PROCEEDINGS OF A SYMPOSIUM IN APPLIED MATHEMATICS OF THE AMERICAN MATHEMATICAL SOCIETY

Held in New York City
April 20-23, 1964

R. Finn
EDITOR

PROCEEDINGS OF
SYMPOSIA IN APPLIED MATHEMATICS
VOLUME XVII

APPLICATIONS OF NONLINEAR PARTIAL DIFFERENTIAL EQUATIONS IN MATHEMATICAL PHYSICS

AMERICAN MATHEMATICAL SOCIETY
PROVIDENCE, RHODE ISLAND

1965

Prepared by the American Mathematical Society with the support of the U.S. Army Research Office (Durham) and the Mathematics Division of the Air Force Office of Scientific Research under Grant No. AF-AFOSR-562-64.

Library of Congress Catalog Number 65-18255

CONTENTS

[1] These abstracts are reprinted from the Notices of the American Mathematical Society, Volume 11, April, 1964.

PREFACE

The contributions to this volume arose from talks presented at a symposium on the nonlinear partial differential equations of mathematical physics, which took place in New York City, April 20–23, 1964. The organizational work and invitations were the responsibility of a committee, consisting of C. B. Morrey, W. Noll, J. B. Serrin, A. H. Taub and myself as chairman.

It was inevitable in view of the broad scope of the subject matter and the severe limitations of time that many important and original contributions could not be included in the program. An attempt was made, however, to organize the meeting in such a way that participants would gain acquaintance with some of the principal lines of modern research in a number of differing but interrelated subjects. Accordingly, the symposium was divided into four sessions of invited addresses, as follows:

1. General Nonlinear Theory
2. Finite Elasticity, Compressible Fluids
3. Viscous Fluids, Magnetohydrodynamics
4. General Relativity, Quantum Field Theory.

In addition, a fifth session was devoted to discussion of the invited talks and to the presentation of selected contributed papers.

The present volume is organized along similar lines, except that the abstracts of contributed papers have been placed in the sections to which they correspond. The underlying cohesive spirit which appeared in the diverse talks at the meeting will, it is hoped, be felt also by the reader who peruses the papers presented here. The volume will have served its purpose if an occasional reader is stimulated to probe more deeply into some of the questions that are discussed, or to discover some unifying principle which unites results that may at first seem to have little connection.

R. Finn

Stanford University

I. GENERAL NONLINEAR THEORY

REMARKS ON NONLINEAR PARABOLIC EQUATIONS

BY

AVNER FRIEDMAN[1]

The present article is concerned with nonlinear parabolic equations of any order. Questions of existence "in the large" and of uniqueness are considered, and the behavior of solutions as $t \to \infty$ is studied.

1. **Abstract Cauchy problem.** Consider the Cauchy problem

$$\frac{du}{dt} - A(t)u = f(t) \qquad (0 < t \leqq T), \tag{1.1}$$

$$u(0) = u_0, \tag{1.2}$$

where $u_0, f(t)$ and the solution $u(t)$ belong to a Banach space E, and $A(t)$ is a closed linear operator in E with a domain D dense in E and independent of t. The solution $u(t)$ is understood to be strongly continuous in $[0, T]$ and to have a strongly continuous (strong) derivative in $(0, T]$. Assume:

(i) For each $t \in [0, T]$, the resolvent set of $A(t)$ contains the half plane $\mathrm{Re}\,\lambda \geqq 0$ and the resolvent $R(\lambda, A) = (\lambda I - A)^{-1}$ satisfies

$$\|R(\lambda, A)\| \leqq C_0(1 + |\lambda|)^{-1} \qquad (C_0 > 0, \mathrm{Re}\,\lambda \geqq 0).$$

(ii) For each $s \in [0, T]$, $A(t)A^{-1}(s)$ is uniformly Hölder continuous (exponent ε) in t with coefficient independent of s, i.e.,

$$\|[A(t) - A(\tau)]A^{-1}(s)\| \leqq C|t - \tau|^{\varepsilon} \qquad (0 \leqq t, s, \tau \leqq T),$$

where $\varepsilon \in (0, 1]$ and C is a constant.

From (i) it follows (see **[60]**) that $A(t)$ is an infinitesimal generator of a strongly continuous semigroup of bounded operators $e^{\tau A(t)}$ $(0 \leqq \tau < \infty)$, and

$$\|e^{\tau A(t)}\| \leqq \text{const } e^{-\delta\tau} \qquad (\delta > 0),$$

$$\|A(t)e^{-\tau A(t)}\| \leqq \text{const } e^{-\delta\tau}\tau^{-1}.$$

Using these inequalities, Sobolevski **[48]** and Tanabe **[53]**, **[54]**, **[55]** constructed, by the parametrix method, a fundamental solution, i.e., an operator $U(t, \tau)$

[1] This work was partially supported by the Alfred P. Sloan Foundation and by the National Science Foundation Grant G14876.

strongly continuous in t, τ $(0 \leqq \tau \leqq t \leqq T)$, having a strongly continuous t-derivative for $0 \leqq \tau < t \leqq T$, and satisfying

$$\frac{\partial U(t, \tau)}{\partial t} - A(t)U(t, \tau) = 0 \qquad (0 \leqq \tau < t \leqq T),$$

$$U(\tau, \tau) = I.$$

They also proved parts (a) and (b) of the following theorem.

THEOREM 1. (a) *If $f(t)$ is Hölder continuous (exponent α) in* $[0, T]$, *then*

$$u(t) = U(t, 0)u_0 + \int_0^t U(t, s)f(s)\, ds \tag{1.3}$$

is the unique solution of the Cauchy problem (1.1), (1.2). *If $u_0 \in D$ then $du(t)/dt$ is strongly continuous in* $[0, T]$.

(b) *Assume that $A(t)A^{-1}(0)$ and $f(t)$ have strongly continuous derivatives up to order k for $0 \leqq t \leqq T$, and that the kth derivatives are Hölder continuous in* $[0, T]$. *Then the solution* (1.3) *has strongly continuous derivatives up to order $k + 1$ for $0 < t \leqq T$.*

(c) *If $A(t)A^{-1}(0)$ and $f(t)$ are analytic in t $(0 \leqq t \leqq T)$, then $u(t)$ is analytic for $0 < t \leqq T$.*

Part (c) was proved by Sobolevski **[48]** and by Komatzu **[24]**, by different methods. A variant of (a) was previously established by Kato **[22]**; he assumed that (i) holds only for λ real $(\lambda \geqq 0)$ but with $C_0 \leqq 1$, that $A(t)A^{-1}(0)$ has a strongly continuous derivative, that $v_0 \in D$ and, finally, that $A(0)f(t)$ is continuous. The last assumption is very restrictive for applications to parabolic equations.

The differentiability assertion in (b) can be extended to $0 \leqq t \leqq T$ provided f satisfies some consistency conditions at $t = 0$. Thus, if $u_0 = 0$ and if $f(t)$ can be extended by 0 to $-1 < t < 0$ so that the extended function satisfies in $[-1, T]$ the same differentiability assumptions which f satisfies in $[0, T]$ (in other words, if $f^{(j)}(0) = 0$ for $j = 0, 1, \cdots, k$), then upon extending $A(t)$ in a suitably smooth manner to $-1 < t < 0$ and applying (b) to the solution $w(t)$ of (1.1) in $(-1, T]$ with $w(-1) = 0$, we find (since $w(t) = 0$ if $-1 \leqq t < 0$, $w(t) = u(t)$ if $0 \leqq t \leqq T$) that $u(t)$ has strongly continuous derivatives up to order $k + 1$ for $0 \leqq t \leqq T$.

Sobolevski **[48]** considered also nonlinear equations. A useful tool employed by him in this connection (as well as in the proof of Theorem 1(c)) is that of a fractional power of $A(t)$. Let A be a closed linear operator with a densely defined domain D and let (i) hold for A. One defines

$$A^{-\alpha} = \frac{1}{\Gamma(\alpha)} \int_0^\infty e^{\tau A} \tau^{\alpha - 1}\, d\tau \qquad (0 < \alpha < \infty). \tag{1.4}$$

$A^{-\alpha}$ is a bounded linear operator mapping E in a one-to-one way into itself, $A^{-\alpha}A^{-\beta} = A^{-(\alpha+\beta)}$, and A^{-1} coincides with the inverse of A. Defining A^{α}

$= (A^{-\alpha})^{-1}$ one finds that the domain $D(A^\alpha)$ of A^α decreases with α, and $A^\alpha A^\beta v = A^\beta A^\alpha v = A^{\alpha+\beta} v$ for any real numbers α, β and $v \in D(A^\gamma)$, $\gamma = \max\{\alpha, \beta, \alpha + \beta\}$. If, further, $-\infty < \alpha < \beta < \gamma < \infty$, then

$$\|A^\beta v\| \leqq C(\alpha, \beta, \gamma)\|A^\gamma v\|^{(\beta-\alpha)/(\gamma-\alpha)}\|A^\alpha v\|^{(\gamma-\beta)/(\gamma-\alpha)}. \tag{1.5}$$

If A^{-1} is completely continuous, then also $A^{-\alpha}$ $(0 < \alpha < \infty)$ is completely continuous.

Consider now the Cauchy problem for a nonlinear equation

$$\frac{du}{dt} - A(t, u)u = f(t, u) \qquad (0 < t \leqq T). \tag{1.6}$$

THEOREM 2 (SOBOLEVSKI [**48**]). *Let $A_0 = A(0, u_0)$ be a closed linear operator with a densely defined domain D. Assume that A_0^{-1} is completely continuous, that the resolvent set of A_0 contains the half plane* $\operatorname{Re} \lambda \geqq 0$, *and that* $\|R(\lambda, A_0)\| \leqq C_0(1 + |\lambda|)^{-1}$ *if* $\operatorname{Re} \lambda \geqq 0$, *where C_0 is a positive constant. Assume next that for some $\alpha \in [0, 1)$, $\varepsilon \in (0, 1]$, $\rho \in (0, 1]$, $R > 0$ and for any $v \in E$, $\|v\| \leqq R$, $A(t, A_0^{-\alpha}v)$ is a closed linear operator with domain D, $f(t, A_0^{-\alpha}v)$ is defined, and*

$$\|[A(t, A_0^{-\alpha}v) - A(\tau, A_0^{-\alpha}w)]A_0^{-1}\| \leqq C(|t - \tau|^\varepsilon + \|v - w\|^\rho), \tag{1.7}$$

$$\|f(t, A_0^{-\alpha}v) - f(\tau, A_0^{-\alpha}w)\| \leqq C(|t - \tau|^\varepsilon + \|v - w\|^\rho) \tag{1.8}$$

for all v, w in E, $\|v\| \leqq R$, $\|w\| \leqq R$, $0 \leqq t, \tau \leqq T$, where C is a constant.

Then, for every $v_0 \in D(A_0^\beta)$ (for some $\beta > \alpha$), $\|A_0^\alpha v_0\| < R$, there exists at least one solution of (1.6), (1.2) *in some interval* $[0, t_0]$. *If $\rho = 1$ then the assumption that A_0^{-1} is completely continuous may be omitted and, furthermore, the solution is unique.*

REMARK 1. t_0 depends upon C_0 and upon upper bounds on $\|A_0^\beta u_0\|$, $[R - \|A_0^\alpha v_0\|]^{-1}$. Hence, if $\rho = 1$ and if one can establish the a priori inequalities

$$\|R(\lambda, A(t, u(t)))\| \leqq \frac{\text{const}}{1 + |\lambda|}, \qquad \|[A(t, u(t))]^\beta u(t)\| \leqq \text{const},$$
$$\|[A(t, u(t))]^\alpha u(t)\| \leqq \text{const} < R, \tag{1.9}$$

then the existence of a unique solution of (1.6), (1.2) follows.

REMARK 2. From the proof of Theorem 2 and from some other facts proved in [**48**] one can show that if $\varepsilon = \rho = 1$ then $du(t)/dt$ belongs to the domain of A_0^α, for $0 < t \leqq t_0$.

Theorem 2 extends part (a) of Theorem 1 to nonlinear equations. Parts (b), (c) can also be extended. It will be enough to mention the analogue of (b). We assume that for any $z \in E$, $\|z\| \leqq R$, $0 \leqq t \leqq T$, the operator $A(t, A_0^{-\alpha}z)A_0^{-1}$ has partial derivatives up to order k (Fréchet derivatives with respect to z and strong derivatives with respect to t) and that the kth derivatives are Hölder continuous with exponents ε, ρ. A similar assumption is made with regard to $f(t, A_0^{-\alpha}z)$. Then the (unique) solution of (1.6), (1.2) has strongly continuous derivatives up to order $k+1$. By Remark 2, they all belong to the domain of A_0^α, provided $\varepsilon = \rho = 1$.

2. **Existence in the large.** Consider the most general quasi-linear parabolic equation

$$(2.1)\quad \frac{\partial u}{\partial t} - \sum_{|\alpha|=2m} a_\alpha(x, t, u, Du, \cdots, D^{2m-1}u)D^\alpha u = f(x, t, u, Du, \cdots, D^{2m-1}u)$$

in a cylinder $Q_T = \Omega \times (0, T]$, where Ω is a bounded domain in R^n, $D^\alpha = D_1^{\alpha_1} \cdots D_n^{\alpha_n}$, $D_i = \partial/\partial x_i$, $|\alpha| = \alpha_1 + \cdots + \alpha_n$, and where D^ju $(j = 1, \cdots, 2m)$ denotes any jth order derivative with respect to the x_i's. Parabolicity means that for any real vector $\xi \neq 0$,

$$(-1)^m \operatorname{Re}\left\{ \sum_{|\alpha|=2m} a_\alpha(x, t, u, \cdots, D^{2m-1}u)\xi^\alpha \right\} < 0$$

where $\xi^\alpha = \xi_1^{\alpha_1} \cdots \xi_n^{\alpha_n}$. For the sake of definiteness we shall consider in the sequel only the first initial-boundary value problem, i.e., the problem of solving (2.1) under the initial condition

$$(2.2)\qquad u(x, 0) = u_0(x) \qquad (x \in \Omega),$$

and the boundary conditions

$$(2.3)\qquad \frac{\partial^j u(x, t)}{\partial \nu^j} = 0 \quad \text{for } j = 0, 1, \cdots, m-1 \qquad (x \in \partial\Omega, 0 < t \leqq T),$$

where ν is the normal to the boundary $\partial\Omega$ of Ω. All the results of §§2, 3, however, can be extended to general elliptic boundary conditions for which (2.5) (below) holds. f and the coefficients a_α are assumed to be real-valued continuous functions for $(x, t) \in \bar{Q}_T$ and all $u, Du, \cdots, D^{2m-1}u$, and $\partial\Omega$ is assumed to be of class C^{2m}.

For $p > 1$, denote by $W_p^{2m}(\Omega)$ the closure of the set $C^{2m}(\bar{\Omega})$ in the norm

$$\|u\|_{W_p^{2m}(\Omega)} = \sum_{|\alpha| \leqq 2m} \|D^\alpha u\|_{L_p(\Omega)}.$$

By Sobolev's lemmas, if $p > n$ then the elements of $W_p^{2m}(\Omega)$ can be identified with functions in $C^{2m-1}(\bar{\Omega})$.

If u_0 belongs to $C^{2m-1}(\bar{\Omega})$, then

$$A_0 u \equiv \sum_{|\alpha|=2m} a_\alpha(0, x, u_0(x), Du_0(x), \cdots, D^{2m-1}u_0(x))D^\alpha u \equiv \sum_{|\alpha|=2m} \tilde{a}_\alpha(x)D^\alpha u$$

is an elliptic operator with continuous coefficients in $\bar{\Omega}$. Consider A_0 is an operator on the set Δ of functions of $C^{2m}(\bar{\Omega})$ which vanish on $\partial\Omega$ together with their first $m - 1$ derivatives, and denote its closure (as an operator in $L_p(\Omega)$) again by A_0. Denote by D the domain of the (closed) operator A_0. According to Koshelev **[25]** and Solomjak **[50]**, there exists a positive number ω such that

$$\|u\|_{W_p^{2m}(\Omega)} \leqq C\|(A_0 - \omega)u\|_{L_p(\Omega)} \qquad (u \in D) \tag{2.4}$$

and

$$\|(\lambda I - A_0)^{-1}\| \leqq C(|\lambda| + 1)^{-1} \qquad (\text{Re}\,\lambda \geqq \omega). \tag{2.5}$$

C depends only on a module of ellipticity, on a bound on the $\tilde{a}_\alpha(x)$ and on a modulus of continuity of the $\tilde{a}_\alpha(x)$. (2.5) was also proved by Browder **[4]** in case $p = 2$. For general elliptic boundary conditions, Agmon, Douglis and Nirenberg **[2]** proved (2.4), and Agmon **[0]** proved (2.5). (Actually, in **[25]**, **[50]**, **[4]** stronger assumptions are made on the $\tilde{a}_\alpha$.) Note that in (2.5), $\lambda I - A_0$ is considered as a mapping from (a subset of) $L_p(\Omega)$ into itself. From (2.4) it follows that D is the closure of Δ in $W_p^{2m}(\Omega)$.

Without loss of generality we shall assume in this section that $\omega = 0$, since the general case follows by the transformation $u = ve^{\omega t}$ which does not change anything. From (2.4), (2.5) (with $\omega = 0$) it follows that A_0 satisfies the assumptions made in Theorem 2 concerning its resolvent and that A_0^{-1} is completely continuous. Next if $(2m - 1)/2m < \alpha < 1$ then there exists a $p > n$ such that $A_0^{-\alpha}$ is completely continuous in L_p and it maps bounded sets in L_p into sets of functions whose first $2m - 1$ derivatives are uniformly continuous and even satisfy a uniform Hölder condition. Hence (1.7), (1.8) hold with $\varepsilon = \rho = 1$ (if a_α, f are Lipschitz continuous). We conclude:

Theorem 2 implies the existence of a unique solution of (2.1)–(2.3) *in* Q_{t_0} *for some* t_0 *sufficiently small. The solution may be taken in the classical sense.*

The last assertion follows from the last paragraph of §1 in conjunction with regularity theorems for elliptic equations and with Sobolev's lemmas (compare **[37**, p. 122]). Note that f is assumed to satisfy some consistency conditions at $t = 0$ in order for u to be continuous at $t = 0$; compare §1.

If f and the a_α are analytic in $(t, u, Du, \cdots, D^{2m-1}u)$ (but not necessarily in x), then the solution $u(x, t)$, as a function of t with values in $L_p(\Omega)$, is analytic in t. Hence, for any C^∞ function $\phi(x)$, $\int u(x, t)\phi(x)\,dx$ is an analytic function in t. In particular it follows that *if* $u(x, t_0) = 0$ *for some* $0 < t_0 < T$ *and for all* x *in some closed subdomain* Ω_0 *of* Ω, *then* $u(x, t) \equiv 0$ *for* $0 \leqq t \leqq T$, $x \in \Omega_0$.

We next consider the question of existence in the large, i.e., in the whole interval $0 \leqq t \leqq T$. Restricting ourselves first to semilinear equations

$$\frac{\partial u}{\partial t} - \sum_{|\alpha| \leqq 2m} a_\alpha(x, t) D^\alpha u = f(x, t, u, Du, \cdots, D^{2m-1}u) \tag{2.6}$$

with real $a_\alpha(x, t)$ ($|\alpha| = 2m$), we shall prove:

THEOREM 3. *Assume that for some* $1 < q \leqq \infty$ *and for any* $0 < \tau < T$, *every solution* $u(x, t)$ *of* (2.6), (2.2), (2.3) *in* Q_τ *satisfies*

$$\|u(x, t)\|_{L_q(\Omega)} \leqq C_0 \tag{2.7}$$

where C_0 *is a constant independent of* τ. *Assume next that if* $q < \infty$ *then*

$$|f(x, t, u, \cdots, D^{2m-1}u)| \leqq C\left\{1 + \sum_{j=0}^{2m-1} |D^j u|^{r_j}\right\} \qquad \left(0 \leqq r_j < \frac{2m + n/q}{j + n/q}\right) \tag{2.8}$$

for some constant C, *whereas if* $q = \infty$ *then for any* $R > 0$ *and for any* u *with* $|u| \leqq R$

$$|f(x, t, u, \cdots, D^{2m-1}u)| \leqq C(R)\left\{1 + \sum_{j=1}^{2m-1} |D^j u|^{r_j}\right\} \qquad \left(0 \leqq r_j < \frac{2m}{j}\right), \tag{2.9}$$

where $C(R)$ *is a constant depending on* R. *Then there exists a unique solution of* (2.6), (2.2), (2.3) *in* Q_T.

The assumption (2.7) *is satisfied for* $q = 2$ *if*

$$\mathrm{Re}\,\{\bar{u}f(x, t, u, \cdots, D^{2m-1}u)\} \leqq C_1|u|^2 + C_2 \tag{2.10}$$

for any possible solution $u = u(x, t)$ *in* Q_τ, *where* C_1, C_2 *are constants independent of* τ.

Note that the variables $u, Du, \cdots, D^{2m-1}u$ occurring in (2.8), (2.9) are independent variables; in (2.8), (2.9), (x, t) varies in Q_T and $Du, \cdots, D^{2m-1}u$ are arbitrary; in (2.8) u is also arbitrary; finally, the notation $|D^j u|^2 = \sum_{|\alpha|=j} |D^\alpha u|^2$ is being used in (2.8), (2.9).

PROOF. Writing (2.6) (in Q_τ) in the form

$$\frac{dv}{dt} - A(t)v = f(t, v), \tag{2.11}$$

we can represent v by

$$v(t) = U(t, 0)v_0 + \int_0^t U(t, s)f(s, v(s))\, ds. \tag{2.12}$$

If we prove that for some $\rho \in (0, 1)$

$$\|f(s, v(s))\|_{L_p} \leqq B_1\{1 + \|A^\rho(s)v(s)\|_{L_p}\} \tag{2.13}$$

where the B_i are used to denote constants independent of v, τ, then upon applying $A^\rho(t)$ to (2.12) we get

$$\|A^\rho(t)v(t)\|_{L_p} \leqq \frac{B_2}{t^\rho} + B_2 \int_0^t (t - s)^{-\rho}\|A^\rho(s)v(s)\|\, ds,$$

i.e., $\|A^\rho(t)v(t)\|_{L_p} \leqq B_3/t^\rho$. This inequality holds also when ρ is increased ($\rho < 1$) since the same is true of (2.13). Combining this inequality for $t \geqq t_0$ with the first italicized statement of this section and with Remark 1 following Theorem 2, the proof of Theorem 3 is completed.

To prove (2.13) note that if $q < \infty$ then, by (2.8),

$$\|f(t, v(t))\|_{L_p} \leqq B_4\left\{1 + \sum_{j=0}^{2m-1} [\|D^j u(x, t)\|_{L_{pr_j}}]^{r_j}\right\}.$$

By the interpolatory inequalities of Nirenberg [**43**] and Gagliardo [**18**], the jth term in the sum is bounded by a constant times

$$(\|D^{2m}u\|_{L_p})^{\alpha r_j}(\|u\|_{L_r})^{r_j(1-\alpha)} + (\|u\|_{\tilde{q}})^{r_j}$$

for any $\tilde{q} > 0$, $j/2m \leqq \alpha \leqq 1$, where $1/r_j p = (j - 2\alpha m)/n + \alpha/p + (1 - \alpha)/r$. Taking $\alpha = 1/r_j$, $1 \leqq r_j \leqq 2m/j$, $r = \tilde{q} = q$ we find, upon using (2.7), (2.4), that if

$$r_j = \frac{2m + n/q}{j + n/q} \tag{2.14}$$

then

$$\|f(t, v(t))\|_{L_p} \leqq B_5(1 + \|D^{2m}u\|_{L_p}) \leqq B_6(1 + \|A(t)v(t)\|_{L_p}). \tag{2.15}$$

If r_j as defined in (2.14) is replaced by $r_j - \varepsilon$ for some $\varepsilon > 0$, then the previous calculation can be slightly modified using interpolatory inequalities for fractional derivatives and an extension of (2.4) to fractional powers of A (see Glushko and Krein [**19**]). We then obtain (2.13) with some $\rho \in (0, 1)$.

For $q = \infty$ the proof is similar. Suppose finally that (2.10) holds. Multiplying both sides of (2.6) by $\overline{u(x, t)}$ and integrating over Ω, we obtain, after using Gårding's inequality and (2.10),

$$\phi'(t) \leqq c\phi(t) + d \qquad (\phi(t) = [\|u(x, t)\|_{L_2(\Omega)}]^2)$$

where c, d are constants, and the a priori boundedness of $\phi(t)$ follows.

From the proof of Theorem 3 we deduce:

COROLLARY. *Theorem 3 remains valid (with $q = \infty$) also in case*

$$a_\alpha = a_\alpha(x, t, u, \cdots, D^k u)$$

for some $k \leqq 2m - 1$, a_α real for $|\alpha| = 2m$, provided for every solution in Q_τ $(0 < \tau \leqq T)$ the first k x-derivatives are a priori bounded and satisfy an a priori Hölder condition in (x, t), independently of τ.

It will be shown in §5 that the restrictions on the r_j cannot be improved in the case of second order parabolic equations. Here we shall only give an example (with $f = f(x, t, u)$) to the effect that (for equations of any order) if in (2.10) $|u|^2$ is replaced by $|u|^{2+\varepsilon}$ for some $\varepsilon > 0$, then (2.7) need not hold for $q = 2$ and in fact the solution may not exist in the large.

EXAMPLE. Let $\zeta(x)$ be a C^∞ function with compact support in Ω, $\zeta \geqq 0$ in Ω, $\max \zeta = \tau^{-1}$ for any given $0 < \tau < T$. For any $\varepsilon > 0$, set

$$w(x, t) = (1 - t\zeta(x))^{-k}$$

where k is a positive number satisfying: $(k + 2m)/k < 1 + \varepsilon$. w satisfies

(2.16) $$\frac{\partial w}{\partial t} - \sum_{|\alpha| \leqq 2m} a_\alpha(x, t) D^\alpha w = f_0(x, t, w)$$

where $f_0(x, t, w) = \sum_{j=0}^{2m} b_j(x, t) w^{(k+j)/k}$ if $w \geqq 1$, and the b_j are as smooth as the a_α's. Defining $f_0(x, t, w)$ for $w < 1$ such that it remains a smooth function in (x, t, w) and such that, say, $f_0(x, t, w) = 0$ if $w < 0$, it follows that $u = w - 1$ satisfies (2.6), (2.2), (2.3) in Q_τ with $f = f(x, t, u)$ which is smooth for $(x, t) \in \bar{Q}_T$ and for all u and which satisfies: $|uf(x, t, u)| \leqq C_1|u|^{2+\varepsilon} + C_2$. u cannot be extended beyond $t = \tau$ since $u(x^0, t) \to 0$ as $t \to \tau$, for any x^0 where $\zeta(x^0) = \max \zeta(x)$.

Theorem 3 in the special case of $m = 1$ was proved by Sobolevski [**49**].

Vishik [**57**], [**59**] and Browder [**5**], [**6**] proved by different methods existence of "strong" solutions in the large for nonlinear elliptic and parabolic equations satisfying some monotonicity properties and whose coefficients have at most a polynomial growth in the unknown function and in its derivatives. In [**58**] Vishik considered also a more general growth condition. Writing the elliptic operator in the form $\sum_{|\alpha| \leqq m} D^\alpha A_\alpha(x, t, u, \cdots, D^m u)$ and introducing

$$h(u, v) = \int_0^T \int_\Omega \sum_{|\alpha| \leqq m} A_\alpha(x, t, u, \cdots, D^m u) \overline{D^\alpha v}\, dx dt,$$

the monotonicity assumption states that for all smooth functions u, v satisfying the homogeneous elliptic boundary conditions

$$\operatorname{Re}\{h(u, u - v) - h(v, u - v)\} \geqq 0.$$

The condition $\operatorname{Re}\{h(u, u)\} \geqq c(\|u\|)\|u\|$ $(0 \leqq c(r) \to \infty$ as $r \to \infty)$ of ellipticity is also assumed.

3. **Convergence of solutions as** $t \to \infty$. If the assumptions of Theorem 3 hold for any $T > 0$ (with constants which may depend on T), then a unique solution exists in Q_∞. We shall now study the behavior of this solution as $t \to \infty$. It is assumed (in addition to sufficient smoothness, locally) that $a_\alpha(x, t)$ are uniformly bounded and uniformly Hölder continuous in Q_∞, and that (2.6) is uniformly parabolic in Q_∞, i.e., $(-1)^m\{\sum_{|\alpha|=2m} a_\alpha(x, t)\xi^\alpha\} \leqq -\gamma|\xi|^{2m}$ where γ is a positive constant independent of $(x, t) \in Q_\infty$. The constants in (2.4), (2.5) (with $A_0 = \sum a_\alpha D^\alpha$) are then independent of t. We finally assume that $\omega = 0$. Then,

(3.1) $$\|A^\rho(t)U(t, s)\| \leqq C_\rho(t - s)^{-\rho} e^{-\delta(t-s)} \qquad (0 \leqq s < t < \infty, 0 \leqq \rho < 1)$$

where C_ρ is independent of t, as can be deduced from [**48**].

THEOREM 4. *Let $u(x, t)$ be a solution of* (2.6), (2.2), (2.3) *in Q_∞ satisfying for some* $1 < q \leqq \infty$, $\tilde{q} > 0$,

(3.2) $$\|u(x, t)\|_{L_q(\Omega)} \leqq R \qquad (R \textit{ a constant}),$$

(3.3) $$\|u(x, t)\|_{L_{\tilde{q}}(\Omega)} \leqq \eta(t), \qquad \eta(t) \to 0 \textit{ as } t \to \infty.$$

Assume that if $q < \infty$ *then*

$$(3.4)\quad |f(x, t, u, \cdots, D^{2m-1}u)| \leqq C \sum_{j=0}^{2m-1} |D^j u|^{r_j} + \varepsilon(t) \qquad \left(0 \leqq r_j < \frac{2m + n/q}{j + n/q}\right)$$

for $(x, t) \in Q_\infty$ *and for all* $u, \cdots, D^{2m-1}u$, *whereas if* $q = \infty$ *then*

$$(3.5)\quad |f(x, t, u, \cdots, D^{2m-1}u)| \leqq C \sum_{j=1}^{2m-1} |D^j u|^{r_j} + \varepsilon(t) \qquad \left(0 \leqq r_j < \frac{2m}{j}\right)$$

for $(x, t) \in Q_\infty$, $|u| \leqq R$ *and for all* $Du, \cdots, D^{2m-1}u$. *If* $\varepsilon(t) \to 0$ *as* $t \to \infty$ *then*

$$(3.6)\qquad \left\{\sum_{j=0}^{2m-1} \operatorname*{l.u.b.}_{\Omega} |D^j u(x, t)|\right\} \to 0 \quad \text{as } t \to \infty.$$

The assumptions (3.2), (3.3) *hold with* $q = \tilde{q} = 2$ *if*

$$(3.7)\qquad -\operatorname{Re}\left\{\int_\Omega \overline{u(x, t)}\left[\sum_{|\alpha| \leqq 2m} a_\alpha(x, t) D^\alpha u(x, t)\right] dx\right\} \geqq \beta \int_\Omega |u(x, t)|^2\, dx \qquad (\beta > 0)$$

and if, for all $(x, t) \in Q_\infty$,

$$(3.8)\qquad \operatorname{Re}\{\bar{u} f(x, t, u, \cdots, D^{2m-1}u)\} \leqq \beta_0 |u|^2 + (|u|^2 + 1)\delta(t) \qquad (\beta_0 < \beta,\ \delta(t) \to 0 \text{ as } t \to \infty),$$

where $u = u(x, t)$.

PROOF. Representing $u(x, t)$ in the form

$$v(t) = U(t, \tau)v(\tau) + \int_\tau^t U(t, s) f(s, v(s))\, ds$$

and applying $A^\rho(t)$ we get, using (3.1),

$$(3.9)\qquad \begin{aligned} \|A^\rho(t)v(t)\| &\leqq C_\rho (t - \tau)^{-\rho} e^{-\delta(t-\tau)} \|v(\tau)\| \\ &\quad + C_\rho \int_\tau^t (t - s)^{-\rho} e^{-\delta(t-s)} \|f(s, v(s))\|\, ds. \end{aligned}$$

Similarly to the proof of Theorem 3, one can show that

$$(3.10)\qquad \|f(t, v(t))\| \leqq B_1 \|A^\rho v(t)\| + B_1 \varepsilon_0(t)$$

for some $\rho \in (0, 1)$, where B_i are used to denote constants independent of t and

$$(3.11)\qquad \varepsilon_0(t) = \varepsilon(t) + (\eta(t))^r \qquad \left(r = \max_j r_j\right).$$

Substituting (3.10) into (3.9) we find that $\phi(t) = e^{\delta(t-\tau)} \|A^\rho(t) v(t)\|$ satisfies

$$\begin{aligned} \phi(t) \leqq &\left\{C_\rho (t - \tau)^{-\rho} \|v(\tau)\| + C_\rho B_1 \int_\tau^t (t - s)^{-\rho} e^{\delta(s-\tau)} \varepsilon_0(s)\, ds\right\} \\ &+ \int_\tau^t (t - s)^{-\rho} \phi(s)\, ds. \end{aligned}$$

The integral in the braces is bounded by $B_2 e^{\delta(t-\tau)}$ l.u.b. $\varepsilon_0(s)$. Denoting by $\chi(t)$ the expression in the braces we find that

$$\phi(t) \leqq \chi(t) + \int_\tau^t \left[\sum_{j=1}^{\infty} \frac{(t-s)^{j-1-j\rho}[\Gamma(1-\rho)]^j}{\Gamma(j(1-\rho))}\right] \chi(s)\, ds.$$

Since the last series is bounded by $B_3(t-s)^{-\rho}\exp[B_3(t-s)^{1-\rho}]$, it follows that for $t - \tau \geqq 1$ and for any $\lambda > 0$

$$\phi(t) \leqq B_4 e^{\lambda(t-\tau)}\|v(\tau)\| + B_4 e^{\delta(t-\tau)} \text{ l.u.b. } \varepsilon_0(s).$$

Hence, for any $0 < \delta_0 < \delta$,

$$\|A^\rho(t)v(t)\| \leqq B_5 e^{-\delta_0(t-\tau)}\|v(\tau)\| + B_4 \operatorname*{l.u.b.}_{\tau<s<t} \varepsilon_0(s). \tag{3.12}$$

Since for any $\varepsilon > 0$ one can first choose τ sufficiently large and then t_0 sufficiently large so that each of two terms on the right-hand side of (3.12) become less than ε if $t > t_0$, we conclude that

$$\|A^\rho(t)v(t)\| \to 0 \quad \text{as } t \to \infty. \tag{3.13}$$

Since ρ can be taken arbitrarily close to 1, (3.6) follows.

To prove the last assertion of Theorem 4, multiply both sides of (2.6) by $\bar{u}(x, t)$ and integrate over Ω. Making use of (3.7), (3.8), we get

$$\psi'(t) + \lambda\psi(t) \leqq \delta(t) \qquad (\psi(t) = [\|u(x, t)\|_{L_2(\Omega)}]^2)$$

for $t \geqq t_0$, for some $\lambda > 0$, $t_0 > 0$. The assertion that $\psi(t) \to 0$ as $t \to \infty$ now easily follows.

From the inequality

$$\|A^\rho(t)v(t)\| \leqq B_6 e^{-\delta_0(t-\tau)}\|A^\rho v(\tau)\| + B_4 \operatorname*{l.u.b.}_{\tau<s<t} \varepsilon_0(s), \tag{3.14}$$

which is a consequence of (3.12), one can derive quantitative results on the rate convergence of $u(x, t)$. Thus we have (compare [**16**, Chapter 6, §2]):

COROLLARY. *If for some* $\lambda > 0$ $(0 < \mu < \delta)$

$$\varepsilon(t) + (\eta(t))^r \leqq \text{const}(1+t)^{-\lambda} \qquad (\leqq \text{const } e^{-\mu t}), \tag{3.15}$$

then

$$\|A^\rho(t)v(t)\| \leqq \text{const}(1+t)^{-\lambda} \qquad (\leqq \text{const } e^{-\mu t}) \tag{3.16}$$

for any $\rho \in (0, 1)$ *and, consequently,*

$$\sum_{j=0}^{2m-1} \operatorname*{l.u.b.}_{\Omega} |D^j u(x, t)| \leqq \text{const}(1+t)^{-\lambda} \qquad (\leqq \text{const } e^{-\mu t}). \tag{3.17}$$

Note that if $\delta(t) \leqq \text{const}(1+t)^{-\lambda}$ $(\leqq \text{const } e^{-\mu t})$ and if (3.7), (3.8) hold, then (3.3) holds with $\tilde{q} = 2$ and $\eta(t) = \text{const}(1+t)^{-\lambda}$ $(\text{const } e^{-\mu t})$.

The proof of Theorem 4 can obviously be applied to solutions of abstract Cauchy problems and to solutions of inequalities

$$|du/dt - A(t)u| \leqq C_1(t)|A^p(t)u| + C_2(t).$$

Consider the Dirichlet problem

$$(3.18)\qquad -B(x, D)w \equiv \sum_{|\alpha|\leqq 2m} b_\alpha(x)D^\alpha w = g(x, w, Dw, \cdots, D^{2m-1}w) \qquad (x \in \Omega),$$

$$(3.19)\qquad \frac{\partial^j w(x)}{\partial \nu^j} = 0 \quad \text{for } j = 0, 1, \cdots, m-1 \qquad (x \in \partial\Omega).$$

If g satisfies the same growth condition as f (in (2.8), (2.9)) with $q = 2$, and if B is strongly elliptic and $-\mathrm{Re}(Bw, w)_{L_2} \geqq \beta(w, w)_{L_2}$ $(\beta > 0)$ for any smooth w satisfying (3.19), then the existence and uniqueness of a solution of (3.18), (3.19) can be established by using (2.4) (which now holds with $\omega = 0$) and Schauder's fixed point theorem. Assuming that, as $t \to \infty$,

$$(3.20)\qquad \begin{aligned} f(x, t, u, \cdots, D^{2m-1}u) &\to g(x, u, \cdots, D^{2m-1}u), \\ a_\alpha(x, t) &\to b_\alpha(x) \end{aligned}$$

uniformly in $x \in \Omega$ and $u, \cdots, D^{2m-1}u$ in bounded sets, and that

$$(3.21)\qquad |g(x, u, \cdots, D^{2m-1}u) - g(x, w, \cdots, D^{2m-1}w)| \leqq \text{const} \sum_{j=1}^{2m-1} |D^j(u - w)|^{r_j},$$

we find that Theorem 4 can be applied to $u - w$.

The asymptotic convergence of solutions of general linear parabolic equations was established by Friedman **[13]**, **[14]**, **[15]** (also for noncylindrical domains and for nonhomogeneous boundary conditions). An abstract convergence theorem for the linear equations (1.1) (with $A(t)$ as in §1) was established by Tanabe **[56]**. Similar theorems were proved by Agmon and Nirenberg **[1]** for much more general operators A, but the operators are independent of t.

4. **Unique continuation.** Let

$$A(x, t, D)u = \sum_{|\rho|=|\sigma|=m} (-1)^\rho D^\rho(a^\rho(x, t)D^\sigma u) \qquad ((x, t) \in \bar{Q}_T)$$

be strongly elliptic and formally self adjoint (i.e., $\overline{a^{\rho\sigma}} = a^{\sigma\rho}$). Let u be a solution of

$$(4.1)\qquad \frac{\partial u}{\partial t} - A(x, t, D)u = f(x, t, u, \cdots, D^m u) \qquad ((x, t) \in Q_T),$$

$$(4.2)\qquad \frac{\partial^j u(x, t)}{\partial \nu^j} = 0 \quad \text{for } j = 0, 1, \cdots, m-1 \quad (x \in \partial\Omega, 0 < t \leqq T).$$

We consider the problem: If $u(x, T) \equiv 0$ does u vanish identically in Q_T?

THEOREM 5. *Assume that* $\partial a^{\rho\sigma}/\partial t$, $D^\alpha a^{\rho\sigma}$ $(0 \leqq \alpha \leqq \rho)$ *exist and are continuous functions in* $\bar{Q}_T$, *that* $u(x, t)$ *is a smooth solution of* (4.1), (4.2), *and that for* $u = u(x, t)$

$$(4.3) \qquad |f(x, t, u, \cdots, D^m u)| \leqq \sum_{j=0}^{m} c_j |D^j u| \qquad (c_j \text{ constants}).$$

If $u(x, T) \equiv 0$ $(x \in \Omega)$ *then* $u \equiv 0$ *in* Q_T.

This theorem was proved by Lees and Protter [**36**] for $m = 1$. The proof for $m > 1$ is similar provided one uses Gårding's inequality and makes an appropriate transformation $v = e^{kt}u$.

In the special case where f is linear in $u, \cdots, D^m u$, Lions and Malgrange [**38**] proved the assertion of Theorem 5 also for weak solutions. Agmon and Nirenberg [**1**] derived a convexity property for any (classical) solution, from which the uniqueness assertion follows.

Note that (4.3) is satisfied whenever

$$|f(x, t, u, \cdots, D^m u)| \leqq \sum_{j=0}^{m} d_j |D^j u|^{r_j} \qquad (d_j \text{ constants})$$

where $r_j \geqq 1$ for all j. If however some of the r_j are less than 1 then the assertion of Theorem 5 is no longer true, as shown by the following counterexample: For any $0 < \delta < 1$, the function $u(x, t) = \phi(t)x(1 - x)$ satisfies

$$|u_t \pm u_{xx}| \leqq a|u|^\delta + a|u_x|^\delta \qquad (0 \leqq x \leqq 1, 0 \leqq t \leqq 1),$$

$$u(x, 0) = 0 \qquad (0 \leqq x \leqq 1), \qquad u(0, t) = u(1, t) = 0 \qquad (0 \leqq t \leqq 1),$$

provided $\phi(t) = [(1 - \delta)t]^{1/(1-\delta)}$ and a is a sufficiently large constant. A similar counterexample, for general m, is given by $\phi(t)x^{m-1}(1 - x)^{m-1}$.

The proof of Theorem 5 extends to solutions of (4.1) in the strip $x \in R^n$, $0 < t \leqq T$, provided

$$\int_0^T \int_{R^n} \sum_{j=0}^{2m} |D^j u|^2 \, dxdt < \infty.$$

Applying this remark to $v(x, t) = u(x, t)\exp[-\lambda(1 + |x|^2)^{1/2}]$ $(\lambda > 0)$, one arrives at the following

COROLLARY. *Let* $u(x, t)$ *be a solution of* (4.1) *in the strip* $x \in R^n$, $0 < t \leqq T$, *satisfying for some* $\mu > 0$,

$$(4.4) \qquad \sum_{j=0}^{2m} \int_0^T \int_{R^n} |D^j u(x, t)|^2 \, e^{-\mu|x|} \, dxdt < \infty.$$

If f *satisfies* (4.3) *and if* $u(x, T) \equiv 0$ $(x \in R^n)$, *then* $u(x, t) \equiv 0$ $(x \in R^n, 0 < t \leqq T)$.

In this corollary, $\partial a^{\rho\sigma}/\partial t$, $D^\alpha a^{\rho\sigma}$ $(0 \leqq \alpha \leqq \rho)$ are assumed to be bounded in the whole strip.

Mizohata [39] proved a uniqueness theorem similar to the corollary, for the special case $m = 1, f \equiv 0$, assuming a polynomial growth instead of the exponential growth in (4.4).

Theorem 5 has an analogue in case $T = \infty$. Assuming that $\partial a^{\rho\sigma}/\partial t$, $D^\alpha a^{\rho\sigma}$ $(0 \leqq \alpha \leqq \rho)$ are bounded continuous functions in $\bar{Q}_\infty$ and that (4.1) is uniformly parabolic in Q_∞, we have:

THEOREM 6. *Let $u(x, t)$ be a smooth solution of* (4.1), (4.2) *in* Q_∞ *and let*

$$|f(x, t, u, \cdots, D^m u)| \leqq \sum_{j=0}^{m} c_j(t)|D^j u| \tag{4.5}$$

hold for $(x, t) \in Q_\infty$, $u = u(x, t)$. *If for some* $\eta > 1$,

$$\begin{aligned} c_0(t) &= O(t^{(\eta-2)/2}), \qquad c_j(t) = o(t^{-1/2}) \qquad (j = 1, \cdots, m), \\ a(t) &\equiv \sum_{|\rho|,|\sigma| \leqq m} \underset{\Omega}{\text{l.u.b.}} \left|\frac{\partial a^{\rho\sigma}(x, t)}{\partial t}\right| = o(t^{-1/2}), \end{aligned} \tag{4.6}$$

and if for any $\lambda > 0$,

$$e^{\lambda t^\eta} \int_\Omega |D^m u(x, t)|^2 \, dx \to 0 \quad \text{as } t \to \infty, \tag{4.7}$$

then $u \equiv 0$ *in* Q_∞.

If instead of (4.6),

$$c_j(t) = O(t^{-(1+\varepsilon)/2}) \qquad (j = 0, 1, \cdots, m), \qquad a(t) = o(c_m(t)) \tag{4.8}$$

for some $\varepsilon > 0$, *and if* (4.7) *holds for* $\eta = 1$ *and for any* $\lambda > 0$, *then* $u \equiv 0$ *in* Q_∞.

The first part of Theorem 6 was proved by Protter [45] in the case $m = 1$; the proof for $m > 1$ is similar. The second part of Theorem 6 is an improvement over Protter's result for $\eta = 1$, and it follows by extending the proof of Theorem 5 of Cohen and Lees [7]. In that theorem the authors stated a result similar to that of Protter [45] for second order equations with coefficients independent of t. Theorems 5, 6 can be extended to any elliptic boundary conditions for which Gårding's inequality holds.

For linear parabolic equations with coefficients independent of t, Krein and Prozorovskaja [30] proved that for any $\varepsilon > 0$ there exists a constant β such that

$$\|u(x, t)\|_{L_p(\Omega)} \geqq \exp[-\beta t^{1+\varepsilon}]\|u(x, 0)\|_{L_p(\Omega)}. \tag{4.9}$$

Bounds of the same type were obtained by Agmon and Nirenberg [1] for general classes of operators A independent of t.

Open questions. (a) Extend Theorems 5, 6 to $f = f(x, t, u, \cdots, D^{2m-1}u)$.

(b) Extend (4.9) to linear parabolic equations with coefficients depending also on t.

(c) Can the condition (4.4) be replaced by the essentially much weaker condition

$$\int_{R^n} |u(x, t)| \exp[-\mu |x|^{2m/(2m-1)}]\, dx \leqq \text{const} < \infty?$$

In the case of general linear parabolic equations with coefficients independent of x, this is true and is well known.

5. **Existence in the large for second order equations.** All functions in this section are real-valued.

For second order nonlinear parabolic equations there are various methods for deriving existence theorems in the large. We consider here only the first initial-boundary value problem (most of the results described below are not known for the second and third initial-boundary value problems). Consider first noncylindrical domains. Thus, Q_T is a bounded $(n + 1)$-dimensional domain contained in a strip $0 < t \leqq T$, whose boundary is composed of $\bar{\Omega}$ (on $t = T$), $\bar{\Omega}_T$ (on $t = T$) and S (in $0 < t < T$). The initial and boundary conditions are given by

$$u = \phi \quad \text{on } \Omega + S. \tag{5.1}$$

Suppose u is a solution of a general nonlinear parabolic equation

$$F(x, t, u, D_x u, D_x^2 u, D_t u) = 0$$

in Q_T, satisfying (5.1). Then there exists a solution w of

$$G(x, t, w, D_x w, D_x^2 w, D_t w) = 0$$

in Q_T satisfying $w = \psi$ on $\Omega + S$ for any functions G, ψ such that $G - F$ and $\psi - \phi$ are uniformly small together with some of their derivatives. The proof of this fact follows with the aid of a priori estimates of the Schauder type derived by Friedman **[10]**, **[11]**.

The above result can be used to prove existence theorems for equations which differ from linear equations only by a small perturbation.

Let

$$Lu = \sum_{i,j=1}^{n} a_{ij}(x, t) \frac{\partial^2 u}{\partial x_i \, \partial x_j} + \sum_{i=1}^{n} b_i(x, t) \frac{\partial u}{\partial x_i} + c(x, t)u - \frac{\partial u}{\partial t} \tag{5.2}$$

be a linear parabolic operator in Q_T with continuous coefficients in $\bar{Q}_T$, and consider the semilinear equation

$$Lu = f(x, t, u, D_x u) \quad \text{in } Q_T \tag{5.3}$$

under the condition (5.1). If

$$-uf(x, t, u, 0) \leqq A_1 u^2 + A_2 \qquad (A_1, A_2 \text{ constants}) \tag{5.4}$$

then by comparison one finds an a priori bound on the solution of (5.3), (5.1) (this bound is valid also when L is quasi-linear). Thus, under the assumption (5.4), Theorems 3, 4 can be applied with $q = \infty$.

Assume, in addition to (5.4),

$$f(x, t, u, D_x u) \leqq C(|u|) + \mu |D_x u| \qquad (\mu \text{ a constant}), \tag{5.5}$$

where $C(r)$ is any monotone increasing function of r. Then (Friedman [**12**]) *if* L, f, S, ϕ *are suitably smooth and* μ *is sufficiently small* (*depending only on* L *and* Q_T), *there exists a unique solution of* (5.3), (5.1). The proof depends on an a priori bound on the Hölder coefficient of $D_x u(x, t)$.

From now on we assume that Q_T is a cylinder, i.e., $S = \partial\Omega \times (0, T)$, and consider quasi-linear equations

$$\sum_{i,j=1}^{n} a_{ij}(x, t, u, D_x u) \frac{\partial^2 u}{\partial x_i \, \partial x_j} - \frac{\partial u}{\partial t} = f(x, t, u, D_x u). \tag{5.6}$$

Ladyzhenskaja and Uraltseva [**34**] extended the a priori inequality of de Giorgi to general second order parabolic equations and up to the boundary. (Similar extension of de Giorgi and Nash inequalities to general elliptic equations was previously obtained by Morrey [**42**], Stampaccia [**51**], [**52**] and by Ladyzhenskaja and Uraltseva [**33**].) By the same method they also derived in [**35**] a priori bounds on $D_x u$ where u is a solution of (5.6), (5.1). This bound involves l.u.b. $|D_x u|$ on the boundary S, but a simple device of S. Bernstein can be used to estimate the latter quantity in terms of l.u.b. $|u|$. From the bound on $D_x u$ follows a bound on its Hölder coefficient (via the extended de Giorgi inequality to parabolic equations). Applying next the a priori estimates of Friedman [**11**], one obtains a priori bounds also on the higher derivatives of u. The Leray–Schauder fixed point theorem can then be used to conclude the existence of a solution of the system (5.6), (5.1) in Q_T.

Observe that once the a priori bounds on $D_x u$ and on its Hölder coefficients are established, one can also derive the existence of a solution in Q_T by applying the corollary to Theorem 3.

In their proof of existence of a solution of (5.6), (5.1) in Q_T, Ladyzhenskaja and Uraltseva assumed, in addition to sufficient smoothness of a_{ij}, f, ϕ, $\partial\Omega$, the following:

(I) (5.4) holds and, for some M (depending on A_1, A_2), if $(x, t) \in Q_T$, $|u| \leqq M$, $p = (p_1, \cdots, p_n) \in R^n$,

$$\nu(|p| + 1)^{m-2}|\xi|^2 \leqq \sum a_{ij}(x, t, u, p)\xi_i\xi_j \leqq \mu(|p| + 1)^{m-2}|\xi|^2, \tag{5.7}$$

where ν, μ are positive constants, and m is an arbitrary constant;

$$|D_x a_{ij}|(|p| + 1) + |D_u a_{ij}|(|p| + 1)^2 + |D_p a_{ij}|(|p| + 1)^3 \leqq \mu(|p| + 1)^m, \tag{5.8}$$

$$|f| + |D_x f|(|p| + 1) + |D_u f| + |D_p f|(|p| + 1) \leqq \mu(|p| + 1)^m. \tag{5.9}$$

(II) Either an a priori modulus of continuity for the solution $u(x, t)$ is already known, or

$$|D_x a_{ij}|(|p| + 1)^{-1} + |D_u a_{ij}| \leqq \varepsilon(|p| + 1)^{m-2} + P(p), \tag{5.10}$$

(5.11) $$|D_x f|(|p| + 1)^{-1} - D_u f \leqq \varepsilon(|p| + 1)^m + P(p)(|p| + 1)^2,$$

where ε is sufficiently small (depending on μ, ν) and $|p|^{2-m}P(p) \to 0$ if $p \to \infty$.

Similar results were derived (in **[34]**) for quasi-linear parabolic equations in divergence form, as well as for some systems of parabolic equations (in **[35]**). For equations in divergence form, similar results were independently proved by Oleinik and Kruzhkov **[44]** in case the principal coefficients are independent of $D_x u$. They employed and extended Nash's inequality for parabolic equations.

In the special case of the semilinear equation (5.3), the conditions (5.7), (5.8), (5.10) are satisfied with $m = 2$ and thus f must satisfy (5.9), (5.11) with $m = 2$. On the other hand, Theorem 3 specialized to second order equations requires only that $|f(x, t, u, p)| \leqq \text{const}(|p| + 1)^{2-\varepsilon}$ for some $\varepsilon > 0$.

Filippov **[8]** has shown, by means of a counterexample, that the condition

$$|f(x, t, u, p)| \leqq \text{const}(|p| + 1)^{2+\varepsilon} \qquad (\text{for some } \varepsilon > 0)$$

is not sufficient for existence of solutions in the large. In fact, for any continuous positive function $\psi(v)$ ($v_0 \leqq v < \infty$, $v_0 > 0$) satisfying

$$\int_{v_0}^{\infty} \frac{dv}{\psi(v)} < \infty,$$

and for every $h > 0$ sufficiently small, he constructed a continuous function $v(x, t)$ in $0 \leqq x \leqq h$, $0 \leqq t \leqq 1$ with $v(0, t) \equiv 0$, such that there exist no solutions of

$$u_{xx} - u_t = -uu_x\psi(u_x) \quad \text{for } 0 < x < h,\ 0 < t \leqq 1,$$

satisfying $u(0, t) = 0$ for $0 \leqq t \leqq 1$, $u(x, 0) \geqq v(x, 0)$ for $0 \leqq x \leqq h$, $u(h, t) \geqq v(h, t)$ for $0 \leqq t \leqq 1$.

For some special nonlinear equations, all the solutions may exist in the large even though the conditions (5.7)–(5.11) are not met. Such equations are those considered by Browder and Vishik (see §2); for some concrete examples see **[58]**. An example of different type, given in **[32]**, is

$$\Delta u - u_t = f(|D_x u|^2),$$

where $f'(\tau) \leqq \text{const}(0 \leqq \tau < \infty)$.

We conclude this section with a result concerning the condition (5.4).

THEOREM 7. *Let L, defined in (5.2), be parabolic in $Q_\infty = \Omega \times (0, \infty)$ (Ω bounded) and let its coefficients be continuous and bounded in $\bar{Q}_\infty$. Let $f(u)$ be any positive monotone increasing function defined in an interval $u_0 \leqq u < \infty$ ($u_0 > 0$), satisfying:*

(5.12) $$\int_{u_0}^{\infty} \frac{du}{f(u)} < \infty,$$

(5.13) $$\frac{f(\mu u)}{\mu f(u)} \geqq K(\mu) \quad \textit{for } u \geqq u_0,\ \mu \geqq \mu_0;\ K(\mu) \to \infty \textit{ if } \mu \to \infty.$$

Then, for any $T_0 > 0$ *and for any closed subdomain* Ω_0 *of* Ω *there exists a constant* N *(depending only on* L, f, Ω_0, T_0*) such that any solution* $u(x, t)$ *of*

$$Lu \leqq -f(u) \quad \text{in } Q_{T_0}, \tag{5.14}$$

$$u \geqq N \quad \text{on } \Omega + \partial\Omega \times (0, T_0) \tag{5.15}$$

tends to ∞ *if* $x \in \Omega_0$, $t \to T_0$.

PROOF. It suffices to construct a function $z(x, t)$ satisfying

$$Lz > -f(z) \quad \text{in } Q_{T_0}, \tag{5.16}$$

$$z < N \quad \text{on } \Omega + \partial\Omega \times (0, T_0), \tag{5.17}$$

$$z(x, t) \to \infty \quad \text{if } x \in \Omega_0,\ t \to T_0, \tag{5.18}$$

since then, by a comparison argument, $u \geqq z$ and the proof is completed. Introduce the function

$$G(v) = \int_v^\infty \frac{dv}{f(v)}$$

and let g be the inverse of G. $g(w)$ is defined for $0 < w \leqq \varepsilon_0$, where $\varepsilon_0 = \int_{u_0}^\infty (1/f(v))\, dv$, and $g(w) > 0$, $g'(w) < 0$, $g''(w) \geqq 0$, $g(w) \to \infty$ if $w \to 0$.

Let $\zeta(x)$ be a C^∞ function in Ω satisfying: $0 \leqq \zeta \leqq \varepsilon_0/T_0$, $\zeta = \varepsilon_0/T_0$ on Ω_0, $\zeta = 0$ near the boundary $\partial\Omega$. Take

$$z(x, t) = \mu g(\varepsilon_0 - t\zeta(x)) \qquad (\mu > 0),$$

where μ is to be determined later on. (5.18) is evidently satisfied, and so is also (5.17) provided $N = \mu g(\varepsilon_0)/2$. To prove (5.16) we use the parabolicity of L and the boundedness of $g(w)/g'(w) = -v/f(v)$ (where $w = G(v)$), and get

$$Lz \geqq H_0 \mu g'(w),$$

where H_0 depends only on L, f, ζ, T_0. Using (5.13) and choosing μ such that $K(\mu) > H_0$, (5.16) follows.

In the special case where the elliptic part of L is self adjoint with sufficiently smooth coefficients which are independent of t and where $\partial\Omega$ is sufficiently smooth, Kaplan **[21]** has also derived, by a different method, a nonexistence theorem.

6. Miscellaneous remarks.

1. Some topological methods, such as the application of fixed point theorems, have become a standard tool in the study of nonlinear differential equations. In the theory of nonlinear integral equations, such methods play a much more fundamental role, and it has therefore been one of the primary objects of workers in this field to develop topological methods applicable to integral equations (see **[26]**). It turns out that the available methods can also be applied to some questions in nonlinear differential equations. As an example we mention the following result of Krasnoselski and Sobolevski **[29]**:

If there exist two distinct solutions u, v of (2.1)–(2.3), where the a_α and $\partial\Omega$ are smooth and f is Hölder continuous, then there also exists a one-parameter family of solutions which connect u to v.

An example where two distinct solutions exist was given by Mlak [**41**].

2. Krein and Rutman [**31**], Krasnoselski [**27**] and others have developed a theory of positive solutions of operator equations in a Banach space. Thus, if E is a real Banach space and K is a cone by which the concept of positivity is defined, then the positive operators A are those which map K into itself. The theory was developed to suit the situations which arise in nonlinear integral equations with positive kernels and can therefore be used also in the study of second order elliptic and parabolic equations. We mention two results obtained in this way, due to Krasnoselski and Sobolevski [**27**], [**28**]:

(i) Let Lu be a linear elliptic operator in a bounded domain Ω, let the coefficient of u in Lu be $\leqq 0$, and assume that L and $\partial\Omega$ are sufficiently smooth. Then there exists a unique non-negative eigenfunction u_0 of $Lu = \lambda u$ in Ω, $u = 0$ on $\partial\Omega$; the corresponding eigenvalue is simple and smaller than the absolute value of any other eigenvalue.

(ii) Let $f(x, u)$ be non-negative continuous function ($x \in \bar{\Omega}$, $0 \leqq u < \infty$), monotone decreasing in u and satisfying

$$f(x, tu) > tf(x, u) \qquad (u > 0,\ x \in \Omega,\ 0 < t < 1).$$

Then the values of λ for which the Dirichlet problem $Lu = \lambda f(x, u)$ in Ω, $u = 0$ on $\partial\Omega$ has a nonzero non-negative solution fill an open interval. The solution $u = u(x, \lambda)$ is unique and decreases with λ.

The method of proof of (i) leads to the following result for second order linear parabolic equations $Lu = 0$ in Q_T: There is precisely one nonzero non-negative solution satisfying $u = 0$ on $\partial\Omega \times (0, T]$, $u(x, T) \equiv \text{const}\ u(x, 0)$ ($x \in \Omega$).

The Dirichlet problem for the generalized Monge-Ampère equation

$$\frac{rt - s^2}{(1 + p^2 + q^2)^\alpha} = f(x, y, z, p, q) \qquad (0 \leqq \alpha < 1)$$

can also be treated by the above methods [**3**], [**27**].

3. The tool of fractional powers of operators in a Banach space has been used by Sobolevski [**46**], [**47**], and more recently by Fujita and Kato [**17**], [**23**], to study the Navier–Stokes equations.

4. Consider the Cauchy problem

$$\begin{aligned} &\frac{dx}{dt} = Ax + f(t, x) \qquad (0 < t \leqq T), \\ &x(0) = a \end{aligned} \tag{6.1}$$

in a real Banach space E where A is an infinitesimal generator of a strongly continuous semigroup of bounded operators. Assume that $f(t, x)$ is convex in x with respect to a cone K, i.e., the Fréchet derivative $f_x(t, x)$ satisfies: $f_x(t, y_1)z \leqq f_x(t, y_2)z$

whenever $y_1 \leqq y_2$, $z \geqq 0$. Given a function $x(t)$, set $y = Hx$ where $y(t)$ is the solution of

$$\frac{dy}{dt} = Ay + f_x(t, x(t))(y - x(t)) + f(t, x(t)), \qquad y(0) = a.$$

Under some assumptions on f, Mlak [**40**] proved that if $x(t)$ satisfies

$$\frac{dx}{dt} \leqq Ax + f(t, x), \qquad x(0) = a,$$

then $y(t)$ satisfies the same inequality and, furthermore, $x(t) \leqq y(t)$. This leads to the construction of a monotone sequence $\{x_m(t)\}$ where $x_{n+1} = Hx_n$, which, under further restrictions on f, converges to the solution of (6.1) provided the latter exists. Some concrete examples of this method were treated by Kalaba [**20**]. It should be interesting to refine this method so that it can be used to prove existence theorems for (6.1); in this connection, see Fleming [**9**].

Added in proof. We have recently proved (Pacific J. Math.) that if E is a Hilbert space then (b), (c) of Theorem 1 hold also if (i) is assumed only with Re $\lambda = 0$.

J. L. Lions and J. Leray have recently proved results of Vishik-Browder type (see §2). See also recent work of J. L. Lions and W. A. Strauss.

References

0. S. Agmon, *On the eigenfunctions and on the eigenvalues of general elliptic boundary value problems*, Comm. Pure Appl. Math. **15** (1962), 119–147.

1. S. Agmon and L. Nirenberg, *Properties of solutions of ordinary differential equations in Banach space*, Comm. Pure Appl. Math. **16** (1963), 121–239.

2. S. Agmon, A. Douglis, and L. Nirenberg, *Estimates near the boundary for solutions of elliptic partial differential equations satisfying general boundary conditions*. I, Comm. Pure Appl. Math. **12** (1959), 623–727.

3. I. Ja. Bakelman and M. A. Krasnoselski, *Nontrivial solutions of the Dirichlet problem for equations with the Monge-Ampère operator*, Dokl. Akad. Nauk SSSR **137** (1961), 1007–1010.

4. F. E. Browder, *On the spectral theory of elliptic differential operators*. I, Math. Ann. **142** (1961), 22–130.

5. ———, *Nonlinear parabolic boundary value problems of arbitrary order*, Bull. Amer. Math. Soc. **69** (1963), 858–861.

6. ———, *Nonlinear elliptic boundary value problems*, Bull. Amer. Math. Soc. **69** (1963), 862–874; **70** (1964), 299–302.

7. P. J. Cohen and M. Lees, *Asymptotic decay of solutions of differential inequalities*, Pacific J. Math. **11** (1961), 1235–1249.

8. A. F. Filippov, *On conditions for existence of solutions of quasi-linear parabolic equations*, Dokl. Akad. Nauk SSSR **141** (1961), 568–570.

9. W. H. Fleming, *Some Markovian optimization problems*, J. Math. Mech. **12** (1963), 131–140.

10. A. Friedman, *Interior estimates for parabolic systems of partial differential equations*, J. Math. Mech. **7** (1958), 393–418.

11. ———, *Boundary estimates for second order parabolic equations and their applications*, J. Math. Mech. **7** (1958), 771–792.

12. ———, *On quasi-linear parabolic equations of the second order*. II, J. Math. Mech. **9** (1960), 539–556.

13. A. Friedman, *Convergence of solutions of parabolic equations to a steady state*, J. Math. Mech. **8** (1959), 57–76.

14. ———, *Asymptotic behavior of solutions of parabolic equations*, J. Math. Mech. **8** (1959), 387–392.

15. ———, *Asymptotic behavior of solutions of parabolic equations of any order*, Acta Math. **106** (1961), 1–43.

16. ———, *Partial differential equations of parabolic type*, Prentice-Hall, Englewood Cliffs, N. J., 1964.

17. H. Fujita and T. Kato, *On the Navier-Stokes initial value problem*. I, Tech. Rep. No. 121, Stanford Univ., Stanford, Calif., 1963.

18. E. Gagliardo, *Ulteriori proprietè di alcune classi di funzioni in piue variabili*, Ricerche Mat. **8** (1959), 24–51.

19. V. P. Glushko and S. G. Krein, *Fractional power of differential operators and inclusion theorems*, Dokl. Akad. Nauk SSSR **122** (1958), 963–966.

20. R. Kalaba, *On nonlinear differential equations, the maximum operation, and monotone convergence*, J. Math. Mech. **8** (1959), 519–574.

21. S. Kaplan, *On the growth of solutions of quasi-linear parabolic equations*, Comm. Pure Appl. Math. **16** (1963), 305–330.

22. T. Kato, *Integration of the equation of evolution in a Banach space*, J. Math. Soc. Japan **5** (1953), 208–234.

23. T. Kato and H. Fujita, *On the non-stationary Navier-Stokes system*, Rend. Sem. Mat. Univ. Padova **32** (1962), 243–260.

24. H. Komatzu, *Abstract analyticity in time and unique continuation property for solutions of parabolic equations*, J. Fac. Sci. Univ. Tokyo Sect. I **9** (1961), 1–11.

25. A. I. Koshelev, *A priori L_p estimate and generalized solutions of elliptic equations*, Uspehi Mat. Nauk SSSR **13** (1958), no. 4, 29–88.

26. M. A. Krasnoselski, *Topological methods in the theory of nonlinear integral equations*, Gosudarstv. Izdat. Tehn.-Teor. Lit., Moscow, 1956.

27. ———, *Positive solutions of operator equations*, Moscow, 1962.

28. M. A. Krasnoselski and P. E. Sobolevski, *On non-negative eigenfunctions of the first boundary value problem for elliptic equations*, Uspehi Mat. Nauk SSSR **16** (1961), no. 2, 197–199.

29. ———, *The structure of the set of solutions of equations of parabolic type*, Dokl. Akad. Nauk SSSR **146** (1962), 26–29.

30. S. G. Krein and O. I. Prozorovskaja, *Analytic semi-groups and incorrect problems for evolutionary equations*, Dokl. Akad. Nauk SSSR **133** (1960), 277–280.

31. M. G. Krein and M. A. Rutman, *Linear operators leaving invariant a cone in a Banach space*, Uspehi Mat. Nauk SSSR **3** (1948), no. 1, 3–95; Amer. Math. Soc. Transl. (1) **10** (1950), 199–325.

32. O. A. Ladyzhenskaja, *On the solution "in the large" of boundary value problems for linear and quasi-linear parabolic equations and the equations of Navier-Stokes*, Trudy Tretovo Vsesoiuznovo Matematicheski S'ezda **1** (1963), 134–157.

33. O. A. Ladyzhenskaja and N. N. Uraltseva, *Quasi-linear elliptic equations and variational problems with many independent variables*, Uspehi Mat. Nauk SSSR **16** (1961), no. 1, 19–60.

34. ———, *Boundary problems for linear and quasi-linear parabolic equations*. I, II, Izv. Akad. Nauk SSSR **26** (1962), 5–52, 753–780.

35. ———, *Boundary problems for linear and quasi-linear equations and systems of parabolic type*. III, Izv. Akad. Nauk SSSR **27** (1963), 161–240.

36. M. Lees and M. H. Protter, *Unique continuation for parabolic differential equations and inequalities*, Duke Math. J. **28** (1961), 369–382.

37. J. L. Lions, *Equations différentielles. Opérationnelles et problèmes aux limites*, Springer, Berlin, 1961.

38. J. L. Lions and B. Malgrange, *Sur l'unicité rétrograde dans les problèmes mixtes paraboliques*, Math. Scand. **8** (1960), 277–286.

39. S. Mizohata, *Le problème de Cauchy pour le passé pour quelques équations paraboliques*, Proc. Japan Acad. **34** (1958), 693–696.

40. W. Mlak, *Note on abstract differential inequalities and Chaplighin method*, Ann. Polon. Math. **10** (1961), 253–271.

41. ———, *An example of the equation* $u_t = u_{xx} + f(x, t, u)$ *with distinct maximum and minimum solutions of a mixed problem*, Ann. Polon. Math. **13** (1963), 101–103.

42. C. B. Morrey, *Second order elliptic equations in several variables and Hölder continuity*, Math. Z. **72** (1959), 146–164.

43. L. Nirenberg, *On elliptic partial differential equations*, Ann. Scuola Norm. Sup. Pisa **13** (1959), 116–162.

44. O. A. Oleinik and S. N. Kruzhkov, *Quasi-linear parabolic equations of the second order with many independent variables*, Uspehi Mat. Nauk SSSR **16** (1961), no. 5, 115–155.

45. M. H. Protter, *Properties of solutions of parabolic equations and inequalities*, Canad. J. Math. **13** (1961), 331–345.

46. P. E. Sobolevski, *On non-stationary equations of hydrodynamics for viscous fluid*, Dokl. Akad. Nauk SSSR **128** (1959), 45–48.

47. ———, *On the smoothness of generalized solutions of the Navier-Stokes equations*, Dokl. Akad. Nauk SSSR **131** (1960), 758–760.

48. ———, *On equations of parabolic type in a Banach space*, Trudy Moskov. Mat. Obšč. **10** (1961), 297–350.

49. ———, *On a method of proving global existence theorems for parabolic equations*, Dopovidi Akad. Nauk Ukraïn. **1961**, no. 12, 1552–1555.

50. M. Z. Solomjak, *Estimates of the norm of the resolvent of elliptic operators in* L_p *spaces*, Uspehi Mat. Nauk **15** (1960), no. 6(96), 141–148.

51. G. Stampacchia, *Contributi alla regolarizzione dell soluzioni dei problemi al contorno per equazioni del secondo ordine ellitiche*, Ann. Scuola Norm. Sup. Pisa **12** (1958), 223–245.

52. ———, *Problemi al contorno ellitiche con dati discontinui soluzioni Hölderiane*, Ann. Mat. Pura Appl. **51** (1960), 1–38.

53. H. Tanabe, *A class of the equations of evolution in a Banach space*, Osaka Math. J. **11** (1959), 121–145.

54. ———, *Remarks on the equations of evolution in a Banach space*, Osaka Math. J. **12** (1960), 145–166.

55. ———, *On the equations of evolution in a Banach space*, Osaka Math. J. **12** (1960), 363–376.

56. ———, *Convergence to a stationary state of the solution of some kind of differential equations in a Banach space*, Proc. Japan Acad. **37** (1961), 127–130.

57. M. I. Vishik, *Quasi-linear strongly elliptic systems of differential equations having a divergence form*, Trudy Moskov. Mat. Obšč. **12** (1963), 125–184.

58. ———, *Solvability of the first boundary value problem for quasi-linear equations with rapidly increasing coefficients in Orlicz classes*, Dokl. Akad. Nauk SSSR **151** (1963), 758–761.

59. M. I. Vishik and G. E. Shilov, *General theory of partial differential equations and some boundary value problems*, Trudy Tretovo Vsesoiuznovo Matematicheski S'ezda **1** (1963), 55–85.

60. K. Yosida, *On the differentiability of semi-groups of linear operators*, Proc. Japan Acad. **34** (1958), 337–340.

Northwestern University,
Evanston, Illinois

EXISTENCE AND UNIQUENESS THEOREMS FOR SOLUTIONS OF NONLINEAR BOUNDARY VALUE PROBLEMS[1]

BY

FELIX E. BROWDER

Introduction. It is the purpose of the present paper to present a survey of the ideas and results in the application to nonlinear boundary value problems for nonlinear partial differential equations of the recently developed theory of monotone nonlinear operators from a Banach space V to its dual V^*.

This approach to nonlinear problems combines in a novel way essential elements of the two basic classic approaches, the direct method of the calculus of variations on the one hand and the Leray–Schauder theory on the other. Like the variational method but in a more general context, one considers problems having essential semiboundedness properties. Like the Leray–Schauder theory, one translates the problems under consideration into functional equations on Banach spaces. Unlike the variational method, one does not restrict oneself to gradients of functionals or Euler–Lagrange equations of multiple integral problems. Unlike the Leray–Schauder theory, one does not restrict oneself to operators of the form $I + C$, C compact.

Let V be a Banach space (over the reals, for most of the present discussion), V^* the space of bounded linear functionals on V. For w in V^*, u in V, we denote the pairing between w and u by $\langle w, u\rangle$.

Let T be a mapping (possibly nonlinear) defined on a subset of V and with values in V^*. Then T is said to be monotone if for all u and v of $D(T)$, the domain of T,

$$\langle Tu - Tv, u - v\rangle \geqq 0.$$

If T is defined on an open set and has a Frechét derivative T'_u for each u in $D(T)$, then monotonicity of T is equivalent to the condition that $(-T'_u)$ is a dissipative operator for each u in the sense that

$$\langle(-T'_u)v, v\rangle \leqq 0$$

for all v in V.

[1] The research for this article was partially supported by National Science Foundation Grant GP-3552.

Monotone nonlinear operators in a Hilbert space H were first studied by Zarantonello [**37**] who proved that if T is monotone and satisfies a Lipschitz condition, then $I + T$ maps H onto H. This result was extended to continuous T by Minty [**25**] and under weaker conditions on continuity and monotonicity by the writer [**2**]–[**4**]. The theory of monotone operators was extended to reflexive Banach spaces independently by the writer [**5**], [**6**] and Minty [**27**], and further extended to densely defined operators by the writer in [**6**], [**8**], [**10**], [**17**] and to multi-valued mappings in [**12**]. Applications to elliptic boundary value problems were first given by the writer in [**1**]–[**4**] and especially in [**5**] and extensions given by the writer in [**7**], [**9**], and [**18**] and by Leray and Lions (unpublished). Applications to parabolic boundary value problems were given by the writer in [**6**], [**8**] and to nonlinear equations of evolution in [**10**]. The latter was extended and strengthened by T. Kato in [**21**]. Applications were given to hyperbolic systems and wave equations by Lions [**22**] and Lions and Strauss [**23**], [**24**], and the writer gave applications to more general equations of evolution and other boundary value problems in [**17**]. Applications of monotone mappings to duality mappings of Banach spaces were given by the writer in [**11**], [**12**]. Sharpened results involving assumptions on $|(Tu - Tv, u - v)|$ rather than on $\mathrm{Re}(Tu - Tv, u - v)$ were given for complex Hilbert spaces by Zarantonello in [**38**] and strengthened and extended to complex Banach spaces by the writer [**14**]–[**16**].

In §1, we give a systematic development of the application of monotone operators to elliptic boundary value problems, motivating the discussion by a brief presentation of the corresponding linear theory. We remark that a somewhat different treatment of a similar class of strongly elliptic quasilinear equations was first given by Višik in [**32**]–[**34**] and [**36**]. In Theorems 1 and 2, we treat monotone operators defined on all of V.

In §2, we pass to the treatment of parabolic problems based upon theorems on densely defined monotone operators. Here again, we should refer to earlier work of Višik on parabolic equations [**35**] based on other arguments. We also consider in this section more general initial value problems and nonlinear symmetric positive systems.

In §3, we state the writer's result from [**10**] on nonlinear equations of evolution in a Hilbert space and refer to Kato's extension of this result in [**21**].

In §4, we present some results in complex Banach spaces along the lines treated by Zarantonello [**38**] and the writer [**14**]–[**16**].

In §5, we discuss duality mappings of Banach spaces and the generalized Beurling–Livingston theorem.

In §6, we sketch briefly the treatment of nonlinear elliptic eigenvalue problems by variational methods given by the writer in [**18**] and note connections with monotone operators.

We give the proofs of representative and especially significant results below, especially when they are improvements upon results and proofs given in earlier papers. We have not attempted to give formal statements to most of the results in the applications to boundary value problems and refer for the latter to the literature.

In statements of hypotheses applied below in discursive discussions, we have used the simplest rather than the technically best hypotheses.

1. Let Ω be an open subset of the Euclidean n-space R^n, where, for the sake of simplicity, we assume that Ω is bounded and smoothly bounded. We denote the general point of Ω by $x = (x_1, \cdots, x_n)$ and the element of Lebesgue n-measure on Ω by dx. We write linear differential operators on Ω by setting

$$D^\alpha = \prod_{j=1}^{n} \left(\frac{\partial}{\partial x_j}\right)^{\alpha_j}, \qquad |\alpha| = \sum_{j=1}^{n} \alpha_j, \tag{1.1}$$

for each n-vector $\alpha = (\alpha_1, \cdots, \alpha_n)$ whose components are non-negative integers.

Let m and r be fixed positive integers. We consider r-vector functions $u = (u_1, \cdots, u_r)$ whose components are real-valued functions on Ω. To write nonlinear differential operators (or systems of such operators) acting on such functions u, we introduce real vectors ξ of the form

$$\xi = \{\xi_\alpha \mid |\alpha| \leqq m\} \tag{1.2}$$

with a component ξ_α in R^r for each index of differentiation α of order $\leqq m$. The set of such vectors ξ forms a real vector space R^M whose dimension M is a function of m, r, and n. Similarly, we may introduce vectors of the form

$$\eta = \{\eta_\alpha \mid |\alpha| \leqq m - 1\} \tag{1.3}$$

and

$$\gamma = \{\gamma_\alpha \mid |\alpha| = m\} \tag{1.4}$$

which form vector spaces R^{M_1} and R^{M_2}.

A nonlinear system of r differential operators of order m acting on r-vector functions u on Ω is given by a function

$$A\colon \Omega \times R^M \to R^r \tag{1.5}$$

whose value at (x, ξ) we write as $A(x, \xi)$. If to an r-vector function u on Ω, we assign the function $\xi(u)$ from Ω to R^M given by

$$\xi(u)(x) = \{D^\alpha u(x) \mid |\alpha| \leqq m\}, \tag{1.6}$$

the differential system given by the function A yields the mapping

$$u \to A(u) \tag{1.7}$$

where

$$A(u)(x) = A(x, \xi(u)(x)), \qquad x \in \Omega. \tag{1.8}$$

This definition makes sense if u and all its derivatives of order $\leqq m$ are defined up to sets of measure zero in Ω.

To motivate the general formulation of variational boundary value problems for nonlinear partial differential operators of strongly elliptic type, we recall briefly the corresponding formulation for the Dirichlet problem for a linear strongly elliptic system.

Let A_0 be a linear system of r differential operators of order $2m$ acting on the r-vector function u, where

$$A_0 u = \sum_{|\alpha| \leqq 2m} A_\alpha(x) D^\alpha u. \tag{1.9}$$

The Dirichlet problem for A_0 on Ω asks for a solution u in $C^{2m}(\Omega)$ of the equation

$$A_0 u = f \quad \text{in } \Omega, \tag{1.10}$$

with the boundary conditions

$$D^\beta u = 0 \quad \text{on } \Gamma, \qquad |\beta| \leqq m - 1, \tag{1.11}$$

where Γ is the boundary of Ω and f is a given function on Ω.

For any real number p with $+1 < p < +\infty$, let

$$W^{m,p}(\Omega) = \{u \mid u \in L^p(\Omega),\ D^\alpha u \in L^p(\Omega) \text{ for } |\alpha| \leqq m\} \tag{1.12}$$

(where distribution derivatives D^α are taken) with the norm

$$\|u\|_{m,p} = \Big\{ \sum_{|\alpha| \leqq m} \| D^\alpha u \|^p_{L^p(\Omega)} \Big\}^{1/p}. \tag{1.13}$$

$W^{m,p}(\Omega)$ is a reflexive (and separable) Banach space which for every p includes as a subset the family $C_c^\infty(\Omega)$ of infinitely differentiable r-vector functions u with compact support in Ω. We set

$$W_0^{m,p}(\Omega) = \text{closure in } W^{m,p}(\Omega) \text{ of } C_c^\infty(\Omega). \tag{1.14}$$

The Hilbert space method of solving the Dirichlet problem for A_0 on Ω is based upon translating the Dirichlet problem into a weaker problem which is a functional equation in the Hilbert space $W_0^{m,2}(\Omega)$, proving the existence of a solution of this functional equation, and then showing that this generalized or variational solution is regular enough if f and Ω are sufficiently smooth to force it to be a solution of the Dirichlet problem in the classical sense. Specifically, the translation process is the following:

We replace the boundary conditions (1.11) by the condition

$$u \in W_0^{m,2}(\Omega) \tag{1.15}$$

a substitution which is justified by the remark that a function u in $C^m(\bar{\Omega})$ will satisfy condition (1.11) if and only if it satisfies condition (1.15). On the other hand, condition (1.15) applies to a wider class of not-so-regular functions u.

Second, we take the scalar product in $L^2(\Omega)$ of both sides of the differential equation (1.10) with an arbitrary ψ in $C_c^\infty(\Omega)$, obtaining

$$(A_0 u, \psi) = (f, \psi), \qquad \psi \in C_c^\infty(\Omega), \tag{1.16}$$

where we set

$$(u, v) = \int_\Omega \sum_{j=1}^{r} u_j(x) v_j(x)\, dx.$$

We assume moreover that A_0 is given to us in the generalized divergence form

$$A_0 u = \sum_{|\alpha|,|\beta| \leq m} D^\alpha (A_{\alpha b}(x) D^\beta u), \tag{1.17}$$

as is always possible if the coefficients of A_0 in formula (1.19) lie in $C^m(\Omega)$. Then, assuming that we have a regular function u, equation (1.16) becomes

$$(f, \psi) = \sum_{|\alpha|,|\beta| \leq m} (D^\alpha (A_{\alpha b} D^\beta u), \psi) = a(u, \psi) \tag{1.18}$$

where

$$a(u, \psi) = \sum_{|\alpha|,|\beta| \leq m} (-1)^{|\alpha|} (A_{\alpha b}(x) D^\beta u, D^\alpha \psi). \tag{1.19}$$

The generalized Dirichlet problem then asks for a solution u of

$$a(u, \psi) = (f, \psi), \qquad \psi \in C_c^\infty(\Omega), \tag{1.20}$$

with u lying in $W_0^{m,2}(\Omega)$. The bilinear function $a(u, \psi)$ is termed the Dirichlet form corresponding to the representation (1.17) of A_0 in generalized divergence form.

The problem of finding a solution for equation (1.20) is equivalent to a simple operator-theoretical question in the Hilbert space $W_0^{m,2}(\Omega)$. Indeed, if we assume that the $A_{\alpha\beta}$ are uniformly bounded on Ω, it follows from the Schwarz inequality that

$$|a(u, \psi)| \leq c_0 \|u\|_{m,2} \|\psi\|_{m,2}, \tag{1.21}$$

and that for each fixed u in $W_0^{m,2}(\Omega)$, $a(u, \psi)$ is a bounded linear functional of ψ in the dense subset $C_c^\infty(\Omega)$ of $W_0^{m,2}(\Omega)$. Hence there exists a unique element Tu of $W_0^{m,2}(\Omega)$ such that for all ψ in $C_c^\infty(\Omega)$,

$$(Tu, \psi)_m = a(u, \psi). \tag{1.22}$$

Similarly there exists a unique w in $W_0^{m,2}(\Omega)$ such that for all ψ in $C_c^\infty(\Omega)$,

$$(w, \psi)_m = (f, \psi). \tag{1.23}$$

Then the equation (1.20) is equivalent to

$$(Tu, \psi)_m = (w, \psi)_m, \qquad \psi \in C_c^\infty(\Omega), \tag{1.24}$$

i.e., simply to

$$Tu = w. \tag{1.25}$$

Hence the problem of proving the existence of the generalized solution u which satisfies equation (1.20) is equivalent to proving that w lies in $R(T)$, the range of the operator T from $W_0^{m,2}(\Omega)$ to $W_0^{m,2}(\Omega)$. Such a solution u will exist for each f if we can show that every w lies in $R(T)$, i.e., that T maps onto $W_0^{m,2}(\Omega)$.

Under what hypotheses can such a conclusion be obtained in the linear case? The hypothesis of strong ellipticity of A_0 and the uniform continuity of the top-order $A_{\alpha\beta}$ implies the Gårding inequality: There exist constants $c > 0$, $k \geqq 0$ such that

$$a(u, u) \geqq c\|u\|_{m,2}^2 - k\|u\|_{0,2}^2, \qquad u \in W_0^{m,2}(\Omega). \tag{1.26}$$

The inequality (1.26) is not quite enough by itself to insure the solvability of equation (1.20), but it is enough to know the stronger form with $k = 0$, i.e.,

$$a(u, u) \geqq c\|u\|_{m,2}^2, \qquad u \in W_0^{m,2}(\Omega). \tag{1.27}$$

Let us observe the reasoning to see the parallels and the differences with the later discussion of the nonlinear case.

It follows from the definition of the operator T by equation (1.23) and the inequality (1.21) that T is a bounded linear mapping of $W_0^{m,2}(\Omega)$ into itself and that

$$\|Tu\|_{m,2} \leqq c_0\|u\|_{m,2}.$$

From the inequality (1.27), we know that

$$(Tu, u)_m = a(u, u) \geqq c\|u\|_{m,2}^2, \qquad u \in W_0^{m,2}(\Omega)$$

where c is a positive constant.

Let V be $W_0^{m,2}(\Omega)$ considered as a Banach space. Then if V^* is the conjugate space of V and if we denote the pairing of the functional w from V^* and the element u of V by $\langle w, u\rangle$, we may identify V^* with $W_0^{m,2}(\Omega)$ since the latter is a Hilbert space and we note that under this identification

$$\langle w, u\rangle = (w, u)_m.$$

Our situation is then the following: T is a bounded linear map of V into V^* such that $\langle Tu, u\rangle \geqq c\|u\|^2$ for all u in V, where V is a reflexive Banach space. We must prove that T maps onto V^*.

PROOF. Since for u in V,

$$c\|u\|^2 \leqq \langle Tu, u\rangle \leqq \|Tu\| \cdot \|u\|,$$

it follows that $c\|u\| \leqq \|Tu\|$ for all u in V. Hence T is one-to-one and $R(T)$ is closed. Let T^* be the adjoint mapping to T. Since V is reflexive, T^* maps V into V^*. Since $N(T^*)$, the nullspace of T^*, equals $R(T)^\perp$, the annihilator of $R(T)$ in V^*, it follows from the closedness of $R(T)$ that $R(T) = N(T^*)^\perp$. However, for all u in V,

$$\langle T^*u, u\rangle = \langle u, Tu\rangle = \langle Tu, u\rangle \geqq c\|u\|^2.$$

Hence T^* is one-to-one, $N(T^*) = \{0\}$, and $R(T) = V^*$. q.e.d.

The key observation to be made about this proof is that it uses the notion of the adjoint operator T^* which is a highly linear concept. We propose now to extend this existence proof by drastically different arguments to the nonlinear case.

We begin then with a nonlinear system in generalized divergence form

$$Au = \sum_{|\alpha| \leqq m} D^\alpha A_\alpha(x, u, Du, \cdots, D^m u) \tag{1.28}$$

where, more precisely, A_α is a nonlinear r-system of partial differential operators of order m on Ω for each α with $|\alpha| \leqq m$. We assume $A_\alpha: \Omega \times R^M \to R^r$ to be continuous in ξ on R^M for fixed x in Ω and measurable in x for fixed ξ. We assume moreover that for a fixed p with $+1 < p < +\infty$, we have

$$|A_\alpha(x, \xi)| \leqq c\{1 + |\xi|^{p-1}\}. \tag{1.29}$$

(Weaker assumptions are made in **[5]** [7], **[9]**, **[18]**.)

Consider the Dirichlet problem for the quasilinear operator A on Ω, i.e.,

$$\begin{aligned} Au &= f, \quad \text{on } \Omega; \\ D^\beta u &= 0 \quad \text{on } \Gamma, \qquad |\beta| \leqq m - 1. \end{aligned} \tag{1.30}$$

We consider the nonlinear Dirichlet form

$$a(u, \psi) = \sum_{|\alpha| \leqq m} (-1)^{(\alpha)}(A_\alpha(x, u, Du, \cdots, D^m u), D^\alpha \psi) \tag{1.31}$$

and replace the classical Dirichlet problem (1.30) as in the linear case by the generalized problem

$$\begin{aligned} a(u, \psi) &= (f, \psi), \qquad \psi \in C_c^\infty(\Omega) \\ u &\in W_0^{m,p}(\Omega) \end{aligned} \tag{1.32}$$

where the first equality is obtained as before by integrating by parts in the equation $(Au, \psi) = (f, \psi)$ which is a consequence of $Au = f$.

The generalized Dirichlet problem (1.32) may be generalized to other boundary value problems of variational type by replacing the subspace $W_0^{m,p}(\Omega)$ by an arbitrary closed subspace V of $W^{m,p}(\Omega)$ which contains $W_0^{m,p}(\Omega)$. We obtain then:

$$\begin{aligned} a(u, v) &= (f, v), \qquad v \in V; \\ u &\in V. \end{aligned} \tag{1.33}$$

The equivalence of the problems (1.32) and (1.33) for the case in which $V = W_0^{m,p}(\Omega)$ is based upon the fact that under the assumption (1.29), we have an inequality of the form

$$|a(u, v)| \leqq g(\|u\|_{m,p})\|v\|_{m,p} \tag{1.34}$$

by Hölder's inequality, for a given function $g(r)$ and all u and v in $W^{m,p}(\Omega)$. Moreover, $a(u, v)$, though nonlinear in u, is linear in v. Hence by continuity in v, the equality $a(u, v) = (f, v)$ will hold for all v in the dense subset $C_c^\infty(\Omega)$ of $W_0^{m,o}(\Omega)$ if and only if it holds for all v in $W_0^{m,p}(\Omega)$.

We turn now to the general problem (1.33). It may be construed in terms of an operator formula as in the linear case if we remark that the inequality (1.34) given above together with the linearity of $a(u, v)$ in v (as follows from the defining formula (1.31)) imply for each u in V that $a(u, v)$ is a bounded linear functional of v in V. Hence there is an uniquely defined element Tu of V^* such that

$$\langle Tu, v \rangle = a(u, v), \qquad v \in V. \tag{1.35}$$

Similarly, there is an unique w in V^* such that

$$\langle w, v \rangle = (f, v), \qquad v \in V. \tag{1.36}$$

Then the problems (1.33) become

$$\langle Tu, v \rangle = \langle w, v \rangle, \qquad v \in V, \tag{1.37}$$

i.e.,

$$Tu = w. \tag{1.38}$$

We now wish to impose hypotheses upon the nonlinear Dirichlet form $a(u, v)$ which parallel the assumption (1.27) in the linear case and which we can verify from concrete-analytical assumptions on the A_α. The simplest such assumptions are the following:

(1.39) *There exists a function* $c\colon R^1 \to R^1$ *with* $c(r) \to +\infty$ *as* $r \to +\infty$ *such that*

$$a(u, u) \geqq c(\|u\|_{m,p})\|u\|_{m,p}, \qquad u \in V,$$

and

$$a(u, u - v) - a(v, u - v) \geqq 0, \qquad u, v \in V. \tag{1.40}$$

Translating (1.39) and (1.40) into the corresponding assumptions on $\langle Tu, u \rangle$, the existence of a solution u of problem (1.33) then follows from the following theorem:

THEOREM 1. *Let T be a mapping (possibly nonlinear) of the reflexive real Banach space V into its conjugate space V^* which satisfies the following three conditions*:

(a) *T is continuous from lines in V to the weak topology of V^*.*

(b) *There exists a real function c on R^1 with* $\lim_{r \to +\infty} c(r) = +\infty$ *such that for all u in V,*

$$\langle Tu, u \rangle \geqq c(\|u\|)\|u\|.$$

(c) *T is monotone, i.e., for all u and v in V,*

$$\langle Tu - Tv, u - v \rangle \geqq 0.$$

Then T maps V onto V^*.

Theorem 1 was proved independently by the writer in **[5]** and G. J. Minty **[27]**. Extensions with weaker versions of condition (c) have been given by the writer [7], **[9]** and Leray and Lions (unpublished) with the purpose of weakening the assumptions (1.40) to make the existence result for the nonlinear boundary value problems properly contain the results of Višik **[32]**–**[34]** and **[36]** obtained by more concrete-analytical methods. The proof of Theorem 1 is contained in that of Theorem 2 given below.

To observe how assumptions of the type of the inequality (1.40) may be verified from concrete-analytic assumptions on the functions A_α, let

$$A_{\alpha\beta}(x, \xi) = \frac{\partial A_\alpha}{\partial \xi_\beta}(x, \xi); \qquad |\alpha|, |\beta| \leqq m. \tag{1.41}$$

Then

$$\begin{aligned} a(u, u-v) - a(v, u-v) &= \sum_{|\alpha| \leqq m} (-1)^{|\alpha|}(A_\alpha(u) - A_\alpha(v), D^\alpha(u-v)) \\ &= \int_0^1 \sum_{|\alpha| \leqq m} (-1)^{|\alpha|} \frac{d}{dt}(A_\alpha(tu + (1-t)v), D^\alpha(u-v))\, dt. \end{aligned}$$

Setting $u_t = tu + (1-t)v$, we have

$$\begin{aligned} &a(u, u-v) - a(v, u-v) \\ &\quad = \int_0^1 \sum_{|\alpha|,|\beta| \leqq m} (-1)^{|\alpha|}(A_{\alpha\beta}(u_t)D^\beta(u-v), D^\alpha(u-v))\, dt. \end{aligned} \tag{1.42}$$

Obviously, we may obtain inequalities from below for $a(u, u-v) - a(v, u-v)$ from inequalities from below for the form

$$c(x, \xi, \rho) = \sum_{|\alpha|,|\beta| \leqq m} \langle A_{\alpha\beta}(x, \xi)\rho_\beta, \rho_\alpha \rangle. \tag{1.43}$$

The object of the strengthened forms of Theorem 1 is to obtain corresponding results from assumptions only on the part of the form $c(x, \xi, \rho)$ which depends upon α and β with order equal to m. No best possible result seems yet to have been obtained in this direction. We shall indicate one below, however, of a very simple type which is as strong in one direction of application as any of the more complicated results.

Let

$$c_0(x, \xi, \rho) = \sum_{|\alpha| \leqq m, |\beta| = m} \langle A_{\alpha\beta}(x, \xi)\rho_\beta, \rho_\alpha \rangle. \tag{1.44}$$

Then, if we redefine the nonlinear Dirichlet form $a(u, v)$ to be a function of three variables by setting

$$a(u, w; v) = \sum_{|\alpha| \leqq m} (-1)^{|\alpha|}(A_\alpha(x, w, Dw, \cdots, D^{m-1}w, D^m u), D^\alpha v), \tag{1.45}$$

lower bounds on $c_0(x, \xi, \rho)$ imply lower bounds on

$$a(u, w; u-v) - a(v, w; u-v).$$

The generalized boundary value problem (1.33) may be turned into a functional equation as follows:

For fixed u and w in V, $a(u, w; v)$ is a bounded linear functional of v in V. Hence there exists an uniquely defined element $S(u, w)$ in V^* such that

$$\langle S(u, w), v \rangle = a(u, w; v), \qquad v \in V. \tag{1.46}$$

The previous operator T is then given by

$$T(u) = S(u, u), \qquad u \in V. \tag{1.47}$$

If we assume the inequality (1.39) as well as

$$a(u, v; u - v) - a(v, v; u - v) \geqq 0 \tag{1.48}$$

for all u and v in V, and if we note that $a(u, w; v)$ is uniformly weakly continuous in w running through bounded sets for u and v in a fixed bounded subset of V, the existence of a solution under the hypotheses (1.39) and (1.48) follows from the following simple strengthened form of Theorem 1, whose proof we give in detail below.

THEOREM 2. *Let V be a reflexive Banach space, V^* its conjugate space, S a mapping of $V \times V$ into V^*. Let T be the mapping of V into V^* given by $T(u) = S(u, u)$, $u \in V$. Suppose that:*

(a) *For fixed w in V, $S(\cdot, w)$ is continuous from lines in V to the weak topology of V^*.*

(b) *For fixed u in V, $S(u, \cdot)$ is completely continuous from V to V^* (i.e., continuous on bounded sets from the weak topology on V to the strong topology of V^*).*

(c) *For u and v in V,*

$$\langle S(u, v) - S(v, v), u - v\rangle \geqq 0.$$

(d) *There exists a real function c on R^1 with $c(r) \to +\infty$ as $r \to +\infty$ such that*

$$\langle Tu, u\rangle \geqq c(\|u\|)\|u\|, \qquad u \in V.$$

Then T maps V onto V^*.

PROOF OF THEOREM 2. We shall carry out the proof here under the mild additional hypothesis that T is continuous from finite dimensional subspaces of V to the weak topology on V^*. (This actually follows from the hypotheses of Theorem 2, but we shall not verify this fact explicitly in the present discussion.)

The proof rests upon two simple lemmas.

LEMMA 1. *Let T be a continuous mapping of the finite dimensional Banach space V into V^* such that*

$$\langle Tu, u\rangle \geqq c(\|u\|)\|u\|, \qquad u \in V,$$

for a given function $c(r)$ such that $c(r) \to +\infty$ as $r \to +\infty$.

Then T maps V onto V^*.

PROOF OF LEMMA 1. V may be taken as a Hilbert space with $V = V^*$. It suffices by considering a new mapping $T(u) - w_0$ for fixed w_0 in V, to show that $0 \in R(T)$. Choose R so large that for $\|u\| = R$, $\langle Tu, u\rangle > 0$. Then if T_t

$= tT + (1 - t)I$, $0 \leqq t \leqq 1$, the mappings T_t of the ball $B_R = \{u \mid \|u\| < R\}$ into V are uniformly continuous, and for $\|u\| = R$,

$$\langle T_t u, u\rangle = t\langle Tu, u\rangle + (1 - t)\|u\|^2 > 0.$$

Hence $T_1 = T$ has the same degree over 0 on B_R as $T_0 = I$, and there exists a solution u in B_R of the equation $Tu = 0$. q.e.d.

LEMMA 2. *Let T_0 be a mapping from the dense linear subset $D(T_0)$ of V into V^* such that T_0 is continuous from lines in $D(T_0)$ to the weak topology of V^*. Suppose that for a given u_0 in $D(T_0)$ and w_0 in V^*, we have*

$$\langle T_0 u - w_0, u - u_0\rangle \geqq 0$$

for all u in $D(T_0)$.

Then $T_0 u_0 = w_0$.

PROOF OF LEMMA 2. If $w_0 - T_0 u_0 \neq 0$, there exists v in the dense subset $D(T_0)$ such that $\langle w_0 - T_0 u_0, v\rangle > 0$. For $t > 0$, $u_t = u_0 + tv$ lies in $D(T_0)$. Hence

$$0 \leqq \langle T_0 u_t - w_0, u_t - u_0\rangle = t\langle T_0 u_t - w_0, v\rangle.$$

Cancelling $t > 0$ and rewriting the inequality, we have

$$\langle T_0 u_t - T_0 u_0, v\rangle \geqq \langle w_0 - T_0 u_0, v\rangle > 0.$$

Since

$$\langle T_0 u_t - T_0 u_0, v\rangle \to 0$$

as $t \to 0+$, we have a contradiction. q.e.d.

PROOF OF THEOREM 2 CONCLUDED. Let Λ be the directed set of the finite dimensional subspaces of V order by inclusion. For $F \in \Lambda$, let j_F be the inclusion map of F into V, j_{F^*} the dual projection map of V^* onto F^*, and set

$$T_F = j_{F^*} T j_F \colon F \to F^*.$$

Then T_F is continuous, and for $u \in F$,

$$\langle T_F u, u\rangle = \langle Tu, u\rangle \geqq c(\|u\|)\|u\|.$$

Applying Lemma 1, we see that there exists u_F in F such that $T_F u_F = 0$. For such u_F, we have $c(\|u_F\|)\|u_F\| \leqq 0$, so that since $c(r) \to +\infty$ as $r \to +\infty$, there exists M independent of F in Λ such that $\|u_F\| \leqq M$.

Since V is reflexive, there exists u_0 in V such that u_0 lies in the weak closure of each set

$$V_{F_0} = \bigcup_{F_0 \subset F} \{u_F\}.$$

Let u be an arbitrary element of V and consider F in Λ containing u. For such F, we have

$$\langle Tu_F, u - u_F \rangle = \langle T_F u_F, u - u_F \rangle = 0.$$

Applying condition (c) of the hypothesis of Theorem 2, we have

$$\langle S(u, u_F) - S(u_F, u_F), u - u_F \rangle \geqq 0,$$

i.e.,

$$\langle S(u, u_F), u - u_F \rangle \geqq \langle Tu_F, u - u_F \rangle = 0.$$

By the hypothesis (b) of complete continuity of S in its second variable, the function of v given by

$$\langle S(u, v), u - v \rangle$$

is continuous on bounded sets of V in the weak topology. Since it is non-negative on V_{F_0} for F_0 containing u, it follows that

$$\langle S(u, u_0), u - u_0 \rangle \geqq 0.$$

Since this is true for all u in V, we apply Lemma 2 to $T_0(u) = S(u, u_0)$ and find that $S(u_0, u_0) = 0$, i.e., $Tu_0 = 0$.

Hence $0 \in R(T)$. Since the substitution of $T(u) - w$ for $T(u)$ does not affect the hypotheses of Theorem 2, it follows that $R(T) = V^*$. q.e.d.

2. The passage from the treatment of elliptic boundary value problems to other types of boundary value problems corresponds on the operator-theoretic level to the passage from operators defined on the whole of a Banach space V to those defined only on a dense linear subset of V. The most useful generalization of Theorems 1 and 2 in this direction is the following:

THEOREM 3. *Let V be a reflexive Banach space, V^* its conjugate space. Let T be an operator defined on a dense linear subset $D(T)$ of V with values in V^*, such that $T = L + G$, where:*

(a) *L is a densely defined closed linear operator from V to V^* such that L^* is the closure of its restriction to $D(L) \cap D(L^*)$.*

(b) *G is a mapping of V into V^* given by $G(u) = H(u, u)$, where H is a mapping of $V \times V$ into V^*. For fixed w in V, $H(\cdot, w)$ is continuous from lines in V to the weak topology on V^*, while for fixed u in V, $H(u, \cdot)$ is completely continuous from V to V^*. G maps bounded sets of V into bounded sets of V^*.*

(c) *For u and v in $D(T)$,*

$$\langle L(u - v) + H(u, v) - H(v, v), u - v \rangle \geqq 0.$$

(d) *There exists a real function c on R^1 with $c(r) \to +\infty$ as $r \to +\infty$ such that*

$$\langle Tu, u \rangle \geqq c(\|u\|)\|u\|$$

for all u in $D(T)$.

Then $R(T) = V^*$.

PROOF OF THEOREM 3. It suffices as before to show that $0 \in R(T)$. Let Λ now be the directed set of finite dimensional subspaces of $D(T)$ ordered by inclusion. For each F in Λ, let j_F, j_{F^*}, and $T_F: F \to F^*$ be defined as in the proof of Theorem 2 with

$$T_F = j_{F^*} T j_F.$$

We shall assume, as in the proof of Theorem 2, the additional (and inessential) hypothesis that T is continuous from finite dimensional subspaces of $D(T)$ to the weak topology of V^*. Then T_F is continuous for each F in Λ and by the same argument as in the proof of Theorem 2, there exists u_F in F with $T_F u_F = 0$, while there exists a constant M independent of F in Λ such that

$$\|u_F\| \leqq M.$$

By the reflexivity of V, there exists u_0 in V such that for each F_0 in Λ, u_0 lies in the weak closure of the set

$$V_{F_0} = \bigcup_{F_0 \subset F} \{u_F\}.$$

Let v be any element of $D(L) \cap D(L^*)$. Then $v \in D(T)$ and for F containing v, we have

$$0 = \langle T_F u_F, v\rangle = \langle T u_F, v\rangle = \langle L u_F, v\rangle + \langle G u_F, v\rangle.$$

However,

$$\langle L u_F, v\rangle = \langle u_F, L^* v\rangle$$

while, since G maps bounded sets into bounded sets, $\|G u_F\| \leqq M_1$ for some M_1 independent of F. Hence

$$|\langle u_F, L^* v\rangle| \leqq M_1 \|v\|.$$

Since for fixed v, both sides of this last inequality are weakly continuous in u_F, we have

$$|\langle u_0, L^* v\rangle| \leqq M_1 \|v\|, \qquad v \in D(L) \cap D(L^*).$$

Since both sides of the preceding inequality are continuous in v in the norm of the graph of L^*, and since the portion of the graph of L^* with v in $D(L) \cap D(L^*)$ is dense, we have

$$|\langle u_0, L^* v\rangle| \leqq M_1 \|v\|, \qquad v \in D(L^*).$$

Hence $u_0 \in D(L^{**}) = D(L) = D(T)$.

Let u be an arbitrary element of $D(T)$ and let F be any element of Λ containing u. Then

$$\langle T u_F, u - u_F\rangle = \langle T_F u_F, u - u_F\rangle = 0.$$

By hypothesis

$$
\begin{aligned}
0 &\leqq \langle Lu - Lu_F + H(u, u_F) - H(u_F, u_F), u - u_F\rangle \\
&= \langle Lu + H(u, u_F), u - u_F\rangle - \langle Tu_F, u - u_F\rangle \\
&= \langle Lu + H(u, u_F), u - u_F\rangle.
\end{aligned}
$$

Since $H(u, \cdot)$ is completely continuous, the term on the right of the last inequality is weakly continuous in u_F on bounded subsets of V. Since it is non-negative for all elements of V_{F_0} for $u \in F_0$, it follows that it is non-negative for u_0, i.e.,

$$\langle Lu + H(u, u_0), u - u_0\rangle \geqq 0$$

for all u in $D(T)$. Let $T_0(u) = Lu + H(u, u_0)$ for u in $D(T)$ and apply Lemma 2. Then $T_0 u_0 = 0$, i.e., $Tu_0 = 0$.

As applications of Theorem 3, we have the following:

THEOREM 4 (PARABOLIC EQUATIONS). *Let Ω be a bounded open subset of R^n and for $t \in R^+ = \{t \mid t \in R^1, t \geqq 0\}$, let*

$$A(t)u = \sum_{|\alpha| \leqq m} D^\alpha A_\alpha(x, t, u, \cdots, D^m u),$$

where the A_α are measurable in (x, t) and continuous in $(u, \cdots, D^m u)$, while for a given p with $1 < p < +\infty$, there exists a continuous function $c(t)$ such that

$$|A_\alpha(x, t, \xi)| \leqq c(t)\{1 + |\xi|^{p-1}\}.$$

Suppose also that if

$$a(t, u, v) = \sum_{|\alpha| \leqq m} (-1)^{|\alpha|}(A_\alpha(\cdot, t, u, \cdots, D^m u), D^\alpha v)$$

we have for all u in a closed subspace V of $W^{m,p}(\Omega)$,

$$a(t, u, u) \geqq c(t)\|u\|^p_{m,p}$$

and

$$a(t, u, u - v) - a(t, v, u - v) \geqq -c(t)\|u - v\|^2_{0,2}.$$

Then there exists one and only one solution u in $L^p_{\mathrm{loc}}(R^+, V) \cap C^0(R^+, L^2(\Omega))$ with $u(0) = 0$ of the equation $\partial u/\partial t + A(t)u = 0$ in the sense that for all ψ in $C^1(R^+, V)$ with bounded support

$$-\int_0^\infty \left(u(t), \frac{d\psi}{dt}\right) dt = \int_0^\infty a(t, u(t), \psi(t))\, dt.$$

The detailed derivation of Theorem 4 from Theorem 3 was given by the writer in **[8]** and announced in **[6]**. Theorem 4 and corresponding results on nonlinear wave equations (including part of the results of **[24]**) are special cases of the following theorem:

THEOREM 5. *Let H be a Hilbert space, V a reflexive Banach space with a continuous injection into H. Let $B(t)$, $t \in R^+$, be a continuous family of mappings of V into V^* such that for some real p with $1 < p < +\infty$ and a continuous positive function $c(t)$ on R^+, we have*

$$\|B(t)u\|_{V^*} \leqq c(t)\|u\|_V^{p-1},$$
$$\langle B(t)u, u\rangle \geqq c(t)\|u\|_V^p$$

for all u in V, while

$$\langle B(t)u - B(t)v, u - v\rangle \geqq 0$$

for all u, v in V.

Then there exists one and only one generalized solution of the equation

$$\frac{du}{dt} + B(t, u(t)) = f(t)$$

on R^+ with $u(0) = u_0$ for given f and u_0, i.e., $u \in L^p(R^+, V) \cap C^0(R^+, H)$, $u(0) = u_0$, and

$$-\int_0^\infty \left(u(t), \frac{d\psi}{dt}(t)\right) dt + \int_0^\infty \langle B(t)u(t), \psi(t)\rangle\, dt = \int_0^\infty \langle f(t), \psi(t)\rangle\, dt + \langle u_0, \psi(0)\rangle$$

for all $\psi \in C_c^1(R^+, H) \cap L^{p'}(R^+, V)$.

Theorem 5 is, in turn, a special case of corresponding theorems for equations of evolution of the form

$$\frac{du}{dt} + A(t)u + B(t)u = f(t)$$

where the additional terms $A(t)$ are a family of closed linear operators in H having suitable extension properties from V to V^*. These results are discussed in detail in the writer's paper on nonlinear initial value problems **[17]**.

Another family of such results of which we give only a very special case here are those given in **[17]** for nonlinear perturbations of the symmetric positive systems of Friedrichs **[19]**.

THEOREM 6. *Let L be a symmetric positive system on a bounded open set Ω of R^n, realized under permissible boundary conditions as in* **[19]**. *Let f be a continuous real-valued function on $\Omega \times R^r$ with*

$$|f(x, u)| \leqq c\{1 + |u|\}$$

and

$$(f(x, u) - f(x, v), u - v) \geqq 0,$$
$$(f(x, u), u) \geqq 0$$

for all u and v in $L^2(\Omega)$.

Then the equation $Lu + f(x, u) = g(x)$ has a solution u in $D(L)$ for every g in $L^2(\Omega)$ and u is unique.

Other results for f having polynomial growth in u are given in **[17]**.

3. A refinement of the proof of Theorem 3 is given in the writer's paper **[10]** to yield the following result about nonlinear equations of evolution in a Hilbert space.

THEOREM 7. *Let H be a Hilbert space, f a continuous mapping of $R^+ \times H$ into H which carries bounded sets into bounded sets. Let $\{A(t); t \in R^+\}$ be a family of closed linear operators in H whose domain $D(A(t)) = W$ is independent of t, while $A(t)$ maps W with the graph norm in a C^1-fashion into H. Suppose that all of the following conditions are fulfilled*:

(1) *There exists a continuous real function c on R^+ such that*

$$\langle f(t, u) - f(t, v), u - v\rangle \leqq c(t)\|u - v\|^2$$

for all u and v in H, $t \in R^+$.

(2) *$D(A(T)^*) \subset W$; for u in $D(A(T))$,*

$$\langle A(t)u, u\rangle \leqq c(t)\|u\|^2.$$

Then there exists one and only one mild solution u of

$$\frac{du}{dt} = A(t)u + f(t, u), \qquad t \in R^+ \tag{3.1}$$

with $u(0) = g$, prescribed in W.

Under the hypotheses given on $A(t)$, the linear equation $du/dt = A(t)u$ has propagators $U(t, s)$, i.e., $u(t) = U(t, s)v$ is the solution of the equation on the interval $[s, \infty)$ with $u(s) = v$ for v in W, and $U(t, s)$ are bounded operators in H. Then a mild solution of the equation (3.1) with $u(0) = g$ is defined to be a solution of the integral equation corresponding to (3.1)

$$u(t) = U(t, 0)g + \int_0^t U(t, s)f(s, u(s))\, ds. \tag{3.2}$$

More recently, T. Kato **[21]** has obtained an extension of Theorem 7 with the hypotheses on $A(t)$ weakened to the following:

(i) *For each t in R^+, $A(t)$ is the infinitesmal generator of a one-parameter contraction semigroup.*

(ii) *$(A(t) + I)^{-1}$ is C^1 in t on R^+ in the strong topology.*

4. If V is a complex rather than real Banach space and V^* is the space of bounded conjugate-linear functionals on V with pairing (w, u) between w in V^* and u in V, we may take $\langle w, u\rangle = \mathrm{Re}(w, u)$ as a pairing between V^* and V considered as real

Banach spaces. The results of §§1 and 2 then go over to the complex case with the hypotheses on $\langle Tu, u\rangle$ and $\langle Tu - Tv, u - v\rangle$ replaced by hypotheses on $\mathrm{Re}(Tu, u)$ and $\mathrm{Re}(Tu - Tv, u - v)$.

A more interesting direction of generalization for the complex case was initiated by Zarantonello **[38]** who considered nonlinear operators in a complex Hilbert space H, continuous and mapping bounded sets into bounded sets, for which

$$|(Tu - Tv, u - v)| \geqq c\|u - v\|^2$$

for all $u, v \in V$ and a fixed $c > 0$, and proved that T mapped onto H. This result was strengthened and extended to complex Banach spaces by the writer in **[14]**, **[15]** and **[16]**. The latter results, especially in the local form given to them in **[16]**, are applicable to existence theorems for solutions of nonlinear elliptic boundary value problems which are not strongly elliptic. We shall not consider these applications in detail here, but content ourselves with giving the proof of two basic and simple results in this direction.

THEOREM 8. *Let V be a complex Banach space, T a mapping of V into V^* such that T is continuous from finite dimensional subspaces of V into the weak topology of V^*. Suppose that there exists a continuous strictly increasing real function c on R^+ with $c(0) = 0$, $c(+\infty) = +\infty$, such that*

$$|(Tu - Tv, u - v)| \geqq c(\|u - v\|)\|u - v\| \tag{4.1}$$

for all u and v in V.

Then T maps V one-to-one, bicontinuously onto V^*.

The proof of Theorem 8 rests upon the following lemma:

LEMMA 3. *Theorem 8 holds if V is of finite dimension.*

PROOF OF LEMMA 3. If V is of finite dimension, the hypothesis of Theorem 8 implies that T is continuous. Since

$$\begin{aligned} c(\|u - v\|)\|u - v\| &\leqq |(Tu - Tv, u - v)| \\ &\leqq \|Tu - Tv\| \cdot \|u - v\|, \end{aligned}$$

we have

$$c(\|u - v\|) \leqq \|Tu - Tv\|.$$

Let $h(r)$ be the continuous strictly increasing function on R^+ which is the inverse function of $c(r)$, $h(0) = 0$. Then

$$\|u - v\| \leqq h(\|Tu - Tv\|).$$

Hence $R(T)$ is closed in V^* and T^{-1} is continuous. Moreover T is one-to-one so that $R(T)$ is open in V^* by the Brouwer theorem on invariance of domain for one-to-one self mappings of an Euclidean space of finite dimension. Hence $R(T) = V^*$. q.e.d.

PROOF OF THEOREM 8. Let Λ be the directed set of finite dimensional subspaces of V ordered by inclusion. For each F in Λ, let j_F be the injection map of F into V, j_{F^*} the projection map of V^* onto F^*, and set

$$T_F = j_{F^*}Tj_F\colon \quad F \to F^*.$$

Then $\|j_F\| = \|j_{F^*}\| = 1$, and T_F is a continuous map of F into F^*. We have for u and v in F,

$$|(T_Fu - T_Fv, u - v)| = |(Tu - Tv, u - v)| \geqq c(\|u - v\|)\|u - v\|.$$

By Lemma 3, T_F maps F one-to-one onto F^*. Suppose w is a given element of V^*. By Lemma 3, there exists a solution u_F in F of the equation

$$T_Fu_F = j_{F^*}w.$$

By the same argument as in the proof of Lemma 3, for all u and v in F,

$$\|u - v\| \leqq h(\|T_Fu - T_Fv\|).$$

Hence

$$\|u_F\| \leqq h(\|j_{F^*}w - T_F(0)\|) \leqq h(\|w\| + \|T(0)\|),$$

i.e.,

$$\|u_F\| \leqq M,$$

where M is a constant independent of F in Λ.

Since V is reflexive, there exists an element u_0 in V such that for every F_0 in Λ, u_0 lies in the weak closure of the set

$$V_{F_0} = \bigcup_{F_0 \subset F} \{u_F\}.$$

Let F and F_1 be two elements of Λ with $F \subset F_1$. Then

$$\begin{aligned} c(\|u_F - u_{F_1}\|)\|u_F - u_{F_1}\| &\leqq |(Tu_F - Tu_{F_1}, u_F - u_{F_1})| \\ &= |(Tu_F - w, u_F - u_{F_1})|. \end{aligned}$$

If $q(r)$ is the inverse function of $rc(r)$ on R^+, we have

$$\|u_F - u_{F_1}\| \leqq q(|(Tu_F - w, u_F - u_{F_1})|).$$

Consider the function of v in V given by

$$\|u_F - v\| - q(|(Tu_F - w, u_F - v)|).$$

This function is weakly lower-semicontinuous in v and is nonpositive on V_F. Hence it is nonpositive on the weak closure of V_F and in particular at u_0, i.e.,

$$\|u_F - u_0\| \leqq q(|(Tu_F - w, u_F - u_0)|).$$

Suppose finally that F contains u_0. Then

$$(Tu_F - w, u_F - u_0) = (T_Fu_F - j_{F^*}w, u_F - u_0) = 0$$

which implies that $\|u_F - u_0\| = 0$, i.e., $u_F = u_0$.

If v is any element of V, let F be an element of Λ which contains both u_0 and v. Then

$$(Tu_0, v) = (Tu_F, v) = (T_F u_F, v) = (j_{F^*} w, v) = (w, v),$$

i.e.,

$$(Tu_0 - w, v) = 0$$

for all v. Hence $Tu_0 = w$, and since w was an arbitrary element of V^*, $R(T) = V^*$. The fact that T is one-to-one and bicontinuous follows as in Lemma 3. q.e.d.

A corresponding generalization of Theorem 3 is the following:

THEOREM 9. *Let T be a mapping of the dense linear subset $D(T)$ of the reflexive complex Banach space V into V^*. Suppose that $T = L + G$, where:*

(a) *L is a densely defined closed linear mapping from V to V^* such that L^* is the closure of its restriction to $D(L) \cap D(L^*)$.*

(b) *G is a nonlinear mapping of V into V^* which is continuous from finite dimensional subspaces of V to the weak topology of V^*. G maps bounded subsets of V into bounded subsets of V^*.*

(c) *There exists a continuous strictly increasing real function c on R^+ with $c(0) = 0$, $c(+\infty) = +\infty$, such that for all u and v of $D(T)$,*

$$|(Tu - Tv, u - v)| \geqq c(\|u - v\|)\|u - v\|.$$

Then $R(T) = V^*$, T is one-to-one, and T^{-1} is a continuous mapping of V^* into V.

PROOF OF THEOREM 9. Let Λ be the directed set of finite dimensional subspaces of $D(T)$ ordered by inclusion. Let j_F, j_{F^*}, and T_F be as in the proof of Theorem 8. Then T_F maps F onto F^* as in the latter proof and if u_F is the unique solution of the equation $T_F u_F = j_{F^*} w$ in F,

$$\|u_F\| \leqq M$$

for a constant M independent of F in Λ. Hence by the reflexivity of V, there exists u_0 in V which lies in the weak closure of the set

$$V_{F_0} = \bigcap_{F_0 \subset F} \{u_F\}$$

for each F_0 in Λ.

Let v be any element of $D(L) \cap D(L^*)$ and F any element of Λ containing v. Then

$$0 = (T_F u_F - w, v) = (Tu_F - w, v),$$

i.e.,

$$|(u_F, L^*v)| = |(w - Gu_F, v)| \leqq M_1\|v\|$$

since G maps bounded sets into bounded sets. Since the function $|(u, L^*v)| - M_1\|v\|$ is weakly continuous in u for fixed v, it follows that

$$|(u_0, L^*v)| \leqq M_1\|v\|, \qquad v \in D(L) \cap D(L^*).$$

Since L^* is the closure of its restriction to $D(L) \cap D(L^*)$, it follows that

$$|(u_0, L^*v)| \leqq M_1\|v\|, \qquad v \in D(L^*),$$

and hence that $u_0 \in D(L) = D(T)$.

Let F and F_1 be two elements of Λ with $F \subset F_1$. Then

$$c(\|u_F - u_{F_1}\|)\|u_F - u_{F_1}\| \leqq |(Tu_F - Tu_{F_1}, u_F - u_{F_1})|$$

while

$$(Tu_F - Tu_{F_1}, u_F - u_{F_1}) = (Tu_F - w, u_F - u_{F_1}) = (Tu_F - w, u_{F_1}).$$

Hence, using the inverse function q of $rc(r)$, we see that

$$\|u_F - u_{F_1}\| \leqq q(|(Tu_F - w, u_{F_1})|)$$

for all u_{F_1} in V_F. Since the difference between the left and right sides of the inequality is weakly lower-semicontinuous in u_{F_1}, the same inequality holds for all elements in the weak closure of V_F and hence for u_0. Thus

$$\|u_F - u_0\| \leqq q(|(Tu_F - w, u_0)|).$$

Since, as we proved above, u_0 lies in $D(T)$, we can find an element F of Λ which contains u_0. For such F, we have

$$(Tu_F - w, u_0) = (T_F u_F - j_{F^*}w, u_0) = 0$$

so that $u_F = u_0$.

For any v in $D(T)$, let F be an element of Λ which contains both u_0 and v. Then

$$(Tu_0 - w, v) = (T_F u_F - j_{F^*}w, v) = 0,$$

and since $D(T)$ is dense, $Tu_0 = w$. q.e.d.

We close this section by remarking that in **[16]**, the writer has obtained a number of strengthened forms of the results given above whose proofs are based upon an interesting variant of Lemma 1 of §1. This is the following:

LEMMA 4. *Let V be a finite dimensional complex Banach space, T a continuous mapping of V into V^* such that for $\|u\| = R > 0$, $(Tu, u) \neq 0$. Then if the dimension of V (as a complex vector space) is greater than* 1, *there exists a solution of $Tu = 0$ with $\|u\| < R$.*

PROOF OF LEMMA 4. If B_R is the ball of radius R about 0 in V, it suffices to show that the degree of B_R under T over 0 differs from zero. This degree depends only upon the behaviour of the mapping T on the boundary S_R or B_R, where $S_R = \{u \mid \|u\| = R\}$. Moreover, if $T|S_R$ is homotopic as a mapping of S_R into $V^* - \{0\}$ to $T_1|S_R$, then T and T_1 have the same degree. By Lemma 1, it suffices to deform T on S_R into a mapping T_1 for which $\mathrm{Re}(T_1 u, u) > 0$ for u in S_R.

Consider the mapping $f: S_R \to S^1$ given by $f(u) = (Tu, u)|(Tu, u)|^{-1}$. If V has complex dimension > 1, S_R is a topological sphere of dimension > 1 and simply connected. Hence by the covering homotopy theorem, every mapping of S_R into the unit circle can be lifted to a map into the line and is contractible. Hence we can find a continuous mapping of $S_R \times [0, 1]$ into the unit circle $|\zeta| = 1$ such that $f(u, 0) = 1, f(u, 1) = \bar{f}(u)$ for all u in S_R.

We then deform $T|S_R$ by the one-parameter family

$$H_t u = f(t, u)T(u).$$

Then $H_0 = T$, while for $t = 1$,

$$(H_1 u, u) = \bar{f}(u)(Tu, u) = |(Tu, u)| > 0. \qquad \text{q.e.d.}$$

5. An interesting application of Theorem 1 is to the proof of the Beurling–Livingston theorem on duality mappings of Banach spaces [**11**].

Let V be a Banach space. If J is a mapping of V into V^*, J is said to be a duality mapping of V with gauge function Φ (where Φ is a given continuous, strictly increasing real function on R^1 with $\Phi(0) = 0$) if the following two conditions are satisfied:

(1) $\langle Ju, u\rangle = \|Ju\| \cdot \|u\|$;
(2) $\|Ju\| = \Phi(\|u\|)$.

THEOREM 10. *Let V be a strictly convex, reflexive Banach space, J a duality mapping of V (such mappings always exist). Let C be a closed subspace of V, $C^\perp$ its annihilator in V^*, f an element of V, g an element of V^*. Let $C + f$ be the translate of C by f, $C^\perp + g$ the translate of $C^\perp$ by g.*

Then $J(C + f) \cap (C^\perp + g)$ has exactly one element.

PROOF OF THEOREM 10. If V is strictly convex, the element Ju of V^* is uniquely determined by conditions (1) and (2). Hence it follows (see [**11**]) that J is continuous from the strong topology of V to the weak topology of V^*. Moreover

$$\langle Ju - Jv, u - v\rangle = \|Ju\| \cdot \|u\| + \|Jv\| \cdot \|v\| - \langle Jv, u\rangle - \langle Ju, v\rangle$$

while

$$\langle Jv, u\rangle \leqq \|Jv\| \cdot \|u\|,$$
$$\langle Ju, v\rangle \leqq \|Ju\| \cdot \|v\|$$

with equality holding only if $u = v$. Hence

$$\begin{aligned}\langle Ju - Jv, u - v\rangle &\geqq (\|Ju\| - \|Jv\|)(\|u\| - \|v\|)\\ &= \Phi(\|u\| - \Phi(\|v\|))(\|u\| - \|v\|) \geqq 0\end{aligned}$$

with equality holding only if $u = v$.

Therefore J is a monotone mapping of V into V^* and we have

$$\langle Ju, u\rangle = \|Ju\| \cdot \|u\| \geqq c(\|u\|)(\|u\| + \|Ju\|)$$

where $c(r) \to +\infty$ as $r \to +\infty$. Theorem 10 then follows from the following more general theorem:

THEOREM 11. *Let V be a reflexive Banach space, T a mapping of V into V^* such that T is continuous from finite dimensional subspaces of V to the weak topology of V^*. Suppose that T is monotone, i.e.,*

$$\langle Tu - Tv, u - v\rangle \geqq 0$$

for all u and v in V, while there exists a real function c on R^1 with $c(r) \to +\infty$ as $r \to +\infty$ such that

$$\langle Tu, u\rangle \geqq c(\|u\|)\{\|u\| + \|Tu\|\}$$

for all u in V. Let C be a closed subspace of V, $C^\perp$ its annihilator in V^*, f an element of V, g an element of V^*.

Then $T(C + f) \cap (C^\perp + g)$ is nonempty.

PROOF OF THEOREM 11. We form a new mapping S of C into C^* by setting

$$Su = j^*T(u + f), \qquad u \in C,$$

where j is the injection map of C into V, j^* the dual projection map of V^* onto C^*. It follows easily that

$$T(C + f) \cap (C^\perp + g)$$

is nonempty if and only if j^*g lies in $R(S)$. Hence it suffices to prove that $R(S) = C^*$.

We remark first that S is continuous from finite dimensional subspaces of C to the weak topology of C^*. Next, S is a monotone operator from C to C^* for if u and v lie in C,

$$\begin{aligned}\langle Su - Sv, u - v\rangle &= \langle T(u + f) - T(v + f), u - v\rangle \\ &= \langle T(u + f) - T(v + f), (u + f) - (v + f)\rangle \geqq 0.\end{aligned}$$

Finally, for u in C,

$$\begin{aligned}\langle Su, u\rangle = \langle T(u + f), u\rangle &= \langle T(u + f), u + f\rangle - \langle T(u + f), f\rangle \\ &\geqq c(\|u + f\|)\{\|u + f\| + \|T(u + f)\|\} - \|f\|\cdot\|T(u + f)\| \\ &\geqq c_1(\|u\|)\|u\|\end{aligned}$$

with $c_1(r) \to +\infty$ as $r \to +\infty$.

Applying Theorem 1, we see that $R(S) = C^*$. q.e.d.

Theorem 10 can be extended to reflexive spaces V which are not strictly convex by using the concept of a multiplevalued duality mapping. Thus the point-to-set mapping J_0 of V into 2^{V^*} is said to be the duality mapping of V with gauge function Φ if

$$J_0(u) = \{v \mid v \in V^*, \|v\| = \Phi(\|u\|), \langle v, u\rangle = \|v\|\cdot\|u\|\}.$$

THEOREM 12. *Let V be a reflexive Banach space, J_0 the duality mapping of V into V^* with gauge function Φ as defined just above. Let C be a closed subspace of V, $C^\perp$ its annihilator in V^*, f an element of V, g an element of V^*.*

Then $J_0(C + f) \cap (C^\perp + g)$ is nonempty.

Theorem 12 follows from the results of the writer in **[12]** on multivalued monotone mappings from V to V^*, which may be described in part in the following summary form:

THEOREM 13. *Theorems 1 and 3 are valid for multivalued mappings T of V into V^*, i.e., mappings T of V into 2^{V^*} where for each u, $T(u)$ is a closed bounded convex subset of V^*.*

We refer for the detailed statement and proof of Theorems 12 and 13 to **[12]**, which also gives a more extensive analysis of the structure of multivalued monotone mappings from V to V^*.

Let us finally refer to the results of **[13]** and **[20]** (see also **[12]**) for the proof of the equivalence of various continuity assumptions on monotone mappings in Banach spaces.

6. An interesting and useful complement to the results of §1 on the existence of solutions for quasilinear strongly elliptic boundary value problems is provided by the results of **[18]** concerning the existence of eigenfunctions for

$$Au = \lambda Bu, \qquad \lambda \in R^1$$

where A and B are nonlinear elliptic operators under variational boundary conditions. These results are obtained by applying the direct method of the calculus of variations in Banach spaces and provide an illuminating insight into the role of monotonicity in existence theorems like those of §1.

Consider the two functionals

$$f(u) = \int_\Omega F(x, u, \cdots, D^m u)\, dx,$$

and

$$g(u) = \int_\Omega G(x, u, \cdots, D^{m-1} u)\, dx$$

on a closed subspace V of $W^{m,p}(\Omega)$, $1 < p < +\infty$. Here F and G are functions on $\Omega \times R^M$ and $\Omega \times R^{M_1}$, respectively, which are measurable in x, C^1 in ξ, and satisfy the inequalities:

$$\text{(I)} \qquad \begin{aligned} |F(x, \xi)| &\leqq c\Big\{1 + |\xi|^p + \sum_{|\beta| \leqq m-1} |\xi_\beta|^{p_\beta}\Big\}, \\ |G(x, \xi)| &\leqq c\Big\{1 + \sum_{|\beta| \leqq m-1} |\xi_\beta|^{p_\beta}\Big\} \end{aligned}$$

where

$$(n - p(m - |\beta|))p_\beta < np \quad \text{if } n - p(m - |\beta|) < 0.$$

Let $F_\alpha = \nabla_{\xi_\alpha}(F)$, $G_\alpha = \nabla_{\xi_\alpha}(G)$. We also assume that:

$$\text{(II)}\quad \begin{aligned} |F_\alpha(x, \xi)| &\leqq c\Big\{1 + |\xi|^{p-1} + \sum_{|\beta| \leqq m-1} |\xi_\beta|^{p'_\beta}\Big\} \\ |G_\alpha(x, \xi)| &\leqq c\Big\{1 + |\xi|^{p-1} + \sum_{|\beta| \leqq m-1} |\xi_\beta|^{q_{\alpha\beta}}\Big\} \end{aligned}$$

where

$$(n - p(m - |\beta|))p'_\beta \leqq n(p - 1)$$

$$(n - p(m - |\alpha|))q_{\alpha\beta} \leqq n(p - 1) + p(m - |\beta|).$$

Assumption (I) implies that g is weakly continuous on bounded subsets of V and that f is continuous on V. If we define

$$\Phi(u, v) = \int_\Omega F(x, v, \cdots, D^{m-1}v, D^m u)\, dx,$$

we find that $\Phi(u, \cdot)$ is weakly continuous on bounded subsets of V, uniformly for u in bounded subsets of V.

Assumption (II) implies that both f and g have continuous Frechét derivatives everywhere in V. Then a minimum point of f with respect to the hypersurface $g(u) = c$ in V will be a solution of the eigenvalue problem

$$f'(u) = \lambda g'(u), \qquad \lambda \in R^1$$

provided that $g'(u) \neq 0$ at that point.

In more concrete-analytic terms, such an eigenfunction would be an eigenfunction of a variational boundary value problem for the system of equations

$$\sum_{|\alpha| \leqq m} (-1)^{|\alpha|} D^\alpha F_\alpha(x, u, \cdots, D^m u) = \lambda \sum_{|\beta| \leqq m-1} (-1)^{|\beta|} D^\beta G_\beta(x, u, \cdots, D^{m-1}u).$$

DEFINITION. *Let Φ be a real functional on $V \times V$. Then Φ is said to be semi-convex if the following conditions hold*:

(a) *For each v in V and each c in R^1, the set*

$$\{u \mid u \in V,\ \Phi(u, v) \leqq c\}$$

is a closed convex subset of V.

(b) *For each bounded set B in V and each sequence $\{v_j\}$ in V such that v_j converges weakly to v in V, we have*

$$\Phi(u, v_j) \to \Phi(u, v)$$

uniformly for u in B.

THEOREM 14. *Let V be a reflexive Banach space, Φ a semiconvex functional on $V \times V$, $f(v) = \Phi(v, v)$ for v in V. Then f is bounded from below on every bounded, weakly closed subset C of V and assumes its minimum on C.*

THEOREM 15. *If Φ has a Frechét derivative at each point, then a necessary and sufficient condition for condition* (a) *for semiconvexity to hold is that Φ_1', the partial gradient of Φ with respect to u, should be a monotone map from V to V^*.*

The proofs of Theorems 14 and 15, as well as their applications to nonlinear eigenvalue problems, are given in [**18**].

BIBLIOGRAPHY

1. F. E. Browder, *The solvability of nonlinear functional equations*, Duke Math. J. **30** (1963), 557–566.

2. ———, *Variational boundary value problems for quasilinear elliptic equations of arbitrary order*, Proc. Nat. Acad. Sci. U.S.A. **50** (1963), 31–37.

3. ———, *Variational boundary value problems for quasilinear elliptic equations.* II, Proc. Nat. Acad. Sci. U.S.A. **50** (1963), 594–598.

4. ———, *Variational boundary value problems for quasilinear elliptic equations.* III, Proc. Nat. Acad. Sci. U.S.A. **50** (1963), 794–798.

5. ———, *Nonlinear elliptic boundary value problems*, Bull. Amer. Math. Soc. **69** (1963), 862–874.

6. ———, *Nonlinear parabolic boundary value problems of arbitrary order*, Bull. Amer. Math. Soc. **69** (1963), 858–861.

7. ———, *Nonlinear elliptic problems.* II, Bull. Amer. Math. Soc. **70** (1964), 299–302.

8. ———, *Strongly nonlinear parabolic boundary value problems*, Amer. J. Math. **86** (1964), 339–357.

9. ———, *Nonlinear elliptic boundary value problems.* II, Trans. Amer. Math. Soc. **117** (1965), 530–550.

10. ———, *Nonlinear equations of evolution*, Ann. of Math. (2) **80** (1964), 485–523.

11. ———, *On a theorem of Beurling and Livingston*, Canad. J. Math. **17** (1965).

12. ———, *Multi-valued monotone nonlinear mappings and duality mappings in Banach spaces*, Trans. Amer. Math. Soc., (to appear).

13. ———, *Continuity properties of monotone nonlinear operators in Banach spaces*, Bull. Amer. Math. Soc. **70** (1964), 551–553.

14. ———, *Remarks on nonlinear functional equations*, Proc. Nat. Acad. Sci. U.S.A. **51** (1964), 985–989.

15. ———, *Remarks on nonlinear functional equations.* II, Illinois J. Math. **9** (1965).

16. ———, *Remarks on nonlinear functional equations.* III, Illinois J. Math. **9** (1965).

17. ———, *Nonlinear initial value problems.* Ann. of Math. **81** (1965).

18. ———, *Variational methods for nonlinear elliptic eigenvalue problems*, Bull. Amer. Math. Soc. **71** (1965), 176–183.

19. K. O. Friedrichs, *Symmetric positive linear differential equations*, Comm. Pure Appl. Math. **11** (1958), 333–418.

20. T. Kato, *Demicontinuity, hemicontinuity, and monotonicity*, Bull. Amer. Math. Soc. **70** (1964), 548–550.

21. ———, *Nonlinear evolution equations in Banach spaces*, (these Proceedings, pp. 50–67).

22. J. L. Lions, *Sur certaines systèmes hyperboliques non linéaires*, C. R. Acad. Sci. Paris **257** (1963), 2057–2060.

23. J. L. Lions and W. A. Strauss, *Sur certaines problèmes hyperboliques non linéaires*, C. R. Acad. Sci. Paris **257** (1963), 3267–3270.

24. ———, *Some nonlinear evolution equations*, (to appear).

25. G. J. Minty, *Monotone (nonlinear) operators in Hilbert space*, Duke Math. J. **29** (1962), 341–346.

26. G. J. Minty, *Two theorems on nonlinear functional equations in Hilbert space*, Bull. Amer. Math. Soc. **69** (1963), 691–692.

27. ———, *On a "monotonicity" method for the solution of nonlinear equations in Banach spaces*, Proc. Nat. Acad. Sci. U.S.A. **50** (1963), 1038–1041.

28. ———, *Maximal monotone sets in Hilbert spaces* (to appear).

29. S. Smale, *Morse theory and a nonlinear generalization of the Dirichlet problem*, Ann. of Math. (2) **80** (1964), 382–396.

30. M. M. Vaĭnberg, *Variational methods for the study of nonlinear operators*, Gosudarstv. Izdat. Tehn.-Teor. Lit., Moscow, 1956.

31. M. M. Vaĭnberg and R. I. Kačurovski, *On the variational theory of nonlinear operators and equations*, Dokl. Akad. Nauk SSSR **129** (1959), 1199–1202.

32. M. I. Višik, *Solution of a system of quasilinear equations in divergence form under periodic boundary conditions*, Dokl. Akad. Nauk SSSR **137** (1961), 502–505.

33. ———, *Boundary value problems for quasilinear strongly elliptic systems in divergence form*, Dokl. Akad. Nauk SSSR **138** (1961), 518–521.

34. ———, *Simultaneous quasilinear equations with lower order terms*, Dokl. Akad. Nauk SSSR **144** (1962), 13–16.

35. ———, *Solvability of boundary problems for quasilinear parabolic equations of higher order*, Mat. Sb. (N.S.) **59** (1962), 289–335.

36. ———, *Quasilinear strongly elliptic systems of differential equations having divergence form*, Trudy Moskov. Mat. Obšč. **12** (1963), 125–184.

37. E. H. Zarantonello, *Solving functional equations by contractive averaging*, Tech. Rep. No. 160, U.S. Army Research Center, Madison, Wis., 1960.

38. ———, *The closure of the numerical range contains the spectrum*, Bull. Amer. Math. Soc. **70** (1964), 781–787.

UNIVERSITY OF CHICAGO,
CHICAGO, ILLINOIS

NONLINEAR EVOLUTION EQUATIONS IN BANACH SPACES[1]

BY

TOSIO KATO

Consider the initial value problem

$$\frac{du}{dt} = f(t, u), \qquad 0 \leqq t \leqq T, \; u(0) = \phi, \tag{1}$$

where the unknown u is a function on the real interval $I = [0, T]$ (or a subinterval of I) to a Banach space X and f is a given function from $I \times X$ (or a subset thereof) to X. (1) is *regular* (in a vague sense) if f is well behaved and *singular* otherwise. We are mainly interested in more or less singular cases, but here we consider certain restricted types of singular equations.

If $f(t, u)$ is linear in u, (1) takes the form

$$\frac{du}{dt} + A(t)u = f(t), \qquad u(0) = \phi, \tag{2}$$

where $\{A(t)\}$ is a family of linear operators in X. (2) is singular if the $A(t)$ are unbounded operators.

For singular nonlinear equations, our discussion will be restricted to "semi-linear" equations

$$\frac{du}{dt} + A(t)u = f(t, u), \qquad u(0) = \phi, \tag{3}$$

where the nonlinear term $f(t, u)$ is either regular or at most relatively regular with respect to $A(t)$ in a sense to be specified below.

The main object of this paper is to give a survey of the results obtained for the singular equations of the form (3) by using the semigroup theory. For convenience, however, we shall also discuss the regular equations (1) briefly. Some typical results are stated as theorems and others as part of remarks, but these are not intended to be exhaustive.

For simplicity we assume throughout the paper that X is *separable*, though this is not always necessary.

[1] This work was partly supported by Air Force Office of Scientific Research under Grant No. AF–AFOSR 553–64.

1. **Regular equations.** A fundamental result for regular equations (1) is

THEOREM 1. *Let $f(t, u)$ be continuous on $I \times X$ to X and uniformly Lipschitz continuous in u:*

$$\|f(t, u) - f(t, v)\| \leqq L\|u - v\|, \qquad t \in I, \quad u, v \in X. \tag{4}$$

Then (1) *has a unique solution $u = u(t) \in C^1(I; X)$ for any $\phi \in X$.*[2] *The solution u depends on the initial value ϕ continuously, i.e., the map $\phi \rightarrow u$ is continuous from X to $C^1(I; X)$.*

REMARKS. 1. This theorem has exactly the same form as the classical theorem of Picard (which is a special case of Theorem 1 with $\dim X < \infty$; we shall refer to this case as the *classical* case). In modern textbooks, even the classical theorem is often proved in the general context of infinite-dimensional Banach spaces (Bourbaki [**1**], Dieudonné [**1**]).

2. There is a corresponding local existence theorem if $f(t, u)$ is defined and Lipschitz continuous only for u in a neighborhood of ϕ or, even when $f(t, u)$ is defined everywhere in X, it is not uniformly Lipschitz continuous. It will not be necessary to state this local version of Theorem 1 explicitly; the result is again the same as in the classical case.

3. In the classical case there is another basic theorem due to Peano, which guarantees the existence (but not uniqueness) of a solution if f is only continuous. This theorem cannot be generalized to the infinite-dimensional case (a counter-example is given in Dieudonné [**1**, p. 287], and cited by Browder [**3**]). If, however, f is assumed to be compact (completely continuous), the existence of a local solution can be proved. More generally, the same is true if $f = f_1 + f_2$ where f_1 is compact and f_2 is locally Lipschitz continuous. For further generalization of this result see Theorem 6 below.

Recently Browder [**3**] proved the following theorem, which is a generalization of Theorem 1 when X is a Hilbert space.

THEOREM 2. *Let X be a Hilbert space. Let f be continuous from $I \times X$ to X and map bounded sets into bounded sets. Let*

$$\operatorname{Re}\,(f(t, u) - f(t, v), u - v) \leqq M\|u - v\|^2, \qquad t \in I, \quad u, v \in X. \tag{5}$$

Then (1) *has a unique solution $u \in C^1(I; X)$ for every $\phi \in X$. The map $\phi \rightarrow u$ is continuous from X to $C(I; X)$.*

REMARKS. 1. The theorem is not essentially changed if we assume $M = 0$, as is easily seen by introducing the transformation $u(t) \rightarrow e^{-Mt}u(t)$. In this case (5) means that $-f$ is a *monotonic* function (see Minty [**1**], [**2**]).

[2] $C(I; X)$ is the Banach space consisting of all continuous X-valued functions $u(t)$ defined on I with the maximum norm $\|u\| = \max_t \|u(t)\|$. $C^1(I; X)$ is the Banach space of all continuously differentiable X-valued functions on I with the norm $\|u\| = \max_t \|u(t)\| + \max_t \|u'(t)\|$.

2. The uniqueness proof in Theorem 2 is almost trivial but the existence proof is rather complicated. Browder uses a generalized Galerkin method in this proof.[3]

3. Again there is a local version of Theorem 2 if (5) is not satisfied uniformly (e.g., M depends on u, v).

4. In Theorem 2 the (strong) continuity of f is not necessary if one is only interested in the solution of the integral equation

$$u(t) = \phi + \int_0^t f(s, u(s))\, ds. \tag{6}$$

It is sufficient, e.g., to assume that f is *demicontinuous* (continuous from $I \times X$ with strong topology in X to X with weak topology; see Browder [**2**]). A solution of (6) may be called a *mild solution* of (1), according to Browder [**3**].

2. **Singular linear equations.** Here we do not want to go into details on linear equations (2), but we need some relevant results for the discussion of nonlinear equations (3).

The basic fact we need is the existence of the *evolution operator* (solution operator, Green's function, resolvent, propagator, etc.) $U(t, s)$ associated with (2). $U(t, s)$ is a family of bounded linear operators on X to itself defined for $0 \leqq s \leqq t \leqq T$, strongly continuous in the two variables jointly and satisfying the conditions

$$U(t, s)\, U(s, r) = U(t, r), \qquad U(s, s) = 1, \tag{7a}$$

$$\frac{\partial U(t, s)u}{\partial t} = -A(t)U(t, s)u, \tag{7b}$$

$$\frac{\partial U(t, s)u}{\partial s} = U(t, s)A(s)u \tag{7c}$$

for some $u \in X$ to be described below. The solution of (2) is formally given by

$$u(t) = U(t, 0)\phi + \int_0^t U(t, s)f(s)\, ds. \tag{8}$$

It should be remarked that (8) need not give a solution of (2) for every ϕ and $f(t)$. The existence of du/dt and $A(t)u$ for (8) can be proved only under certain assumptions on ϕ and $f(t)$. In any case, however, (8) may be regarded as a generalized solution of (2) for any $\phi \in X$ and any integrable $f(t)$ (a *mild solution* by Browder [**3**]). A solution of (2) for which $u(t)$ is continuous on $[0, T]$, continuously differentiable on $(0, T]$ and $A(t)u(t)$ exists on $(0, T]$ is called a *strict solution*. If $u'(t)$ and $A(t)u(t)$ are continuous on $[0, T]$, it is a *strict solution on the closed interval* $[0, T]$. Thus (8) is necessary, but not sufficient, for u to be a strict solution on the closed interval.

[3] A simplified proof of Theorem 2 is given in the Appendix at the end of this paper, assuming that X is separable.

There are various known sufficient conditions for the existence of the evolution operator $U(t, s)$ (see Kato **[1]**, **[2]**, **[3]**, Kato and Tanabe **[1]**, Lions **[1]** and Yosida **[1]**). In practically all cases so far considered, $-A(t)$ is assumed to be the infinitesimal generator of a strongly continuous semigroup of bounded linear operators on X (semigroup of class C_0 by Hille and Phillips **[1]**). In addition $A(t)$ is assumed to depend on t smoothly in some sense or other.

Roughly speaking there are two important cases of (2) to be distinguished, which we call "hyperbolic" and "parabolic" although they do not conform exactly to the standard usage of the words.[4] Let us state some typical set of assumptions in each case.

In the hyperbolic case one assumes, e.g., that (1) $-A(t)$ is, for each t, the infinitesimal generator of a *contraction* semigroup, (2) the domain $D(A(t))$ of $A(t)$ is independent of t and (3) $A(t)(A(0) + 1)^{-1}$, which is a bounded operator for each t, is strongly continuously differentiable.[5] The case $A(t) = A =$ const. is permissible as a hyperbolic case if $-A$ is the infinitesimal generator of a semigroup of class C_0 even if it is not a contraction semigroup.

In the parabolic case one assumes, e.g., that (1) $-A(t)$ is the infinitesimal generator of an *analytic semigroup*[6] of class $H(-\theta, \theta)$ by Hille-Phillips (so that the resolvent set of $-A(t)$ covers a sector $|\arg z| < \pi/2 + \theta$), (2) $\|(d/dt)(\lambda + A(t))^{-1}\| \leqq N|\lambda|^{-\alpha}$ for some $\alpha > 0$ for all λ with Re $\lambda > 0$ and (3) $(d/dt)(1 + A(t))^{-1}$ is Hölder-continuous in norm.[7]

The characteristic result in the parabolic case is that for $s < t$ the range of $U(t, s)$ is contained in $D(A(t))$ and

$$\|A(t)\,U(t, s)\| \leqq N(t - s)^{-1}, \qquad s < t. \tag{7d}$$

This implies that (2) has a strict solution for any initial value ϕ if $f(t) = 0$. On the other hand, a strict solution exists in the hyperbolic case only for $\phi \in D(A(0))$. More generally, (7b) is true for any $u \in X$ and $s < t$ in the parabolic case but only for $u \in D(A(s))$ in the hyperbolic case.

Regarding the differentiability of the mild solution (8), the following is known (see Kato **[1]**, **[3]**; Kato and Tanabe **[1]**, Krasnosel'skii, Krein and Sobolevskii **[1]**, **[2]**). In the hyperbolic case, (8) is a strict solution on the closed interval $[0, T]$ if $\phi \in D(A(0))$ and $f(t)$ is continuously differentiable. In the parabolic case, a strict solution exists if $f(t)$ is Hölder continuous (ϕ is arbitrary).

---

[4] In particular these two notions are not mutually exclusive, and in many cases "parabolic" is a stronger notion than "hyperbolic."

[5] These assumptions are made in Kato **[1]** but are replaced by weaker assumptions in Kato **[2]**. See also Yosida **[1]**.

[6] This is the characteristic assumption in the parabolic case. This condition is satisfied if, e.g., $A(t)$ is a nonnegative selfadjoint operator or, more generally, the numerical range of $A(t)$ is contained in a sector $|\arg z| \leqq \omega < \pi/2$.

[7] These conditions are assumed in Kato and Tanabe **[1]**. For other possible assumptions see Kato **[3]**.

3. **Singular equations with regular nonlinear term.** Let us now consider the equation (3) in which $A(t)$ is unbounded but $f(t, u)$ is regular. *We make the standing assumption that $\{A(t)\}$ is such that the evolution operator $U(t, s)$ exists* (see §2). Then (3) is formally reduced to the integral equation

$$u(t) = U(t, 0)\phi + \int_0^t U(t, s)f(s, u(s))\, ds. \tag{9}$$

Actually a solution of (9) is a *mild solution* but need not be a strict solution of (3).

Sufficient conditions for the existence and uniqueness of the solution of (9) have been studied rather extensively. The simplest condition will be the Lipschitz continuity of f; we have namely

THEOREM 3. *Let f satisfy the assumptions of Theorem* 1. *Then* (9) *has a unique solution $u \in C(I; X)$ for any $\phi \in X$. The map $\phi \to u$ is continuous from X to $C(I; X)$.*

REMARKS. 1. Again the proof can be based on a straightforward iteration method (Krasnosel'skii et al. **[1]**, Segal **[1]**).

2. Again there is a local version of Theorem 3; cf. Remark 2 to Theorem 1. Also there is an analog of Theorem 2 due to Browder **[3]**:

THEOREM 4. *Let X be a Hilbert space. Let f be demicontinuous from $I \times X$ to X and map bounded sets into bounded sets, and let* (5) *be satisfied. Let $-A(t)$ be the infinitesimal generator of a contraction semigroup, with $(A(t) + 1)^{-1}$ strongly continuously differentiable. Then* (9) *has a unique solution $u \in C(I; X)$ for any $\phi \in X$. The map $\phi \to u$ is continuous from X to $C(I; X)$.*

REMARK. Browder proved Theorem 4 under the additional assumption that $D(A(t))$ is constant and $D(A(t)^*) \subset D(A(t))$. Actually it turns out that the theorem is true for more general $A(t)$ under consideration.[8]

Under certain compactness assumption related to $A(t)$, it can be shown that the continuity of $f(t, u)$ is sufficient for the existence (but not for uniqueness) of a solution of (9):

THEOREM 5. *Assume that we are in the parabolic case and that $A(t)$ has compact resolvent for each t. If f is continuous from $I \times X$ to X, then* (9) *has at least one local solution $u \in C(I_0; X)$ for any $\phi \in X$, where $I_0 = [0, T_0]$ is a subinterval of I depending on ϕ.*

REMARKS. 1. Theorem 5 was proved by Krasnosel'skii et al. **[2]** in the special case in which $A(t)$ is a nonnegative selfadjoint operator with compact resolvent.

---

[8] The proof is given in the Appendix at the end of this paper. This rather lengthy proof is included partly to illustrate how the monotonicity is useful in an existence proof.

2. In view of Remark 3 to Theorem 1, Theorem 5 shows that the singular equation (3) can be more easily solved than the regular equation (1) with the same f.

There is another theorem, due to Krasnosel'skii et al. **[1]**, based on a compactness assumption.

THEOREM 6. *Let $S \subset X$ be an open neighborhood of ϕ. Let $f = f_1 + f_2$, where $f_1(t, u)$ is compact (completely continuous) on $I \times S$ to X and $f_2(t, u)$ is continuous on $I \times S$ to X and locally Lipschitz continuous in u. Then there is at least one local solution $u \in C(I_0; S)$ of (9).*

REMARK. In the theorems given above we considered only solutions of (9), i.e., mild solutions of (3). In order to show that a mild solution is a strict solution, we need somewhat stronger assumptions on f so that $f(t, u(t))$ satisfies the conditions imposed on $f(t)$ in §2. In Theorem 3, for example, it suffices to add the assumption that $f(t, u)$ is Hölder continuous in t if we are in the parabolic case; in the hyperbolic case we further assume that $\phi \in D(A(0))$ and $f(t, u)$ has continuous derivatives f_t and f_u, where f_u means the Fréchet derivative (see Krasnosel'skii et al. **[1]**, Foiaş et al. **[1]**, Segal **[1]**). Segal **[1]** considers also the higher order differentiability of a mild solution assuming the existence of higher order derivatives of f (in the special case $A(t) = A =$ const.).

EXAMPLE. Consider the nonlinear wave equation

$$\frac{\partial^2 u}{\partial t^2} - \Delta u + m^2 u + cu^3 = 0, \qquad m^2 > 0, \tag{10}$$

in R^3. Introduce the selfadjoint operator $B = (m^2 - \Delta)^{1/2}$ acting in the Hilbert space $L^2(R^3)$. If we set $Bu = v$, $du/dt = w$, (10) reduces to a system of equations of first order:

$$\frac{d}{dt}\begin{pmatrix} v \\ w \end{pmatrix} + \begin{pmatrix} 0 & -B \\ B & 0 \end{pmatrix}\begin{pmatrix} v \\ w \end{pmatrix} + c\begin{pmatrix} 0 \\ (B^{-1}v)^3 \end{pmatrix} = 0. \tag{11}$$

The operator

$$A = \begin{pmatrix} 0 & -B \\ B & 0 \end{pmatrix}$$

acting in the space $X = L^2(R^3) \oplus L^2(R^3)$ is skew-adjoint and the map

$$\begin{pmatrix} v \\ w \end{pmatrix} \to c\begin{pmatrix} 0 \\ (B^{-1}v)^3 \end{pmatrix}$$

is continuously differentiable on X to X; the latter fact is due to the Sobolev inequality. Thus Theorem 3 is directly applicable to prove the existence of a local mild solution of (11) for any initial value of

$$\begin{pmatrix} v \\ w \end{pmatrix}$$

belonging to X. This means that a "mild" solution of (10) exists if the initial value of u and du/dt belong to $D(B)$ and $L^2(R^3)$, respectively. This solution is strict if

$$\begin{pmatrix} v \\ w \end{pmatrix} \in D(A)$$

initially, i.e., if $u \in D(B^2) = D(\Delta)$ and $du/dt \in D(B)$ initially. For details see Browder [**1**], Browder and Strauss [**1**], Segal [**1**], [**2**]. It will be noted that a similar and somewhat stronger result has been obtained by Jörgens [**1**] by a different method. For global solutions of (10) see also §5.

4. **Singular equations with relatively regular nonlinear term.** We now consider the equation (3) in which f is not regular but "regular relative to $A(t)$." For simplicity we assume that $A(t) = A$ is independent of t[9] and that $-A$ is the infinitesimal generator of a semigroup of class C_0. In general we are in the hyperbolic case, but the parabolic case will occur if $-A$ is the generator of an analytic semigroup. We denote by $[D(A)]$ the domain $D(A)$ of A regarded as a Banach space with the graph norm $\|u\| + \|Au\|$. Most of the results stated below will be true in more general cases in which $A(t)$ is variable but has domain independent of t.

The following theorem, due to Segal [**1**], is useful mainly in the hyperbolic case, for there is a stronger theorem like Theorem 8 in the parabolic case.

THEOREM 7. *Let $f(t, u)$ be defined on $I \times [D(A)]$ to X and differentiable in t and u. Let $f_t(t, u)$ be continuous on $I \times [D(A)]$ to X and Lipschitz continuous in u. Let $f_u(t, u)$ have an extension as a bounded linear operator on X to X (denoted by the same symbol $f_u(t, u)$), and let the map $t, u \to f_u(t, u)$ be continuous from $I \times [D(A)]$ to $B(X)$*[10] *and Lipschitz continuous in u. Then* (3_0)[9] *has a unique local strict solution $u \in Y(I_0) \equiv C(I_0; [D(A)]) \cap C^1(I_0; X)$ for any $\phi \in D(A)$. The map $\phi \to u$ is continuous in an appropriate sense.*[11]

REMARKS. 1. If $f(t, u) = B(t)u$ is linear in u, the assumptions of Theorem 7 imply that $B(t)$ is a bounded operator. In this case the theorem reduces to a perturbation theorem for the linear evolution equation due to Phillips [**1**]. It seems that even in this simple case, no stronger result is known without further assumptions on A.

2. If X is reflexive and $-A$ is the generator of a *group* (i.e., both A and $-A$ are generators of semigroups), the assumptions of Theorem 7 can be partly weakened. It suffices to assume that $f(t, u)$ is Lipschitz continuous in the sense that

$$\|f(t, u) - f(s, v)\| \leqq (l(\|Au\|) + l(\|Av\|))(|t - s| + \|u - v\|) \tag{11}$$

for $u, v \in D(A)$, where $l(x)$ is a positive nondecreasing function of $x \geqq 0$.

---

[9] In this special case we shall denote (3) by (3_0).

[10] $B(X)$ is the Banach space of all bounded linear operators on X to X.

[11] For any $\phi \in D(A)$, there is an interval $I_0' = [0, T_0']$ such that the solution u_1 of (3_0) with the initial value ϕ_1 exists on I_0' and u_1 is arbitrarily close to u in $Y(I_0')$ if ϕ_1 is sufficiently close to ϕ in $[D(A)]$.

If we assume that $-A$ is the infinitesimal generator of an analytic semigroup (parabolic case), the assumptions of Theorem 7 can be weakened to a great extent. For example we have

THEOREM 8. *Let* α, β *be real numbers such that* $0 \leqq \alpha < 1$, $\alpha \leqq \beta \leqq 1$. *Let* $f(t, u)$ *be defined for* $u \in D(A^\beta)$ *and let*

$$(12) \quad \|f(t, u) - f(s, v)\| \leqq (l(\|A^\beta u\|) + l(\|A^\beta v\|))(|t - s|^{1-\alpha} + \|A^\alpha u - A^\alpha v\|).$$

Then a unique local strict solution of (3_0) *exists for any* $\phi \in D(A^\beta)$.

REMARK. In the parabolic case, many other theorems of a similar kind could be stated and more detailed results obtained depending on the special properties of the inequality similar to (12). We shall not do this in general terms since it will be of little interest, but illustrate this by an example of the Navier-Stokes equation in hydrodynamics. Regarding other results more or less related to Theorems 7 and 8, we refer also to Carroll [**1**], Sobolevskii [**1**], [**3**], [**4**].

EXAMPLE (Navier-Stokes equation). Let Ω be a bounded domain in R^m, $m = 2$ or 3, with a smooth boundary. Let $\mathbf{L}^2(\Omega)$ be the set of vector-valued functions on Ω with all components in $L^2(\Omega)$. Let X be the subspace of $\mathbf{L}^2(\Omega)$ spanned by the set $C_{0,\sigma}^\infty(\Omega)$ of infinitely differentiable vector-valued functions with compact supports and with divergence zero (solenoidal vectors), and let P be the projection of $\mathbf{L}^2(\Omega)$ onto X. Let A be the Friedrichs extension of $-P\Delta$ defined on $C_{0,\sigma}^\infty$, regarded as an operator in X; A is a positive-definite, selfadjoint operator in X. Then the Navier-Stokes equation can be expressed by (3_0), where $f(t, u) = -P(u, \operatorname{grad} u) + f(t)$ and $f(t)$ is the external force.

For $m = 3$ it can be proved that

$$(13) \quad \|f(t, u) - f(t, v)\| \leqq M\|A^{3/4}u\| \, \|A^{1/2}(u - v)\| + M\|A^{1/2}v\| \, \|A^{3/4}(u - v)\|.$$

This special estimate on $f(t, u)$ enables one to construct a strict local solution of (3_0) under the assumption that $\phi \in D(A^{1/4})$ and $f(t)$ is Hölder continuous. Further differentiability of $u(t)$ can be proved by assuming higher differentiability of $f(t)$. For $m = 2$ we have a similar but stronger estimate on $f(t, u)$, which leads to the existence and uniqueness of a strict local solution for any $\phi \in X$ and Hölder continuous $f(t)$. For details see Fujita and Kato [**1**], Kato and Fujita [**1**], Sobolevskii [**2**], [**5**]. For global solutions, see §5.

5. **Global solutions.** Most of the solutions of the nonlinear equations we have considered above are local in t, i.e., they exist only in some interval $I_0 = [0, T_0]$ smaller than the given interval $I = [0, T]$. Exceptions occur when (1) the Lipschitz or monotonicity condition is satisfied uniformly for all $u \in X$ or (2) the initial data and the external force are sufficiently small (e.g., in the example of the Navier-Stokes equation).

To prove the existence of a global solution in more general cases, we have to depend on some other principles. Usually such a principle is furnished by the so-called energy inequality, which expresses the physical fact that certain functional $E = E(t) = E[u(t)]$ of $u(t)$ does not increase without limit. When such a quantity E exists, it is expected that it prevents the solution $u(t)$ from "blowing up" in a finite time and therefore the local solution will continue to exist until $t = T$.

It is not always possible, however, to give this intuitive reasoning a mathematical justification. The difficulty lies in the fact that the finiteness of E at the initial time does not always guarantee the existence of a local solution. Thus there is often a gap between the energy principle and the local existence theorem.

Let us illustrate this situation by the two examples discussed above. For the nonlinear wave equation (10), the energy principle implies that

$$E = \|du/dt\|^2 + \|Bu(t)\|^2$$

is bounded in t (assuming that $c \geqq 0$). But we can construct a local solution if E is finite at the initial time, and it can be shown that the length T_0 of the interval of existence of the local solution has a lower bound depending only on $E(0)$. Hence follows immediately the existence of a global solution. In the case of the Navier-Stokes equation, the conserved quantity with a natural physical meaning is simply $E = \|u(t)\|^2$. If we depend on the local existence theorem stated above, however, we need the finiteness of $\|A^{1/4}u(0)\|$ to construct a local solution in the three-dimensional flow. But $\|A^{1/4}u(t)\|$ is probably not conserved; here is the difficulty to prove the global existence of a solution. In the two-dimensional flow, on the other hand, the local solution exists for any ϕ with $\|\phi\| < \infty$. Furthermore, it can be shown that $E' = \|A^{1/4}u(t)\|^2$ is conserved together with E. Thus there is no gap between the energy principle and the local existence theorem, and the global solution is known to exist (see the papers cited above).

APPENDIX

The main purpose of this Appendix is to prove Theorem 4. Since the proof is based on Theorem 2, we shall also give a proof of Theorem 2 and its generalization stated in Remark 4 to Theorem 2.

Part A. Proof of Theorem 2 and its generalization. The assumptions are

(i) f is demicontinuous on $I \times X$ to X and maps bounded sets into bounded sets.

(ii) $-f$ is monotonic, i.e., (5) is satisfied with $M = 0$ (see Remark 1 to Theorem 2).

The existence proof is based on Galerkin's method and monotonicity argument.

We introduce the Hilbert space $Y = L^2(I; X)$. We use the notations $(\ ,\ )_X$, $\|\ \|_X$, $(\ ,\ )_Y$, $\|\ \|_Y$, etc., to denote inner products and norms in various spaces.

Let L' be the linear operator in Y defined by

(A1) $$(L'u)(t) = u'(t) = du(t)/dt$$

with $D(L') = \{u \mid u \in C^1(I; X),\ u(0) = 0\}$. It is easily seen that L' is preclosed (has a closed extension); we denote by L the closure of L' as an operator in Y.

LEMMA A1. *L is densely defined with $D(L) \subset C(I; X)$. L is closed, maximal accretive*[12] *and invertible with $D(L^{-1}) = Y$. Furthermore,*

$$\text{(A2)} \qquad \operatorname{Re}(Lu, u)_Y = \tfrac{1}{2} \|u(T)\|_X^2 \geqq 0, \qquad u \in D(L);$$

$$\text{(A3)} \qquad (L^{-1}v)(t) = \int_0^t v(s)\, ds, \qquad v \in Y.$$

A mild solution u of (1) is by definition a solution of the integral equation (6). According to (A3), it is a solution of

$$\text{(A4)} \qquad u = \phi - L^{-1}Gu \quad \text{or} \quad L(u - \phi) + Gu = 0,$$

where ϕ will also denote an element of Y such that $\phi(t) = \text{const.} = \phi \in X$ and where G is a nonlinear operator in Y defined by

$$\text{(A5)} \qquad (Gu)(t) = -f(t, u(t)), \qquad D(G) = C(I; X).$$

Note that $Gu \in Y$ is well defined if $u(t)$ is strongly continuous, for then $f(t, u(t))$ depends on t weakly continuously.

Setting $v = u - \phi$, (A4) can be written

$$\text{(A6)} \qquad (L + G_1)v = 0,$$

where G_1 is defined by $G_1 v = G(v + \phi)$. $-G_1$ is associated with the nonlinear operator $f_1(t, u) = f(t, u + \phi)$ in the same way as $-G$ is associated with $f(t, u)$ by (A5).

LEMMA A2. *G is monotonic, i.e.,*

$$\text{(A7)} \qquad \operatorname{Re}(Gu - Gv, u - v)_Y \geqq 0, \qquad u, v \in D(G).$$

G is demicontinuous from $C(I; X)$ to Y, i.e., $u_n \to u$ in $C(I; X)$ implies $Gu_n \rightharpoonup Gu$ in Y.[13] *Furthermore, G sends bounded sets in $C(I; X)$ into bounded sets in Y. The same results hold when G is replaced by G_1.*

PROOF. The results follow easily from the assumptions (i), (ii) on f. In the proof of the demicontinuity, the principle of dominated convergence may be used.

CONSTRUCTION OF A SOLUTION BY GALERKIN'S METHOD. Let $X_1 \subset X_2 \subset \cdots$ be an ascending sequence of finite-dimensional subspaces of X such that $\bigcup X_n$ is dense in X. Let P_n be the orthogonal projection of X onto X_n. Then $0 \leqq P_1 \leqq P_2 \leqq \cdots$ and $P_n \to 1$ strongly.

---

[12] A linear operator A in a Hilbert space H is *accretive* if $(Au, u)_H \geqq 0$ for $u \in D(A)$. A is maximal accretive if there is no proper accretive extension of A. Obviously a linear operator is accretive if and only if it is monotonic.

[13] For convenience we denote by $\to$ strong convergence and by $\rightharpoonup$ weak convergence.

Consider the differential equation

(A8) $$v_n' = dv_n'/dt = P_n f_1(t, v_n), \qquad v_n(0) = 0,$$

where the unknown v_n takes values in X_n. This is a classical differential equation (a differential equation in a finite-dimensional space X_n) with the right member continuous in t and v_n. Hence there exists at least one local solution $v_n = v_n(t)$. This solution can be continued to the whole interval I of t, for $\|v_n(t)\|_X$ is bounded by a given constant independent of the interval of existence. In fact

(A9) $$\begin{aligned}(d/dt)\|v_n(t)\|_X^2 &= 2\,\mathrm{Re}\,(v_n'(t), v_n(t))_X \\ &= 2\,\mathrm{Re}\,(P_n f_1(t, v_n(t)), v_n(t))_X \\ &= 2\,\mathrm{Re}\,(f_1(t, v_n(t)), v_n(t))_X \\ &\leqq 2\,\mathrm{Re}\,(f_1(t, 0), v_n(t))_X \\ &\leqq 2\|f_1(t, 0)\|_X\|v_n(t)\|_X\end{aligned}$$

so that

(A10) $$\|v_n(t)\|_X \leqq \int_0^t \|f_1(s, 0)\|_X\,ds \leqq \int_0^T \|f_1(s, 0)\|_X\,ds \equiv C_1.$$

Thus $v_n \in C(I; X)$ and $\{v_n\}$ is bounded in $C(I; X)$. Hence $\{Gv_n\}$ is bounded in Y by Lemma A2. These results are summarized in the following lemma.

LEMMA A3. *For each n there exists a $v_n \in Y$ such that $P_n v_n = v_n$, $P_n(L + G_1)v_n = (L + P_n G_1)v_n = 0$ and the sequence $\{G_1 v_n\}$ is bounded in Y. (We use P_n also to denote the projection operator in Y defined by $(P_n u)(t) = P_n u(t)$.)*

Since $\{G_1 v_n\}$ is bounded in Y, we may assume that

(A11) $$-G_1 v_n \rightharpoonup z \quad \text{in } Y, \qquad n \to \infty,$$

by replacing $\{v_n\}$ by a subsequence if necessary. Since $P_n^* = P_n \to 1$ strongly, it follows by Lemma A3 that

(A12) $$Lv_n = -P_n G_1 v_n \rightharpoonup z \quad \text{in } Y.$$

Since L^{-1} is bounded, we have

(A13) $$v_n \rightharpoonup v \equiv L^{-1}z \quad \text{in } Y.$$

(A13) implies that $v \in D(L) \subset D(G)$. We can now prove that v satisfies (A6) by using a monotonicity argument due to Minty **[1]**, **[2]**, Browder **[2]**, **[3]**, and others.

Let $w \in D(L)$. Then

(A14) $$\mathrm{Re}\,(L(w - v_n) + G_1 w - G_1 v_n, w - v_n)_Y \geqq 0$$

by Lemmas A1 and A2. But $((L + G_1)v_n, v_n) = (P_n(L + G_1)v_n, v_n) = 0$ by Lemma A3. Using (A11)–(A13), we thus obtain from (A14) on letting $n \to \infty$

(A15) $$\mathrm{Re}\,((L + G_1)w, w - v) \geqq 0 \quad \text{for any } w \in D(L).$$

Set $w = w_n = v + n^{-1}x$, $x \in D(L)$, in (A15). Then

$$\operatorname{Re}(Lv + n^{-1}Lx + G_1 w_n, x) \geqq 0.$$

Since $G_1 w_n \rightharpoonup G_1 v$, $n \to \infty$, by Lemma A2, this gives $\operatorname{Re}(Lv + G_1 v, x) \geqq 0$. Since this is true for every x of a dense set $D(L)$, we have $Lv + G_1 v = 0$, q.e.d.

On setting $u = v + \phi$, we obtain a solution of (A4).

UNIQUENESS AND CONTINUOUS DEPENDENCE ON THE INITIAL VALUE. This is contained in

LEMMA A4. *Let u_1, u_2 be two solutions of* (A4) *for the initial values ϕ_1, ϕ_2, respectively. Then $\|u_1(t) - u_2(t)\|_X \leqq \|\phi_1 - \phi_2\|_X$ for all t.*

PROOF. We have $L(u_i - \phi_i) + Gu_i = 0$, $i = 1, 2$. Set $u = u_1 - u_2$, $\phi = \phi_1 - \phi_2$. Then

$$\text{(A16)} \qquad \operatorname{Re}(L(u - \phi), u)_Y = -\operatorname{Re}(Gu_1 - Gu_2, u_1 - u_2)_Y \leqq 0.$$

But the left member of (A16) is equal to $\operatorname{Re}(L(u - \phi), u - \phi)_Y + \operatorname{Re}(L(u - \phi), \phi)_Y = \frac{1}{2}\|u(T) - \phi\|_X^2 + \operatorname{Re}(u(T) - \phi, \phi)_X = \frac{1}{2}(\|u(T)\|_X^2 - \|\phi\|_X^2)$. Hence $\|u(T)\|_X \leqq \|\phi\|_X$, and a similar argument can be used to show that $\|u(t)\|_X \leqq \|\phi\|_X$ for all t.

REMARK. If f is not only demicontinuous but continuous, then the mild solution u obtained above is a strict solution, for $L(u - \phi) = -Gu \in C(I; X)$. This proves Theorem 2 in the original form.

Part B. Proof of Theorem 4. First we state precisely the assumptions we need. In addition to (i), (ii) stated in Part A we assume the following.

(iii) For each $t \in I = [0, T]$, $-A(t)$ is the infinitesimal generator of a contraction semigroup of bounded operators on X. This is equivalent to the condition that $A(t)$ is a densely defined, closed, maximal accretive operator in X. This further implies that

$$\text{(B1)} \qquad \|(A(t) + \lambda)^{-1}\| \leqq \lambda^{-1} \quad \text{for } \lambda > 0.$$

(iv) $(A(t) + 1)^{-1}$ is strongly continuously differentiable in t. (By (iii) this implies that the same is true for $(A(t) + \lambda)^{-1}$ for any $\lambda > 0$.)

(v) There exists a family $\{U(t, s)\}$ of bounded operators on X to X defined and strongly continuous for $0 \leqq s \leqq t \leqq T$ with the following properties. If u is a strict solution of (2) on the closed interval I, then u must be given by (8). Conversely, (8) is a strict solution of (2) on the closed interval I if $f \in C^1(I; X)$ and $\phi \in D(A(0))$.

REMARKS. 1. Regarding the sufficient conditions for the existence of $U(t, s)$ with the property (v), see the reference given in §2 of text.

2. There is no loss of generality if we replace $A(t)$ by $A(t) + 1$ (cf. Remark 1 after Theorem 2). Thus we may assume the following condition slightly stronger than (iv):

(iv)′ $(A(t) + \lambda)^{-1}$ is strongly continuously differentiable in t for $\lambda \geqq 0$, with

$$\text{(B1)}' \qquad \|(A(t) + \lambda)^{-1}\| \leqq (1 + \lambda)^{-1}, \qquad \lambda \geqq 0.$$

EXISTENCE PROOF. We introduce the Hilbert space Y and the operator L' as in Part A, and set $S' = L' + A$, where A is the multiplication operator by $A(t)$, i.e., $(Au)(t) = A(t)u(t)$, with $D(A) = \{u \mid u \in Y, Au \in C(I; X) \subset Y\}$.

LEMMA B1. *S' is densely defined.*

PROOF. Let $u(t) = A(t)^{-1}v(t)$ where $v \in C^1(I; X)$ and $v(0) = 0$. Then $u \in D(L') \cap D(A) = D(S')$ by (iv)'. The set of all these v is dense in Y, and the same is true for the set of all u, for A^{-1} is a bounded operator in Y with $(A^{-1})^* = A^{*-1}$ invertible.

LEMMA B2. *S' is accretive.*

LEMMA B3. *S' is preclosed.*

PROOF. It suffices to show that S'^* is densely defined. Consider the functions

$$y(t) = (A(t)^{-1})^* x(t),$$
$$z(t) = -\left(\frac{d}{dt} A(t)^{-1}\right)^* x(t) - (A(t)^{-1})^* x'(t) + x(t)$$

where $x \in C^1(I; X)$ with $x(T) = 0$. Obviously $y, z \in Y$. A simple calculation gives $(u, z)_Y = (S'u, y)_Y$ for any $u \in D(S')$. This implies that $y \in D(S'^*)$ with $S'^*y = z$. But the set of the y considered is dense in Y, just as in the proof of Lemma B1.

Next we define an operator U in Y by

$$(Ux)(t) = \int_0^t U(t, s)x(s)\, ds. \tag{B2}$$

Since $U(t, s)$ is strongly continuous in s, the integral is well defined for any $x \in Y$.

LEMMA B4. *U is a bounded linear operator on Y to Y with $R(U) \in C(I; X)$. U is even bounded as an operator on Y to $C(I; X)$.*

PROOF. Since $\|U(t, s)\| \leqq C$ *with a constant* C,[14] it follows from (B2) that $\|Ux(t)\|_X \leqq CT^{1/2}\|x\|_Y$. But the assumption (v) implies that $Ux \in C(I; X)$ whenever $x \in C^1(I; X)$. Since $C^1(I; X)$ is dense in Y, the result follows by continuity.

LEMMA B5. *$US'u = u$ for $u \in D(S')$, and $S'Ux = x$ for $x \in C^1(I; X)$.*

PROOF. This is another expression of the assumption (v).

LEMMA B6. *Let S be the closure of S' (which exists by Lemma* B3). *S is densely defined with $D(S) \subset C(I; X)$. S is closed, maximal accretive and invertible with $S^{-1} = U$.*

---

[14] Actually it can be shown that $\|U(t, s)\| \leqq 1$.

PROOF. If $u \in D(S)$, there is a sequence $u_n \in D(S')$ such that $u_n \to u$, $S'u_n \to Su$ in Y. It follows from Lemmas B4, B5 that $USu = \lim US'u_n = \lim u_n = u$. Hence S^{-1} exists and $S^{-1} \subset U$. Thus S^{-1} is bounded and closed, so that $R(S)$ is closed. But since $R(S')$ is dense in Y by Lemma B5, we must have $R(S) = Y$ and $S^{-1} = U$. All other assertions of the lemma follow easily from preceding lemmas.

LEMMA B7. *For any $\lambda \geqq 0$, $(S + \lambda)^{-1} = U_\lambda$ is a bounded linear operator on Y to Y given by*

(B3) $$(U_\lambda x)(t) = \int_0^t e^{-\lambda(t-s)}U(t, s)x(s)\, ds.$$

PROOF. Define the operator B_λ by $(B_\lambda x)(t) = e^{\lambda t}x(t)$. Then $S'B_\lambda x = B_\lambda(S' + \lambda)x$ for $x \in D(S')$. Hence $SB_\lambda x = B_\lambda(S + \lambda)x$ for $x \in D(S)$ by continuity. This implies that $(S + \lambda)^{-1} = B_\lambda^{-1}UB_\lambda$, q.e.d.

LEMMA B8. *The operator $\lambda(S + \lambda)^{-1}$ is uniformly bounded for $\lambda \geqq 0$ as an operator from $L^\infty(I; X)$ to $C(I; X)$.*

PROOF. It follows easily from (B3) that $\lambda\| U_\lambda x(t)\|_X \leqq C\|x\|_\infty$ for all t, where $\| \ \|_\infty$ denotes the norm in $L^\infty(I; X)$ and C is independent of t and x.

A mild solution u of (3) is by definition a solution of the integral equation (9). By Lemma B6 this means that

(B4) $$u - g + S^{-1}Gu = 0, \qquad g(t) = U(t, 0)\phi,$$

where G is defined in Part A. Setting $v = u - g$, this is equivalent to

(B5) $$v + S^{-1}G_2v = 0 \quad \text{or} \quad (S + G_2)v = 0$$

where $G_2v = G(v + g)$. $-G_2$ is associated with the nonlinear operator $f_2(t, u) = f(t, u + U(t, 0)\phi)$ as $-G$ was associated with $f(t, u)$. Note that $g \in C(I; X)$.

LEMMA B9. *G_2 has the same properties as G stated in Lemma* A2.

LEMMA B10. *G is S-demicontinuous, i.e., $Su_n \to Su$ in Y implies $Gu_n \rightharpoonup Gu$ in Y. The same is true of G_2.*

PROOF. $Su_n \to Su$ implies $u_n = USu_n \to USu = u$ in $C(I; X)$ by Lemma B4. Hence $Gu_n \rightharpoonup Gu$ in Y by Lemma A2. Similarly for G_2.

CONSTRUCTION OF A MILD SOLUTION. Let

B6) $$A_n(t) = A(t)(1 + n^{-1}A(t))^{-1}, \qquad n = 1, 2, 3, \cdots.$$

We define the operator A_n in Y from $\{A_n(t)\}$ just as we defined A from $\{A(t)\}$. Since $A_n(t)$ is bounded with $\|A_n(t)\|_X \leqq n$, A_n is a bounded operator in Y.

Furthermore A_n is accretive since $A_n(t)$ is accretive for each t. Hence it follows that there is a solution v_n to the equation

(B7) $$Lv_n + (A_n + G_2)v_n = 0.$$

This follows from Part A, for the nonlinear function $f^n(t, v) = A_n(t)v + f_2(t, v)$ satisfies the assumptions (i) and (ii) as well as $f_2(t, v)$ and $f(t, v)$. It follows also that

$$\|v_n(t)\|_X \leqq \int_0^T \|f^n(t, 0)\| \, dt = \int_0^T \|f_2(t, 0)\| \, dt \equiv C_2$$

by (A10). Thus we can extract a subsequence N of the sequence of the positive integers such that

(B8) $$v_n \rightharpoonup v \quad \text{in } Y \quad \text{for } n \to \infty \text{ along } N,$$

(B9) $$\|v(t)\|_X \leqq C_2.$$

We shall show that v is a solution of (B5) so that $u = v + g$ is a mild solution of (3).

For simplicity set $L + A_n = S_n$ so that (B7) can be written

(B10) $$(S_n + G_2)v_n = 0.$$

LEMMA B11. *$S_n w \to Sw$ in Y for $w \in D(S')$.*

PROOF. This follows from the fact that $(S_n w - Sw)(t) = (A_n(t) - A(t))w(t) = [(1 + n^{-1}A(t))^{-1} - 1]A(t)w(t) \to 0$, $n \to \infty$, boundedly in t, for $A(t)w(t)$ is strongly continuous in t for $w \in D(S')$.

LEMMA B12. *Let v be as in* (B8). *We have*

(B11) $$\text{Re}\,((S + G_2)w, w - v)_Y \geqq 0 \quad \textit{for every } w \in D(S).$$

PROOF. Let $w \in D(S')$. Then $\text{Re}\,((S_n + G_2)w - (S_n + G_2)v_n, w - v_n)_Y \geqq 0$, for $S_n + G_2$ is monotonic. But $(S_n + G_2)v_n = 0$ by (B10), $S_n w \to Sw$ by Lemma B11 and $v_n \rightharpoonup v$ by (B8). Hence (B11) follows in the limit $n \to \infty$. For a general $w \in D(S)$, there is a sequence $w_m \in D(S')$ such that $w_m \to w$, $Sw_m \to Sw$ in Y. Then $G_2 w_m \rightharpoonup G_2 w$ by Lemma B10. Hence (B11) follows by going to the limit starting from the corresponding inequalities for w_m.

LEMMA B13. *$v \in D(S)$.*

PROOF. The proof is based on (B11). In (B11) set $w = v_\lambda \equiv \lambda(S + \lambda)^{-1}v \in D(S) \subset C(I; X)$. Since $(S + G_2)v_\lambda = G_2 v_\lambda - \lambda(v_\lambda - v)$, we obtain

$$\lambda\|v_\lambda - v\|_Y^2 \leqq \text{Re}\,(G_2 v_\lambda, v_\lambda - v)_Y \leqq \|G_2 v_\lambda\|_Y \|v_\lambda - v\|_Y$$

or

$$\lambda\|v_\lambda - v\|_Y \leqq \|G_2 v_\lambda\|_Y.$$

Since $v \in L^\infty(I; X)$ by (B9), $v_\lambda = \lambda(S + \lambda)^{-1}v$ is uniformly bounded for $\lambda \geqq 0$ as an element of $C(I; X)$; see Lemma B8. Hence $G_2 v_\lambda$ is uniformly bounded in Y by Lemma B9. Hence there is a constant C such that $\lambda \|v_\lambda - v\|_Y \leqq C$ for every $\lambda \geqq 0$. But since $v_\lambda - v = -\lambda^{-1} S v_\lambda$, we obtain $\|Sv_\lambda\|_Y \leqq C$. Since $v_\lambda \to v$ in Y for $\lambda \to +\infty$ and since S is a closed operator in a Hilbert space, it follows that $v \in D(S)$.

COMPLETION OF THE EXISTENCE PROOF. Once $v \in D(S)$ has been proved, we conclude from (B11) that v satisfies $(S + G_2)v = 0$ by the same argument as was used in Part A for the proof of $(L + G_1)v = 0$.

PROOF OF UNIQUENESS AND CONTINUOUS DEPENDENCE ON THE INITIAL VALUE. Suppose we have two solutions u_1, u_2 of the equation (B4) for two initial values ϕ_1, ϕ_2, respectively: $S(u_i - g_i) + Gu_i = 0$, $g_i = U(t, 0)\phi_i$, $i = 1, 2$. Setting $u = u_1 - u_2$, $\phi = \phi_1 - \phi_2$ and $g = g_1 - g_2$, we obtain $\mathrm{Re}\,(S(u - g), u)_Y \leqq 0$ as in (A16). By Lemma B14 proved below, it follows that $\|u(T)\|_X \leqq \|\phi\|_X$. In the same way we can prove that $\|u(t)\|_X \leqq \|\phi\|_X$ for all t, q.e.d.

LEMMA B14. *For any $v \in D(S)$ and $\phi \in X$, set $u = v + g$ where $g(t) = U(t, 0)\phi$. Then*

$$2\,\mathrm{Re}\,(Sv, u)_Y \geqq \|u(T)\|_X^2 - \|\phi\|_X^2. \tag{B12}$$

PROOF. First assume that $v \in D(S')$ and $\phi \in D(A(0))$. Then $g \in C^1(I; X) \cap D(A)$ and $g' + Ag = 0$ by the assumption (v). Hence $u \in C^1(I; X)$, $Sv = S'v = v' + Av = u' + Au$ and

$$\begin{aligned} 2\,\mathrm{Re}\,(Sv, u)_Y &= 2\,\mathrm{Re}\,(u' + Au, u)_Y \geqq 2\,\mathrm{Re}\,(u', u)_Y \\ &= \|u(T)\|_X^2 - \|u(0)\|_X^2 = \|u(T)\|_X^2 - \|\phi\|_X^2. \end{aligned}$$

This proves (B12) in the particular case considered. In the general case, let $v_n \in D(S')$ and $\phi_n \in D(A(0))$ such that $v_n \to v$, $Sv_n \to Sv$ in Y and $\phi_n \to \phi$ in X. Then $g_n \to g$ in Y, where $g_n(t) = U(t, 0)\phi_n$, and $u_n = v_n + g_n \to v + g = u$ in Y. Since (B12) is true for u, v, ϕ replaced by u_n, v_n, ϕ_n, respectively, it suffices to show that $u_n(T) \to u(T)$ in X to deduce (B12) for the general case. But $g_n(T) = U(T, 0)\phi_n \to U(T, 0)\phi = g(T)$ in X, and $v_n(T) \to v(T)$ in X by Lemma B4 since $v_n = USv_n$, $v = USv$ and $Sv_n \to Sv$ in Y.

BIBLIOGRAPHY

N. BOURBAKI,

[1] *Éléments de mathématique, fonctions d'une variable réelle*, Chapitre IV, *Équations différentielles*, Hermann, Paris, 1951.

F. E. BROWDER,

[1] *On non-linear wave equations*, Math. Z. **80** (1962), 249–264.

[2] *Nonlinear parabolic boundary value problem of arbitrary order*, Bull. Amer. Math. Soc. **69** (1963), 858–861.

[3] *Non-linear equations of evolution*, Ann. of Math. (to appear).

F. E. Browder and W. A. Strauss,
[1] *Scattering for non-linear wave equations*, Pacific J. Math. **13** (1963), 23–43.
R. Carrol,
[1] *On some singular quasi-linear Cauchy problems*, Math. Z. **81** (1963), 135–154.
J. Dieudonné,
[1] *Foundations of modern analysis*, Academic Press, New York, 1960.
C. Foiaş, G. Gussi and V. Poenaru,
[1] *Sur les solutions généralisées de certaines équations linéaires et quasi linéaires dans l'espace de Banach*, Rev. Math. Pures Appl. **3** (1958), 283–304.
H. Fujita and T. Kato,
[1] *On the Navier-Stokes initial value problem*. I, Arch. Rational Mech. Anal. **16** (1964), 269-315.
E. Hille and R. S. Phillips,
[1] *Functional analysis and semi-groups*. Amer. Math. Soc. Colloq. Publ. Vol. 31, Amer. Math. Soc., Providence, R. I., 1957.
K. Jörgens,
[1] *Das Anfangswertproblem im Grossen für eine Klasse nichtlinearer Wellengleichungen*, Math. Z. **77** (1961), 295–308.
T. Kato,
[1] *Integration of the equation of evolution in a Banach space*, J. Math. Soc. Japan **5** (1953), 208–234.
[2] *On linear differential equations in Banach spaces*, Comm. Pure Appl. Math. **9** (1956), 479–486.
[3] *Abstract evolution equations of parabolic type in Banach and Hilbert spaces*, Nagoya Math. J. **19** (1961), 93–125.
T. Kato and H. Fujita,
[1] *On the nonstationary Navier-Stokes system*, Rend. Sem. Mat. Univ. Padova **32** (1962), 243–260.
T. Kato and H. Tanabe,
[1] *On the abstract evolution equation*, Osaka Math. J. **14** (1962), 107–133.
M. A. Krasnosel'skii, S. G. Krein and P. E. Sobolevskii,
[1] *On differential equations with unbounded operator in Banach spaces*, Dokl. Akad. Nauk SSSR **111** (1956), 19–22. (Russian)
[2] *On differential equations with unbounded operators in Hilbert space*, Dokl. Akad. Nauk SSSR **112** (1957), 990–993. (Russian)
J. L. Lions,
[1] *Équations différentielles opérationnelles*, Springer, Berlin, 1961.
G. J. Minty,
[1] *Monotone (nonlinear) operators in Hilbert space*, Duke Math. J. **29** (1962), 541–546.
[2] *Two theorems on nonlinear functional equations in Hilbert space*, Bull. Amer. Math. Soc. **69** (1963), 691–692.
R. S. Phillips,
[1] *Perturbation theory for semi-groups of linear operators*, Trans. Amer. Math. Soc. **74** (1954), 199–221.
I. E. Segal,
[1] *Non-linear semi-groups*, Ann. of Math. (2) **78** (1963), 339–364.
[2] *The global Cauchy problems for a relativistic scalar field with power interaction*, Bull. Soc. Math. France **91** (1963), 129–135.
P. E. Sobolevskii,
[1] *Generalized solutions of differential equations of the first order in Hilbert space*, Dokl. Akad. Nauk SSSR **122** (1958), 994–996. (Russian)
[2] *On nonstationary equations of hydrodynamics for viscous fluid*, Dokl. Akad. Nauk SSSR **128** (1959), 45–48. (Russian)

[3] *The use of fractional powers of selfadjoint operators in the investigation of some nonlinear differential equations in Hilbert space*, Dokl. Akad. Nauk SSSR **130** (1960), 272–275. (Russian)

[4] *On equations of parabolic type in a Banach space*, Trudy Moscow Mat. Obšč. **10** (1961), 297–350. (Russian)

[5] *On the application of the method of fractional powers to the study of the Navier-Stokes equation*, Dokl. Akad. Nauk SSSR **155** (1964), 50–53. (Russian)

K. Yosida,

[1] *On the integration of the equation of evolution*, J. Fac. Sci. Univ. Tokyo Sect. I **9** (1963), 397–402.

University of California,
Berkeley, California

SINGULARITIES OF SOLUTIONS OF NONLINEAR EQUATIONS

BY

JAMES SERRIN

An important and fundamental chapter in the theory of linear elliptic equations deals with the behavior of solutions near isolated singularities. The purpose of this paper is to make a beginning on related problems for nonlinear equations.

Let us consider, more particularly, multiple integral variational problems of the form

$$\delta \int F(x, u_x)\, dx = 0. \tag{1}$$

Here F is a given scalar function of the variables x and u_x, where

$$u_x = (\partial u/\partial x_1, \cdots, \partial u/\partial x_n)$$

denotes the gradient of the dependent variable $u = u(x) = u(x_1, \cdots, x_n)$. It will be assumed once and for all that the integrand function $F(x, p)$ is strictly convex in $p = (p_1, \cdots, p_n)$. The extremals of (1) are then solutions of the nonlinear elliptic equation

$$\operatorname{div} F_p(x, u_x) \equiv \frac{\partial}{\partial x_i} F_{p_i}(x, u_x) = 0. \tag{2}$$

Existence and differentiability of solutions of (2) have been major problems of the calculus of variations for many years, but recently with the work of Morrey, De Giorgi, Ladyzhenskaya, and Gilbarg, this theory has been brought to a certain degree of completeness. Very little effort, however, has been spent in determining the type of singularities which solutions may have.

In order to see what may happen, it is instructive to consider several examples. When $F(x, p) = p \cdot p = |p|^2$ we have, of course, the Dirichlet integral, and the corresponding extremals are then solutions of the Laplace equation. In this case, at a positive isolated singularity a solution is necessarily either $O(r^{2-n})$ or $O(\log 1/r)$, depending on the dimension.[1] Singularities which have both positive and negative infinities are naturally far more complicated, but here we shall be interested only in those which are of one sign.

[1] Similar results also hold for linear elliptic equations, cf. [8], [10], [11]. A survey of the local properties of solutions of elliptic equations will be found in reference [3].

Now consider the nonquadratic integrand

$$F(p) = (1 + |p|^2)^{\alpha/2} \tag{3}$$

where $\alpha = \text{const} > 1$, and let u be a corresponding positive solution of (2) in the domain $0 < |x| < 1$. Altogether, the behavior of u near the origin is a much more delicate problem than for the case of Laplace's equation, but in a recent paper I did show that if the exponent α is not greater than n, then u either tends to infinity at the origin, or else it has a removable singularity there. Moreover, the asymptotic behavior as x tends to 0 can be described precisely (cf. **[12]**). This is, however, just one case; we must also determine the behavior when $\alpha > n$ and when the singularity occurs at infinity (that is, when the solution u is defined in some exterior domain). Anticipating some of the results of this paper, the general situation for the integrand (3) is as follows:

1° *Let u be a positive extremal with an isolated nonremovable singularity at the origin. Then u tends to a limit at the origin, the limit being infinite if $\alpha \leqq n$ and finite if $\alpha > n$.*

2° *Let u be a positive extremal defined in an exterior domain. Then u tends to a limit at infinity, the limit necessarily being finite if $n > 2$.*

For a description of the precise asymptotic behavior in these cases the reader is referred directly to Theorems 1 and 2, which contain the main results of the paper.

A final example involves the integrand $F(p) = |p|^\alpha$. Here one easily checks that the functions $Ar^{(\alpha-n)/(\alpha-1)} + B$, for $\alpha \neq n$, and $A \log 1/r + B$, for $\alpha = n$, are solutions of (2) in the domain $0 < |x| < \infty$. In the neighborhood of the origin the behavior of these solutions is in complete agreement with the above results, as might be foreseen from the close similarity of the respective integrands. On the other hand, in spite of this similarity, these solutions have an asymptotic behavior in the neighborhood of infinity which is quite different from that indicated in 2° above. This unexpected phenomenon makes it quite clear that the case of a singularity at infinity is *not* dual with that of a finite singularity, but instead requires its own separate and distinct treatment.

In the work to follow it is convenient to replace (2) by the somewhat more general equation

$$\operatorname{div} \mathscr{A}(x, u_x) = 0, \tag{4}$$

where $\mathscr{A}(x, u_x)$ is a given continuous function of x and u_x. We assume throughout the paper that $\mathscr{A}$ satisfies the following "natural" hypotheses, for some constants $a \geqq 1$, $b \geqq 0$, and $\alpha > 1$,

$$\begin{aligned} |\mathscr{A}(x, p)| &\leqq a|p|^{\alpha-1} + b^{\alpha-1}, \\ p \cdot \mathscr{A}(x, p) &\geqq |p|^\alpha - b^\alpha \end{aligned} \tag{5}$$

(the apparently more general assumption $p \cdot \mathscr{A} \geqq a^{-1}|p|^\alpha - b^\alpha$ can be reduced to the present case by suitably normalizing the function $\mathscr{A}$). We shall also suppose that $\mathscr{A}$ is *monotonic* in the variable p, in the sense that

$$(p - q)\cdot(\mathscr{A}(x, p) - \mathscr{A}(x, q)) > 0 \quad \text{when } p \neq q. \tag{6}$$

For the case of a variational equation (2), condition (6) is a consequence of the convexity of $F(x, p)$, while (5) follows readily from the assumptions

$$F \geqq \text{Const}\,(|p|^\alpha - 1), \qquad |F_p| \leqq \text{Const}\,(|p|^{\alpha-1} + 1).$$

In order to avoid technical difficulties, we shall here understand by a *solution of* (4) *in a domain* (*open set*) D a continuously differentiable function $u = u(x)$ defined in D, such that

$$\int \phi_x \cdot \mathscr{A}\, dx = 0 \tag{7}$$

for all continuously differentiable functions $\phi = \phi(x)$ with compact support in D. Obviously any classical solution of (4) would be a solution in the sense just defined, but not conversely.

In §§1 through 3 we consider the behavior of a positive solution of (4) defined in the domain $0 < |x| < 1$. For this work we suppose that (4) has the following supplementary property, in addition to the given structure (5), (6):

P1. *The Dirichlet problem is solvable for smoothly bounded domains and given continuous boundary data.*

This assumption is satisfied by a wide class of equations of the form (4), as shown by the work of Morrey, Ladyzhenskaya, and Uraltseva, Gilbarg, and Stampacchia. It would be superfluous to elaborate on this, however, for on the one hand new classes of equations for which P1 holds will certainly be found, while on the other it seems that only in pathological circumstances will P1 generally fail. The integrand (3) is a specific case where all the above conditions are satisfied (here $\mathscr{A} = F_p = p(1 + |p|^2)^{(\alpha-2)/2}$, a trivial multiplicative constant being suppressed).

The results of the first three sections are summarized in Theorem 1, (page 79). In this theorem one should note the strikingly different asymptotic behavior which holds when $\alpha < n$, $\alpha = n$, and $\alpha > n$, and especially the occurrence of a *cusped singularity* when $\alpha > n$.

§4 contains a corresponding treatment of the behavior of a positive solution defined in an exterior domain. Here also, we shall need to make certain additional assumptions concerning the structure of equation (4), though it will be convenient to defer the statement of these conditions until later. The results for this case are summarized in Theorem 2, (page 84).

We shall use several of the results of **[12]**, and will therefore require of the reader a certain facility in the general theory of nonlinear elliptic equations. Nevertheless, an effort has been made to keep the proofs and the statements of the theorems as nontechnical as possible. This has occasionally caused the work to overlap with parts of **[12]** (cf. especially Lemmas 3 and 4), but any alternative would considerably increase the difficulty of reading the paper.

1. **Preliminary considerations.** It is known that solutions of (4) satisfy a maximum principle and a Harnack inequality. More particularly, the following specific conclusions are valid:

(i) *Let u be a solution of* (4) *in a domain D. If $u \leqq M$ on the boundary of D then $u \leqq M + bC$* meas $(D)^{1/n}$ *at all points x contained in D. Here b is the constant in* (5), *and C depends only on α and n.*

(ii) *Let u be a positive solution of* (4) *in an annulus $\sigma/2 < |x| < 2\sigma$. Then*

$$\max u \leqq C'(\min u + b\sigma) \quad \text{on } |x| = \sigma,$$

where C' depends only on α, n, and a.

These results are proved in the first chapter of reference **[12]**; cf. also **[13**, Theorem 8]. [The case $\alpha > n$ of (i) actually is not discussed in these references, but can be handled by essentially the same methods.]

Now let u be a positive solution of (4) in the domain $0 < |x| < 1$. Our goal is to determine the asymptotic behavior of u in the neighborhood of the origin. We assert to begin with that *u must tend to a limit u_0 (finite or infinite) as x tends to the origin.* To see this, one need only apply the argument of Theorem 2 of **[5]**. In fact, since both the maximum principle and the Harnack inequality hold for solutions of (4), the proof given there carries over almost intact to the present case.

This much being established, our further considerations of the asymptotic behavior of u depend crucially on the following result.

Lemma 1. *Let Θ be a Lipschitz continuous function with compact support in $|x| < 1$, which is identically one in some neighborhood of the origin. Then*

$$\int \Theta_x \cdot \mathscr{A}\, dx = \text{const} = \omega_n K$$

where the constant is independent of the particular choice of Θ.

Proof. Let $\bar{\Theta}$ and Θ be two test functions obeying the given conditions. Then $\bar{\Theta} - \Theta$ has compact support in $0 < |x| < 1$, whence

$$\int (\bar{\Theta} - \Theta)_x \cdot \mathscr{A}\, dx = 0,$$

that is,

$$\int \bar{\Theta}_x \cdot \mathscr{A}\, dx = \int \Theta_x \cdot \mathscr{A}\, dx,$$

and the lemma is proved. (Note that $K = 0$ if the singularity is removable.)

In what follows it may obviously be assumed without loss of generality that u is continuous in $0 < |x| \leqq 1$, and then, by subtracting an appropriate constant, that

$u < 0$ on $|x| = 1$. This being the case, let $m = m(\sigma)$ denote the minimum value of u on the sphere $|x| = \sigma < 1$. We assert that

$$m \leqq b + |K + b^{\alpha-1}|^{1/(\alpha-1)} \begin{cases} |(\sigma^\tau - 1)/\tau|, & \alpha \neq n, \\ \log 1/\sigma, & \alpha = n, \end{cases} \tag{8}$$

where $\tau = (\alpha - n)/(\alpha - 1)$. Since (8) is trivial for any value of σ for which $m \leqq b$, it may be supposed at the outset that $m > b$. For all x contained in the set $\sigma \leqq |x| \leqq 1$ we define the function

$$v = v(x, \sigma) = \begin{cases} 0 & \text{if } u \leqq 0, \\ u & \text{if } 0 < u < m, \\ m & \text{if } u \geqq m. \end{cases}$$

This definition of v can be continuously extended to all of $|x| \leqq 1$ by setting $v \equiv m$ for $|x| \leqq \sigma$. Clearly then v is Lipschitz continuous, has compact support in $|x| < 1$, and is identically equal to m in the set $|x| \leqq \sigma$. Thus by Lemma 1 we have for fixed σ, and $v = v(x, \sigma)$, $m = m(\sigma)$,

$$\omega_n mK = \int v_x \cdot \mathscr{A}(x, u_x)\, dx = \int v_x \cdot \mathscr{A}(x, v_x)\, dx, \tag{9}$$

since $u_x = v_x$ almost everywhere in the set where $v_x \neq 0$. Using inequality (5)

$$\int v_x \cdot \mathscr{A}(x, v_x)\, dx \geqq \int (|v_x|^\alpha - b^\alpha)\, dx. \tag{10}$$

Moreover, by standard techniques in the calculus of variations[2] it can be shown that

$$\int |v_x|^\alpha\, dx \geqq \omega_n m^\alpha \begin{cases} |(\sigma^\tau - 1)/\tau|^{1-\alpha}, & \alpha \neq n, \\ (\log 1/\sigma)^{1-n}, & \alpha = n. \end{cases} \tag{11}$$

Hence by (9), (10), and (11),

$$m^\alpha \leqq (mK + b^\alpha) \begin{cases} |(\sigma^\tau - 1)/\tau|^{\alpha-1}, & \alpha \neq n, \\ (\log 1/\sigma)^{n-1}, & \alpha = n. \end{cases} \tag{12}$$

Since $m > b$, we have $b^\alpha \leqq mb^{\alpha-1}$. Making this replacement in (12), and then solving for m, proves (8).

Now if $\alpha > n$, then $\tau > 0$, and (8) implies that m is uniformly bounded. This establishes

LEMMA 2. *If $\alpha > n$, then u tends to a finite limit u_0 as x tends to the origin.*

Next suppose $\alpha \leqq n$. If the singularity is *not* removable we assert that $u_0 = \infty$ and $K > 0$. Indeed if u_0 were finite then u would be bounded in the neighborhood of the origin, and by Theorem 11 of **[12]** the singularity would be removable.

[2] Cf. Lemmas 9 and 10 of **[12]**, or, alternately, Lemma 8 below.

Thus in fact $u_0 = \infty$. Next suppose for contradiction that $K \leqq 0$. Then according to (12),

$$m \leqq b\begin{cases} |\tau|^{(1-\alpha)/\alpha}\sigma^{(\alpha-n)/\alpha}, & \alpha < n, \\ (\log 1/\sigma)^{1-1/n}, & \alpha = n. \end{cases}$$

Hence by the Harnack inequality $u = O(r^{(\alpha-n)/\alpha})$ or $u = O(|\log r|^{1-1/n})$ in the neighborhood of the origin. Using Theorem 11 again, it follows once more that the singularity is removable. Thus $K > 0$. We have therefore proved

LEMMA 3. *If $\alpha \leqq n$ then necessarily $K \geqq 0$. The singularity at 0 is removable if and only if $K = 0$, and is not removable if and only if $K > 0$. In the latter case u tends to infinity as x tends to 0.*

2. **The case $\alpha \leqq n$.** In this section we shall establish the asymptotic behavior of u at the origin when $\alpha \leqq n$. In view of the preceding results we may obviously suppose $u_0 = \infty$ and $K > 0$.

As in the previous section it can be assumed that u is continuous in $0 < |x| \leqq 1$ and $u < 0$ on $|x| = 1$. Then according to (8) we have

$$m \leqq b + (K + b^{\alpha-1})^{1/(\alpha-1)}\begin{cases} |\tau|^{-1}\sigma^{\tau}, & \alpha < n, \\ \log 1/\sigma, & \alpha = n. \end{cases} \tag{13}$$

The following calculation has as its purpose the demonstration of the important inequality (16), reverse to (13).

Let σ_0 be such that $u > 0$ for $|x| < \sigma_0$. For any fixed $\sigma < \sigma_0$ we introduce the function

$$\Theta = \Theta(x, \sigma) = \begin{cases} 0 & \text{when } |x| \geqq \sigma_0, \\ \dfrac{r^{\tau} - \sigma_0^{\tau}}{\sigma^{\tau} - \sigma_0^{\tau}} & \text{when } \sigma < |x| < \sigma_0, \\ 1 & \text{when } |x| \leqq \sigma \end{cases}$$

(we assume $\alpha < n$ for simplicity, and write $r = |x|$). By Lemma 1 and Hölder's inequality there results

$$\omega_n K = \int \Theta_x \cdot \mathscr{A}\, dx \leqq \left(\int |\Theta_x|^{\alpha}\, dx\right)^{1/\alpha}\left(\int |\mathscr{A}|^{\alpha/(\alpha-1)}\, dx\right)^{(\alpha-1)/\alpha}.$$

The first integral on the right-hand side equals $\omega_n|\tau|^{\alpha-1}(\sigma^{\tau} - \sigma_0^{\tau})^{1-\alpha}$, whence obviously

$$\omega_n|\tau|^{-1}K^{\alpha/(\alpha-1)}(\sigma^{\tau} - \sigma_0^{\tau}) \leqq \int_{\Sigma} |\mathscr{A}|^{\alpha/(\alpha-1)}\, dx \tag{14}$$

where Σ denotes the annulus $\sigma < |x| < \sigma_0$.

The next problem is to obtain an estimate for the integral $\int_\Sigma |\mathscr{A}|^{\alpha/(\alpha-1)}\, dx$. Let $M = M(\sigma)$ denote the maximum value of u on the sphere $|x| = \sigma < \sigma_0$. We define

$$V = V(x, \sigma) = \begin{cases} \text{Max}\,(0, u) & \text{if } \sigma \leqq |x| \leqq 1, \\ \text{Min}\,(M, u) & \text{if } 0 \leqq |x| < \sigma. \end{cases}$$

Evidently V is Lipschitz continuous, has compact support in $|x| < 1$, and is identically equal to M in a neighborhood of the origin. Let Δ denote the set where $V = u$. Obviously Δ contains the annulus $\sigma < |x| < \sigma_0$, so that

$$\begin{aligned} \int_\Sigma |\mathscr{A}|^{\alpha/(\alpha-1)}\, dx &\leqq \int_\Delta |\mathscr{A}|^{\alpha/(\alpha-1)}\, dx \\ &\leqq \text{const} \int_\Delta (|u_x|^\alpha + b^\alpha)\, dx \\ &\leqq \text{const} \int_\Delta (u_x \cdot \mathscr{A} + 2b^\alpha)\, dx, \quad \text{(using (5))}, \\ &\leqq \text{const} \int (V_x \cdot \mathscr{A} + 2b^\alpha)\, dx, \end{aligned}$$

the last step holding since $V_x = u_x$ almost everywhere in Δ, and $V_x = 0$ almost everywhere in the complement of Δ. Now by Lemma 1

$$\int V_x \cdot \mathscr{A}\, dx = \omega_n M K,$$

so that altogether

$$\int_\Sigma |\mathscr{A}|^{\alpha/(\alpha-1)}\, dx \leqq \text{const}\,(MK + b^\alpha).$$

This being the case, (14) implies

$$M \geqq \text{const}\, K^{1/(\alpha-1)}(\sigma^\tau - \sigma_0^\tau) - b^\alpha K^{-1}, \tag{15}$$

where the constant is strictly positive. If σ is small enough, the term σ^τ in (15) is dominant. Hence for all sufficiently small values of σ we have

$$M \geqq \text{const}\, \sigma^\tau \quad \text{if } \alpha < n, \tag{16'}$$

where the constant remains strictly positive. By a similar calculation, which may be omitted here, we find also

$$M \geqq \text{const} \log 1/\sigma \quad \text{if } \alpha = n. \tag{16''}$$

The following lemma is now an immediate consequence of (13), (16) and the Harnack inequality.

LEMMA 4. *Suppose $\alpha \leqq n$. If the singularity at 0 is not removable, then*

$$u \approx \begin{cases} r^{(\alpha-n)/(\alpha-1)}, & \alpha < n, \\ \log 1/r, & \alpha = n, \end{cases}$$

in the neighborhood of the origin.

The notation $f \approx g$ here means that there exist positive constants C' and C'' such that $C'g \leqq f \leqq C''g$.

3. **The case** $\alpha > n$. Our purpose is to obtain for the present case results corresponding to Lemmas 3 and 4 for the case $\alpha \leqq n$. Thus suppose that the singularity at the origin is *not* removable. According to Lemma 2 the solution then tends to a finite limit u_0 as x tends to the origin. We first show that the problem can be reduced to the case $u_0 = 0$, $u \geqq 0$ in $0 < |x| < 1$, and $u > 0$ on $|x| = 1$. At the same time, it will be shown that we can assume $p \cdot \mathscr{A}(x, p) > 0$ for $p \neq 0$.

To carry out the reduction, let w denote the solution of (4) in $|x| < 1/2$ which agrees with u on the boundary $|x| = 1/2$ (this construction is possible in view of property P1). Set $w_0 = w(0)$. We assert that $w_0 \neq u_0$. Indeed, because of (6) the difference of two solutions of (4) satisfies a simple maximum principle. Thus, if $u_0 = w_0$, the two solutions u and w agree on the boundary of $0 < |x| < 1/2$, and are consequently identical. But this contradicts our assumption that u has a nonremovable singularity at 0. Hence $w_0 \neq u_0$. This being shown, we now set $\kappa = w_0 - u_0$ and define

$$\bar{u} = \kappa(\kappa + u - w) \qquad (0 < |x| < 1/2).$$

Evidently $\bar{u}_0 = 0$, and $\bar{u} = \kappa^2 > 0$ on $|x| = 1/2$. Moreover, since $\bar{u}$ is a multiple of the difference of two solutions of (4), it satisfies the simple maximum principle. Consequently

$$0 \leqq \bar{u} \leqq \kappa^2 \quad \text{for } 0 < |x| < 1/2.$$

Thus $\bar{u}$ is a function having the required properties, at least with respect to the ball $|x| \leqq 1/2$.

It is easy to see that $\bar{u}$ is a solution of the differential equation

$$\operatorname{div} \bar{\mathscr{A}}(x, \bar{u}_x) = 0,$$

where

$$\bar{\mathscr{A}}(x, p) = \kappa\{\mathscr{A}(x, p/\kappa + w_x) - \mathscr{A}(x, w_x)\}.$$

By continuity there exists a number ρ, $0 < \rho < 1/2$, such that $\bar{u} > 0$ on $|x| = \rho$. Since the gradient of w is bounded in $|x| \leqq \rho$, it is therefore clear that $\bar{\mathscr{A}}(x, p)$ satisfies (5) in $|x| \leqq \rho$ for appropriate constants a and b.[3] Moreover, a simple calculation shows that $p \cdot \bar{\mathscr{A}}(x, p) > 0$ for $p \neq 0$. A trivial normalization from the radius ρ to the radius 1 now completes the reduction.

The asymptotic behavior of u is effectively determined by that of the new solution $\bar{u}$. Therefore, in what follows we can concentrate on the behavior of $\bar{u}$. Moreover, no confusion will result if we temporarily drop the bars from $\bar{u}$ and $\bar{\mathscr{A}}$. Thus for the moment u will denote the new solution, with $u_0 = 0$, $u \geqq 0$ in $0 < |x| < 1$, and $u > 0$ on $|x| = 1$.

[3] This may require preliminary multiplication of $\bar{\mathscr{A}}$ by a suitable constant, a normalization which we suppose is automatically carried out.

Let $m = m(\sigma)$ denote as in the previous sections the minimum value of u on the sphere $|x| = \sigma < 1$. We assert that for some appropriate constant,

$$m \leqq \text{const}\, \sigma^{\tau}, \tag{17}$$

where $\tau = (\alpha - n)/(\alpha - 1)$. Since this is trivial when $m = 0$, we need consider only values of σ for which $m > 0$. Let ε be a fixed number, $0 < \varepsilon < m(\sigma)$. For $0 \leqq |x| \leqq \sigma$ we define

$$v = v(x, \sigma, \varepsilon) = \begin{cases} \varepsilon & \text{if } u \leqq \varepsilon, \\ u & \text{if } \varepsilon < u < m, \\ m & \text{if } u \geqq m. \end{cases}$$

The definition of v may be extended to the entire unit ball by setting $v \equiv m$ for $|x| \geqq \sigma$. Now the function $(m - v)/(m - \varepsilon)$ has its support in the ball $|x| \leqq \sigma$ and is identically one in some neighborhood of the origin. Thus by Lemma 1 and the fact that $u_x = v_x$ in the set where $v_x \neq 0$,

$$\omega_n(m - \varepsilon)\bar{K} = \int v_x \cdot \mathscr{A}(x, u_x)\, dx = \int v_x \cdot \mathscr{A}(x, v_x)\, dx \tag{18}$$

(here $-\bar{K}$ is the constant for the new function u; it is obviously a nonzero multiple of the original constant K). Now by (5)

$$\int v_x \cdot \mathscr{A}(x, v_x)\, dx \geqq \int (|v_x|^{\alpha} - b^{\alpha})\, dx$$

where the right-hand integral is evaluated over $|x| \leqq \sigma$. By standard techniques in the calculus of variations (cf. footnote 2) it can easily be shown that

$$\int |v_x|^{\alpha}\, dx \geqq \omega_n \tau^{\alpha-1} \sigma^{n-\alpha} (m - \varepsilon)^{\alpha}.$$

Consequently, (18) implies

$$(m - \varepsilon)\bar{K} \geqq \tau^{\alpha-1}\sigma^{n-\alpha}(m - \varepsilon)^{\alpha} - b^{\alpha}\sigma^{n}.$$

Letting ε tend to zero, and then solving for m, we obtain (17). This inequality serves the same purpose for the case $\alpha > n$ as does (13) for the case $\alpha \leqq n$.

LEMMA 5. $K = 0$ *if and only if the singularity at* 0 *is removable.*

PROOF. It is enough to prove that $\bar{K} \neq 0$ when the singularity is not removable. Let $\sigma < 1$ be chosen so that $m(\sigma) > 0$; this choice is possible since u is continuous and positive on $|x| = 1$. Consider the corresponding function $v = v(x, \sigma, \varepsilon)$. It is obviously nonconstant on a set of positive measure, whence $v_x \cdot \mathscr{A}(x, v_x)$ is positive on a set of positive measure. Thus for this value of σ,

$$\int v_x \cdot \mathscr{A}(x, v_x)\, dx > 0.$$

Comparing with (18) yields $\bar{K} > 0$, and the lemma is proved.

Now let $M = M(\sigma)$ denote the maximum value of u on the sphere $|x| = \sigma < 1$. Our goal is to prove inequality (24), reverse to (17). Since u is continuous and positive on $|x| = 1$ it is clear that there exists some constant σ_2 such that

(19) $$M(\sigma) < \min_{r=1} u \quad \text{for } \sigma < \sigma_2.$$

For fixed σ and σ_1, $0 < \sigma_1 < \sigma < \sigma_2$, we define

$$\Theta = \Theta(x, \sigma, \sigma_1) = \begin{cases} 0 & \text{when } |x| \geqq \sigma, \\ \dfrac{\sigma^\tau - r^\tau}{\sigma^\tau - \sigma_1^\tau} & \text{when } \sigma_1 < |x| < \sigma, \\ 1 & \text{when } |x| \leqq \sigma_1. \end{cases}$$

By Lemma 1 and Hölder's inequality (recall that $\bar{K} > 0$)

$$\omega_n \bar{K} = -\int \Theta_x \cdot \mathscr{A}\, dx \leqq \left(\int |\Theta_x|^\alpha\, dx\right)^{1/\alpha} \left(\int |\mathscr{A}|^{\alpha/(\alpha-1)}\, dx\right)^{(\alpha-1)/\alpha}.$$

Since the first integral on the right-hand side equals $\omega_n \tau^{\alpha-1}(\sigma^\tau - \sigma_1^\tau)^{1-\alpha}$, this yields at once

(20) $$\omega_n \tau^{-1} \bar{K}^{\alpha/(\alpha-1)} (\sigma^\tau - \sigma_1^\tau) \leqq \int_\Sigma |\mathscr{A}|^{\alpha/(\alpha-1)}\, dx$$

where Σ denotes the annulus $\sigma_1 < |x| < \sigma$.

Now let ε be a number satisfying $0 < \varepsilon < M(\sigma)$. We define

$$V = V(x, \sigma, \varepsilon) = \begin{cases} \operatorname{Max}(\varepsilon, u) & \text{if } 0 \leqq |x| < \sigma, \\ \operatorname{Min}(M, u) & \text{if } \sigma \leqq |x| \leqq 1. \end{cases}$$

It is easy to see that the annulus Σ is contained in the union of the sets

$$\Delta = \{u = V\} \quad \text{and} \quad \Delta' = \{u < \varepsilon\} \cap \Sigma.$$

Therefore, using (5) and the fact that $u_x \cdot \mathscr{A} \geqq 0$, we have

$$\int_\Sigma |\mathscr{A}|^{\alpha/(\alpha-1)}\, dx \leqq \text{const} \int_\Sigma (|u_x|^\alpha + b^\alpha)\, dx$$

(21) $$\leqq \text{const} \int_\Sigma (u_x \cdot \mathscr{A} + 2b^\alpha)\, dx$$

$$\leqq \text{const} \left\{ b^\alpha \sigma^n + \int_\Delta u_x \cdot \mathscr{A}\, dx + \int_{\Delta'} u_x \cdot \mathscr{A}\, dx \right\}.$$

Using (5) once more,

(22) $$\int_{\Delta'} u_x \cdot \mathscr{A}\, dx \leqq \text{const} \int_{\Delta'} (|u_x|^\alpha + |u_x|)\, dx.$$

On the other hand, since $u_x = V_x$ almost everywhere in Δ, and $V_x = 0$ almost everywhere in the complement of Δ,

$$\int_\Delta u_x \cdot \mathscr{A}\, dx = \int V_x \cdot \mathscr{A}\, dx = \omega_n(M - \varepsilon)\bar{K}, \tag{23}$$

the last step following in the usual way, since by (19) the function $M - V$ has compact support in $|x| < 1$. From (20), (21), (22), and (23) we obtain the inequality

$$\bar{K}^{\alpha/(\alpha-1)}(\sigma^\tau - \sigma_1^\tau) \leqq \text{const}\left\{b^\alpha\sigma^n + (M - \varepsilon)\bar{K} + \int_{\Delta'} (|u_x|^\alpha + |u_x|)\, dx\right\}.$$

Here we may let ε tend to zero, and then σ_1 tend to zero. Since as $\varepsilon \to 0$

$$\int_{\Delta'} (|u_x|^\alpha + |u_x|)\, dx \to \int_{\{u=0\}\cap\Sigma} (|u_x|^\alpha + |u_x|)\, dx = 0,$$

it follows that

$$\bar{K}^{\alpha/(\alpha-1)}\sigma^\tau \leqq \text{const}\,(b^\alpha\sigma^n + M\bar{K}).$$

Hence for all sufficiently small values of σ,

$$M \geqq \text{const}\ \sigma^\tau \tag{24}$$

where the constant is strictly positive.

The required asymptotic behavior of u follows from inequalities (17) and (24). Indeed by (17) and the Harnack inequality we have for all sufficiently small values of σ,

$$M \leqq \text{const}\,(m + b\sigma) \leqq \text{const}\ \sigma^\tau,$$

while on the other hand, using (24),

$$m \geqq \text{const}\ M - b\sigma \geqq \text{const}\ \sigma^\tau.$$

Returning to the bar notation for the new solution, we have thus proved that $\bar{u} \approx r^\tau$ in the neighborhood of the origin.

Now $\bar{u} = \kappa(\kappa + u - w)$ where $\kappa = w_0 - u_0$. Hence

$$u - u_0 = \bar{u}/\kappa + w - w_0.$$

Since $w - w_0 = O(r)$, the following result is proved.

LEMMA 6. *Suppose $\alpha > n$. If the singularity at* 0 *is not removable, then either $u - u_0 \approx r^\tau$ or $u - u_0 \approx -r^\tau$ in the neighborhood of the origin.*

The content of Lemmas 2 through 6 can be summarized in the following basic theorem. It holds for any equation (4) such that conditions (5), (6), and property P1 are valid.

THEOREM 1. *Let $u = u(x)$ be a positive solution of equation* (4) *in the domain* $0 < |x| < 1$. *Then u tends to a limit u_0 as x tends to the origin.*

The origin is a removable singularity if and only if the constant K in Lemma 1 *vanishes. If the singularity is not removable, then u_0 is infinite if $\alpha \leqq n$, and finite if $\alpha > n$; moreover, in the neighborhood of the origin we have*

$$u \approx r^{(\alpha-n)/(\alpha-1)} \qquad \text{if } \alpha < n,$$

$$u \approx \log 1/r \qquad \text{if } \alpha = n,$$

and

$$u - u_0 \approx \pm r^{(\alpha-n)/(\alpha-1)} \qquad \text{if } \alpha > n.$$

(Here $f \approx g$ means that there exist positive constants C' and C'' such that $C'g \leqq f \leqq C''g$.)

REMARKS. 1. It is of interest to give a formula for K which is independent of test functions. Using the fact that solutions are here assumed to be continuously differentiable functions, it is easily shown that

$$K = -\frac{1}{\omega_n} \oint \mathscr{A} \cdot \mathbf{n}\, ds, \tag{25}$$

where the integral is taken over any smooth nonintersecting closed surface in $0 < |x| < 1$ which contains the origin in its interior, and $\mathbf{n}$ denotes the outer normal vector to this surface. Thus K has the physical significance of an "inflow" of flux $\mathscr{A}/\omega_n$.

2. Theorem 1 also holds for any solution of (4) which is bounded below by a constant, as can be seen by adding an appropriate constant to the solution.

3. We remark finally that condition (6) and property P1 are required only to establish the asymptotic behavior of u when $\alpha > n$.

4. **Positive solutions in an exterior domain.** We now turn to the case of a positive solution of (4) defined in an exterior domain.

As in the case of a singularity at a finite point, we must augment the "natural" hypotheses (5) and (6) with certain further conditions. In particular, we shall suppose that (4) has the following additional properties:

P2. *There exist constants $c > 0$ and $\beta > 1$ such that the inequalities*

$$\begin{aligned} |\mathscr{A}(x,p)| &\leqq c|p|^{\beta-1}, \\ p \cdot \mathscr{A}(x,p) &\geqq c^{-1}|p|^{\beta} \end{aligned} \tag{26}$$

hold for all $|p| \leqq 1$.

P3. *Let u be a bounded solution of* (4) *in a ball of radius R and center z. Then $|u_x(z)|$ can be estimated by the ratios*

$$\frac{\max |u|}{R} \quad \text{and} \quad \frac{R}{1 + |z|}. \tag{27}$$

Property P2 deserves some special remarks. It is apparent that it can hold only if $\mathscr{A}(x, 0) = 0$. Suppose in particular that $\mathscr{A}(x, 0) = 0$ and that $\mathscr{A}$ is of class C^1 in p. Then (26) holds with $\beta = 2$ provided the quadratic form $\mathscr{A}_{i,k}\xi_i\xi_k$ is uniformly positive definite for $|p| \leqq 1$. Since $\mathscr{A}_{i,k}\xi_i\xi_k$ is non-negative by virtue of (6), we see that $\beta = 2$ is in a sense the normal case of property P2. In any event, the exponent β turns out to be the salient parameter governing the behavior of solutions at infinity, just as the exponent α was fundamental in the investigation of finite singularities. It may be observed that for linear elliptic equations of the form

$$\frac{\partial}{\partial x_i}\left(a_{ij}(x)\frac{\partial u}{\partial x_j}\right) = 0 \tag{28}$$

we have $\alpha = \beta = 2$. Thus for (28) there is a certain duality between the case of a singularity at a finite point and a singularity at infinity, a duality which disappears in the general nonlinear case.

Turning to assumption P3, we note that, like property P1, it is satisfied by a wide variety of equations of the form (4); cf. in particular the work of Ladyzhenskaya and Uraltseva [7]. For example, it follows from [7] that P3 holds whenever $\mathscr{A}$ is independent of x, and

$$\mathscr{A}_{i,k}\xi_i\xi_k \geqq \text{Const}\,(1 + |p|)^{\alpha-2}\xi^2, \qquad |\mathscr{A}_{i,k}| \leqq \text{Const}\,(1 + |p|)^{\alpha-2}.$$

The integrand (3) is a specific case where all the above conditions are satisfied (here $\beta = 2$). We note finally that P3 does not necessarily hold for the linear equation (28) if the coefficients a_{ij} are only assumed to be bounded and measurable. Nevertheless the final conclusion (Theorem 2) still remains valid for this case; cf. footnote 4.

The following lemmas will be useful in the sequel. Their proofs are given in §5.

Lemma 7. *After multiplication by a suitable constant* (*which we automatically assume done*), *the vector* $\mathscr{A}$ *satisfies the condition*

$$p\cdot\mathscr{A} \geqq |p|^\beta(1 + |p|)^{\alpha-\beta}. \tag{29}$$

Lemma 8. *Let* $v = v(x)$ *be a Lipschitz continuous function which vanishes for* $|x| \leqq 1$, *and is identically equal to* m *for* $|x| \geqq \sigma$ $(m > 0, \sigma > 1)$. *Then for* $\alpha > 1$, $\beta > 1$ *we have*

$$\int |v_x|^\beta(1 + |v_x|)^{\alpha-\beta}\,dx \geqq \omega_n\kappa m\,\text{Min}\,(J^{\alpha-1}, J^{\beta-1})$$

where κ *is a positive constant depending only on* α *and* β,

$$J = m\begin{cases}|(\sigma^\lambda - 1)/\lambda|^{-1}, & \beta \neq n,\\ |\log\sigma|^{-1}, & \beta = n,\end{cases}$$

and $\lambda = (\beta - n)/(\beta - 1)$.

REMARK. In particular, we may take $\kappa = \beta/\alpha$ if $\beta \leqq \alpha$ and $\kappa = 2^\alpha\alpha/2^\beta\beta$ if $\alpha < \beta$. When $\alpha = \beta$ this yields inequality (11).

Now let u be a positive solution of (4) in an exterior domain, say $1 < |x| < \infty$ for simplicity. Our consideration of the behavior of u near infinity depends crucially on the following basic result corresponding to Lemma 1.

LEMMA 9. *Let Θ be a Lipschitz continuous function with compact support in $1 < |x| \leqq \infty$, which is identically one in some neighborhood of infinity. Then*

$$\int \Theta_x \cdot \mathscr{A}\, dx = \text{const} = \omega_n K$$

where the constant is independent of the particular choice of Θ.

The proof is exactly the same as the proof of Lemma 1.

In what follows it may be assumed without loss of generality that u is continuous in $1 \leqq |x| < \infty$, and then, by subtracting an appropriate constant, that $u < 0$ on $|x| = 1$. This being the case, let $m = m(\sigma)$ denote the minimum value of u on the sphere $|x| = \sigma > 1$. We assert that

$$m \leqq \text{const}\begin{cases} |(\sigma^\lambda - 1)/\lambda|, & \beta \neq n, \\ \log \sigma, & \beta = n, \end{cases} \tag{30}$$

where $\lambda = (\beta - n)/(\beta - 1)$. Since (30) is trivial when $m \leqq 0$, it may be supposed at the outset that $m > 0$. For $1 \leqq |x| \leqq \sigma$ we define the function

$$v = v(x, \sigma) = \begin{cases} 0 & \text{if } u \leqq 0, \\ u & \text{if } 0 < u < m, \\ m & \text{if } u \geqq m. \end{cases}$$

This definition of v can be extended to all of $|x| \geqq 1$ by setting $v \equiv m$ for $|x| \geqq \sigma$. Then v is Lipschitz continuous, has compact support in $1 < |x| \leqq \infty$, and is identically equal to m in the set $|x| \geqq \sigma$. Thus by Lemma 9 we have for fixed σ, and $v = v(x, \sigma)$, $m = m(\sigma)$,

$$\omega_n mK = \int v_x \cdot \mathscr{A}(x, u_x)\, dx = \int v_x \cdot \mathscr{A}(x, v_x)\, dx.$$

Moreover, it follows from Lemmas 7 and 8 that

$$\int v_x \cdot \mathscr{A}(x, v_x)\, dx \geqq \int |v_x|^\beta (1 + |v_x|)^{\alpha-\beta}\, dx \geqq \omega_n \kappa m \operatorname{Min}(J^{\alpha-1}, J^{\beta-1}).$$

Combining the last two displays yields

$$\operatorname{Min}(J^{\alpha-1}, J^{\beta-1}) \leqq K/\kappa.$$

Thus J is bounded, and the assertion is proved.

LEMMA 10. *$|u_x|$ is uniformly bounded in the set $|x| > 2$.*

PROOF. Irrespective of the values of α and β, inequality (30) implies

$$m \leqq \text{const}\ \sigma. \tag{31}$$

Consequently, by the Harnack inequality (cf. §1),

$$u(x) \leqq \text{const}\ r. \tag{32}$$

Let z be any fixed point outside the sphere $|x| = 2$, and let S denote the ball of radius $|z|/2$ and center z. Clearly $\max_S |u| \leqq \text{const}\ |z|$. Therefore, both the ratios (27) are uniformly bounded, and $|u_x(z)| \leqq$ const. This completes the proof.

Lemma 10 being shown, it is now clear that in considering the asymptotic behavior of u in the neighborhood of infinity, there is no loss of generality in supposing $|u_x|$ to be uniformly bounded in the entire set $|x| > 1$, say $|u_x| \leqq B$. Now by (26) and (29) there exists a constant c' such that for $|p| \leqq B$,

$$|\mathscr{A}(x, p)| \leqq c'|p|^{\beta-1},$$
$$p \cdot \mathscr{A}(x, p) \geqq c'^{-1}|p|^{\beta}.$$

A trivial normalization, which we automatically assume carried out, then allows us to write

$$\begin{aligned} |\mathscr{A}(x, p)| &\leqq a'|p|^{\beta-1}, \\ p \cdot \mathscr{A}(x, p) &\geqq |p|^{\beta} \end{aligned} \tag{33}$$

for all $|p| \leqq B$, where a' is an appropriate constant. Since $|u_x| \leqq B$ for the solution under consideration, it is clear that the behavior of $\mathscr{A}$ for $|p| > B$ can be altered at will without affecting the fact that u is a solution of (4). We may therefore suppose that (33) continues to hold for all values of p. In summary, *in considering the asymptotic behavior of u near infinity we may assume without loss of generality that the function* $\mathscr{A}(x, p)$ *satisfies* (33) *for all values of x and p.*[4]

This being the case, the maximum principle and the Harnack inequality (§1) now hold with $b = 0$ and $C' = C'(\beta, n, a')$.

LEMMA 11. *u tends to a limit u_0 as x tends to infinity. If $\beta < n$ then u_0 is finite.*

PROOF. The first part of the lemma is a consequence of the argument of Theorem 3 of [5]. In fact, since both the maximum principle and the Harnack inequality now hold with $b = 0$, the proof given there carries over almost word for word (cf. also [3, p. 135], where the idea appears in somewhat simpler form). Next, if $\beta < n$ then $\lambda < 0$, and (30) implies that m is uniformly bounded. Thus u_0 is finite.

[4] For linear equations this statement is clearly valid even though P3 and Lemma 10 may not hold. Since the further discussion depends only on this statement, and not on the particular validity of either property P3 or Lemma 10, the final conclusion (Theorem 2) thus holds also for linear equations.

Our remaining considerations, though quite analogous to those at a finite singular point, are nevertheless not quite so sharp, since we no longer have necessary and sufficient conditions for the constant K to vanish. The following Lemma 12 is a partial substitute. Here we say that u satisfies a *strong maximum principle at infinity* if in any fixed neighborhood of infinity it is either identically constant or else takes on values both greater and less than u_0. (Note that this definition automatically requires u_0 to be finite.)

If u does *not* satisfy this maximum principle, we assert that either $u < u_0$ or $u > u_0$ is some neighborhood of infinity. This is obvious if $u_0 = \infty$. On the other hand, if u_0 is finite and u does not satisfy the maximum principle, then certainly either $u \leqq u_0$ or $u \geqq u_0$ in some neighborhood of infinity. But by the Harnack inequality we cannot have $u = u_0$ at any point of this neighborhood without at the same time having $u \equiv u_0$. Thus either $u < u_0$ or $u > u_0$, proving the assertion.

LEMMA 12. *If $K = 0$ then u satisfies a strong maximum principle at infinity.*

PROOF. If the maximum principle does not hold, then either $u < u_0$ or $u > u_0$ in some neighborhood of infinity. To be specific, suppose that $u < u_0$. By adding an appropriate (positive or negative) constant to u it can be assumed that $u_0 > 0$, while for some $\hat{\sigma} \geqq 1$

$$u < 0 \quad \text{on } |x| = \hat{\sigma}.$$

Consider the function

$$\hat{v} = \hat{v}(x) = \begin{cases} 0 & \text{if } u \leqq 0, \\ u & \text{if } 0 < u < l, \\ l & \text{if } u \geqq l, \end{cases}$$

where $l = \text{Min}\,(1, u_0/2)$ and $|x| > \hat{\sigma}$. Then according to Lemma 9

$$0 = \int \hat{v}_x \cdot \mathscr{A}(x, u_x)\, dx = \int \hat{v}_x \cdot \mathscr{A}(x, \hat{v}_x)\, dx.$$

Since $p \cdot \mathscr{A} \geqq |p|^\beta$ it follows that $|\hat{v}_x| \equiv 0$, which is an obvious contradiction. This completes the proof.

LEMMA 13. *Suppose $\beta \geqq n$. If the maximum principle does not hold, then $u_0 = \infty$ and*

$$u \approx \begin{cases} r^{(\beta - n)/(\beta - 1)}, & \beta > n, \\ \log r, & \beta = n, \end{cases} \tag{34}$$

in the neighborhood of infinity.

PROOF. By hypothesis and Lemma 12, we have $K \neq 0$. Since the maximum principle does not hold, we can assume without loss of generality that $u_0 > 0$

while $u < 0$ on $|x| = 1$. Proceeding as in the demonstration of Lemma 4, one then finds in analogy with (15),

$$M \geqq \text{const}\,|K|^{1/(\beta-1)}\begin{cases}\sigma^\lambda - \sigma_0^\lambda, & \beta > n,\\ \log \sigma/\sigma_0, & \beta = n.\end{cases} \tag{35}$$

Since $\lambda > 0$ it follows that M tends to infinity as σ tends to infinity. Consequently $u_0 = \infty$. Finally, according to (30), (35), and the Harnack principle, (34) is valid in the neighborhood of infinity. This completes the demonstration.

LEMMA 14. *Suppose $\beta < n$. If the maximum principle does not hold, then either $u - u_0 \approx r^\lambda$ or $u - u_0 \approx -r^\lambda$ in the neighborhood of infinity.*

PROOF. Since u_0 is finite when $\beta < n$, one may easily reduce the lemma to the case where $u_0 = 0$, $u > 0$ in $|x| \geqq 1$, and $K \neq 0$. The result is now proved in the same way as Lemma 6. We omit the details.

The content of Lemmas 11 through 14 is summarized in the following theorem. It holds for any equation (4) such that conditions (5), (6), and properties P2 and P3 are valid.

THEOREM 2. *Let $u = u(x)$ be a positive solution of equation* (4) *in the exterior domain* $1 < |x| < \infty$. *Then u tends to a limit u_0 as x tends to infinity.*

If the constant in Lemma 9 *vanishes, then u satisfies a strong maximum principle at infinity. On the other hand, if the maximum principle does not hold, then u_0 is infinite if $\beta \geqq n$ and finite if $\beta < n$; moreover, in the neighborhood of infinity we have*

$$\begin{aligned} &u \approx r^{(\beta-n)/(\beta-1)} && \text{if } \beta > n,\\ &u \approx \log r && \text{if } \beta = n,\end{aligned} \tag{36}$$

and

$$u - u_0 \approx \pm r^{(\beta-n)/(\beta-1)} \quad \text{if } \beta < n.$$

REMARKS. 1. Although Theorem 2 is closely analogous to Theorem 1, it is nevertheless not quite so strong since we do not have necessary and sufficient conditions for the maximum principle to hold.

2. The conclusion of Theorem 2 applies also to solutions of (4) which are uniformly bounded below, as one sees by adding an appropriate constant to the solution.

COROLLARY. *Suppose $\beta < n$, and let property* P1 *be satisfied in addition to the assumptions of this section. Then*

$$|u - u_0| = O(r^{(\beta-n)/(\beta-1)}) \tag{37}$$

as x tends to infinity.

PROOF. By standard methods (cf. [**12**, Theorem 13]) it can be shown that there exists a solution w of (4) in $2 < |x| < \infty$ such that

(1) on $|x| = 2$, w is constant and $\geqq u, u_0 + 1$,

(2) $w_0 = u_0$.

Since the difference of two solutions of (4) obeys a maximum principle, it follows that $u \leqq w$ in $2 \leqq |x| < \infty$. Moreover, by Theorem 2, $w - w_0 \approx r^{(\beta-n)/(\beta-1)}$ in the neighborhood of infinity. Consequently for large r,

$$u - u_0 \leqq w - w_0 \leqq \text{const } r^{(\beta-n)/(\beta-1)}.$$

The opposite inequality is proved similarly, and the demonstration is complete.

For the case of linear equations of the form (28), Finn and Gilbarg obtained various results which overlap Theorem 2 and the preceding corollary.

5. **Proof of Lemmas 7 and 8.** To prove Lemma 7 we recall that $p\cdot\mathscr{A} \geqq |p|^\alpha - b^\alpha$ according to (5). Therefore, if $|p| \geqq 1 + 2b$,

$$p\cdot\mathscr{A} \geqq (1 - 2^{-\alpha})|p|^\alpha \geqq 2^{-\alpha}|p|^\beta(1 + |p|)^{\alpha-\beta}.$$

On the other hand, (6) implies

$$p\cdot(\mathscr{A}(x, p) - \mathscr{A}(x, \theta p)) \geqq 0$$

for any real number θ between 0 and 1. For $|p| \leqq 1 + 2b$ and $\theta = (1 + 2b)^{-1}$ this gives

$$p\cdot\mathscr{A}(x, p) \geqq p\cdot\mathscr{A}\left(x, \frac{p}{1 + 2b}\right) \geqq c^{-1}(1 + 2b)\left|\frac{p}{1 + 2b}\right|^\beta$$
$$\geqq c^{-1}(2 + 2b)^{2-\alpha-\beta}|p|^\beta(1 + |p|)^{\alpha-\beta}.$$

The lemma follows at once.

PROOF OF LEMMA 8. Consider the variational problem

$$I[v] = \int |v_x|^\beta(1 + |v_x|)^{\alpha-\beta}\, dx = \text{Minimum}, \tag{38}$$

where the admissible functions $v(x)$ are Lipschitz continuous, vanish for $|x| \leqq 1$, and are identically equal to m for $|x| \geqq \sigma$. There is clearly no loss of generality in restricting the domain of integration to the annulus $\Gamma: 1 < |x| < \sigma$, and we shall suppose this done from here on.

We shall show that the Euler-Lagrange equation of (38) has a unique radially symmetric solution $h = h(r)$ in Γ, such that $h = 0$ on $|x| = 1$ and $h = m$ on $|x| = \sigma$. Once this is done, it follows that

$$I[v] \geqq I[h] \tag{39}$$

since the Weierstrass E-function is non-negative.[5] The proof is then completed by showing

$$I[h] \geqq \omega_n \kappa m \text{ Min } (J^{\alpha-1}, J^{\beta-1}). \tag{40}$$

[5] This follows from the fact that $|p|^\beta(1 + |p|)^{\alpha-\beta}$ is convex.

Step 1. *Existence of* $h(r)$. Clearly $h = h(r)$ is a solution of the Euler-Lagrange equation for (38) if and only if it is an extremal of the one-dimensional problem

$$\delta \int |h'|^\beta (1 + |h'|)^{\alpha-\beta} r^{n-1}\, dr = 0, \tag{41}$$

where $h' = dh/dr$. The Euler equation for (41) is

$$\frac{d}{dr}[|h'|^{\beta-1}(1 + |h'|)^{\alpha-\beta-1}(\alpha|h'| + \beta)r^{n-1}] = 0,$$

which has the first integral

$$|h'|^{\beta-1}(1 + |h'|)^{\alpha-\beta-1}(\alpha|h'| + \beta) = kr^{1-n} \tag{42}$$

(k = constant). The boundary conditions on h can be satisfied only if $k > 0$ and $h' > 0$; (42) therefore becomes

$$p^{\beta-1}(1 + p)^{\alpha-\beta-1}(\alpha p + \beta) = kr^{1-n}, \tag{43}$$

where we have set $p = h'$ for simplicity. The left-hand side of (43) is a monotone increasing function of p. Consequently, we can invert (43) to obtain

$$p = f(kr^{1-n}), \tag{44}$$

where $f(t)$ is an increasing function of its argument with $f(0) = 0$. The functions

$$h = h(r, k) = \int_1^r f(kr^{1-n})\, dr, \qquad k > 0, \tag{45}$$

therefore represent all possible radially symmetric extremals of (38) such that $h = 0$ when $r = 1$ and $h > 0$ when $r = \sigma$.

It remains to show that there is a unique value of k for which $h(\sigma, k) = m$. Now $dh/dk > 0$ and $h(\sigma, 0) = 0$, so that it is enough to prove

$$h(\sigma, k) \to \infty \quad \text{as} \quad k \to \infty. \tag{46}$$

But

$$p^{\beta-1}(1 + p)^{\alpha-\beta-1}(\alpha p + \beta) \leqq (\alpha + \beta)(1 + p)^{\alpha-1}$$

whence obviously

$$f(t) \geqq \left(\frac{t}{\alpha + \beta}\right)^{1/(\alpha-1)} - 1.$$

Thus by (45),

$$h(\sigma, k) \geqq \left(\frac{k}{\alpha + \beta}\right)^{1/(\alpha-1)} \int_1^\sigma r^{(1-n)/(\alpha-1)}\, dr - \sigma,$$

and (46) holds. This completes the first part of the proof.

Step 2. *Estimation of* $I[h]$. Retaining the notation $p = h'$, we easily find that

$$I[h] = \omega_n \int_1^\sigma p^\beta(1 + p)^{\alpha-\beta} r^{n-1}\, dr = \omega_n k \int_1^\sigma \left(\frac{1 + p}{\beta + \alpha p}\right) p\, dr,$$

where (43) was used at the second step. Now $(1 + p)/(\beta + \alpha p) \geqq \mathrm{Min}\,(\alpha^{-1}, \beta^{-1})$, and, using the boundary conditions for h,

$$\int_1^\sigma p\, dr = h(\sigma) - h(0) = m.$$

Thus

$$I[h] \geqq \omega_n k m\, \mathrm{Min}\,(\alpha^{-1}, \beta^{-1}). \tag{47}$$

It remains to estimate the constant k from below. The cases $\alpha < \beta$ and $\alpha \geqq \beta$ are best treated separately.

(i) $\alpha < \beta$. We assert that

$$1 + p \leqq \mathrm{Max}\left\{2, 2^{(\beta-1)/(\alpha-1)}\left(\frac{k}{\alpha}\right)^{1/(\alpha-1)}\right\}. \tag{48}$$

This is obvious if $p \leqq 1$; on the other hand, if $p > 1$ then (43) implies,

$$(1 + p)^{\alpha-1} = kr^{1-n}\left(\frac{1 + p}{p}\right)^{\beta-1}\left(\frac{1 + p}{\beta + \alpha p}\right) \leqq 2^{\beta-1}\frac{k}{\alpha}.$$

Thus (48) holds in all cases. Using (43) and (48),

$$\begin{aligned} p^{\beta-1} &= kr^{1-n}(1 + p)^{\beta-\alpha}\left(\frac{1 + p}{\beta + \alpha p}\right) \\ &\leqq \frac{kr^{1-n}}{\alpha}\,\mathrm{Max}\left\{2^{\beta-\alpha}, 2^{(\beta-\alpha)(\beta-1)/(\alpha-1)}\left(\frac{k}{\alpha}\right)^{(\beta-\alpha)/(\alpha-1)}\right\}. \end{aligned}$$

Raising both sides to the $1/(\beta - 1)$ power gives an estimate for p. With the help of this estimate,

$$m = \int_1^\sigma p\, dr \leqq \mathrm{Max}\left\{\left(\frac{2^{\beta-\alpha}k}{\alpha}\right)^{1/(\beta-1)}, \left(\frac{2^{\beta-\alpha}k}{\alpha}\right)^{1/(\alpha-1)}\right\}\cdot \int_1^\sigma r^{(1-n)/(\beta-1)}\, dr.$$

Evaluating the last integral and recalling the definition of J, this can be rewritten

$$J \leqq \mathrm{Max}\left\{\left(\frac{2^{\beta-\alpha}k}{\alpha}\right)^{1/(\beta-1)}, \left(\frac{2^{\beta-\alpha}k}{\alpha}\right)^{1/(\alpha-1)}\right\}.$$

Therefore

$$k \geqq 2^{\alpha-\beta}\alpha\, \mathrm{Min}\,(J^{\alpha-1}, J^{\beta-1}). \tag{49}$$

Combining (47) and (49) yields inequality (40), with $\kappa = 2^\alpha\alpha/2^\beta\beta$.

(ii) $\alpha \geqq \beta$. By (43),

$$p^{\beta-1} = kr^{1-n}(1 + p)^{\beta-\alpha}\left(\frac{1 + p}{\beta + \alpha p}\right) \leqq \frac{kr^{1-n}}{\beta}. \tag{50}$$

Thus we have at once

$$m = \int_1^\sigma p\,dr \leqq \left(\frac{k}{\beta}\right)^{1/(\beta-1)} \int_1^\sigma r^{(1-n)/(\beta-1)}\,dr;$$

hence

$$k \geqq \beta J^{\beta-1} \geqq \beta \operatorname{Min}(J^{\alpha-1}, J^{\beta-1}).$$

Consequently (40) again holds, with $\kappa = \beta/\alpha$. This completes the proof of Lemma 8.

Note. This work was partially supported by the United States Air Force Office of Scientific Research under Grant No. AF-AFOSR 372-63.

References

1. E. De Giorgi, *Sulla differenziabilità e l'analiticità delle estremali degli integrali multipli regolari*, Mem. Accad. Sci. Torino (3) **3** (1957), 25–43.

2. R. Finn and D. Gilbarg, *Three dimensional subsonic flows and asymptotic estimates for elliptic partial differential equations*, Acta Math. **98** (1957), 265–296.

3. D. Gilbarg, *Some local properties of elliptic equations*, Proc. Sympos. Pure Math. Vol. 4, pp. 127–142, Amer. Math. Soc., Providence, R. I., 1961.

4. ———, *Boundary value problems for non-linear elliptic equations*, Nonlinear Problems, pp. 151–160, Univ. of Wisconsin Press, Madison, Wis., 1963.

5. D. Gilbarg and J. Serrin, *On isolated singularities of solutions of second order elliptic differential equations*, J. Analyse Math. **4** (1955–1956), 309–340.

6. O. A. Ladyzhenskaya and N. N. Uraltseva, *Quasi-linear elliptic equations and variational problems with many independent variables*, Russian Math. Surveys **16** (1961), 17–91.

7. ———, *On the smoothness of weak solutions of quasi-linear equations in several variables and of variational problems*, Comm. Pure Appl. Math. **14** (1961), 481–495.

8. W. Littman, G. Stampacchia and H. Weinberger, *Regular points for elliptic equations with discontinuous coefficients*, Ann. Scuola Norm. Sup. Pisa (3) **17** (1963), 45–79.

9. C. B. Morrey, Jr., *Multiple integral problems in the calculus of variations and related topics*, Ann. Scuola Norm. Sup. Pisa (3) **14** (1960), 1–62.

10. J. Moser, *On Harnack's theorem for elliptic differential equations*, Comm. Pure Appl. Math. **14** (1961), 577–591.

11. H. Royden, *The growth of a fundamental solution of an elliptic divergence structure equation*, Studies in Mathematical Analysis and Related Topics; Essays in honor of G. Pólya, pp. 333–340, Stanford Univ. Press, Stanford, Calif., 1962.

12. J. Serrin, *Local behavior of solutions of quasi-linear equations*, Acta Math. **111** (1964), 247–302.

13. ———, *Isolated singularities of solutions of quasi-linear equations*, Acta Math. (1965) (to appear).

14. G. Stampacchia, *On some multiple integral problems in the calculus of variations*, Comm. Pure Appl. Math. **16** (1963), 382–422.

University of Minnesota,
Minneapolis, Minnesota

SOME NONLINEAR EVOLUTION EQUATIONS

BY

J. L. LIONS AND W. A. STRAUSS

We consider equations of the form $A(t)u + u'' + \beta(t; u, u') = f(t)$ $(0 \leqq t \leqq T)$ $(u' = \partial u/\partial t,\ u'' = \partial^2 u/\partial t^2)$, where each $A(t)$ is an elliptic operator and β, which depends nonlinearly on u and u', is in an appropriate sense close to a monotonic operator. Beginning with a Galerkin type of approximation to a solution, there are three methods of passing to the limit: using a monotonicity argument or else proving strong (as opposed to weak) convergence by virtue of either the weak convergence of derivatives or the convergence of the norms in a uniformly convex space. Existence, uniqueness and continuity of weak solutions is proved for mixed initial boundary value problems for the equation $\Box u = h(x, t)|u'|^{p-1}u'$ $(t > 0,$ $x \in \Sigma)$ where Σ is an open set in Euclidean space, $p > 0$, $h(x, t)$ is positive, bounded and bounded away from zero. The boundary conditions may be nonlinear in some cases. Applications are also made to equations where the nonlinear term involves derivatives of arbitrarily high order and to equations where it involves u as well as u'. (Received October 2, 1964.)

UNIVERSITY OF PARIS,
PARIS, FRANCE

STANFORD UNIVERSITY,
STANFORD, CALIFORNIA

RESULTS FOR A QUASI-LINEAR HYPERBOLIC EQUATION

BY

R. C. MacCAMY AND V. J. MIZEL

Solutions of the quasi-linear hyperbolic equation (E) $u_{tt} = Q^2(u_x)u_{xx}$ on the semi-infinite strip S: $0 \leqq x \leqq L$, $0 \leqq t < \infty$ are studied, subject to conditions of the following type: (A) $u(0, t) = u(L, t) = 0$; (B) $u(x, 0) = 0$; (C) $u_t(x, 0) = f(x)$, $f(0) = f(L) = 0$. The following assumptions are made on the C^1 function $Q^2(u_x)$: (i) $Q(\xi) > 0$, $-\infty < \xi < \infty$; (ii) $Q(-\xi) = Q(\xi)$; (iii) $Q'(\xi) < 0$ for $\xi > 0$; (iv) $Q(0) = 1$ (Normalization of t-scale). The following main results are obtained.

THEOREM. *Whenever the inequality* (I) $\max_{0 \leqq x \leqq L}|f(x)| < \int_0^\infty Q(\xi)\,d\xi$ *holds,* (E) *has no smooth* (C^2) *solution satisfying* (A), (B), (C) *and defined on all of S. In particular* (E) *unlike* $u_{tt} = u_{xx}$ *has no smooth periodic solution satisfying* (A), (B), (C).

THEOREM. *Whenever* (I) *is violated there exists on certain subregions of S a unique smooth stable solution of* (E) *satisfying* (A), (B), (C).

These subregions contain points (x, t) *with t arbitrarily large.* The arguments involve use of the Legendre transformation and an explicit proof that, given (I), weak shocks will occur for any initial function $f(x) \neq 0$. This equation arises in the study of the elastic-plastic vibrations of a bar fixed at both ends. (Received February 24, 1964.)

CARNEGIE INSTITUTE OF TECHNOLOGY,
PITTSBURGH, PENNSYLVANIA

II. FINITE ELASTICITY, COMPRESSIBLE FLUIDS

THE EQUATIONS OF FINITE ELASTICITY

BY

WALTER NOLL

1. **Introduction.** I do not believe that the partial differential equations of finite elasticity have been given as much attention by expert analysts as they deserve. This may be in part due to the fact that these equations are not as widely known as other differential equations of mathematical physics. It is the purpose of this lecture to help make the equations of finite elasticity better known. A comprehensive modern exposition of the theory of finite elastic deformations will be given in a forthcoming treatise by C. Truesdell and W. Noll [**1**, Chapter D].

Ideal materials are defined by *constitutive equations*. These are relations connecting the possible motions and deformations of a body and the internal contact forces acting between the parts of the body. In this way an elastic material is defined by a stress-strain relation, which asserts that the present stress depends only on the present strain. Substituting such a stress-strain relation into Cauchy's equation of motion, which expresses the balance of forces, one obtains a particular differential equation of finite elasticity.

In the first part of this lecture I shall make the concept of elasticity mathematically precise. While this is done, the term "strain" will not be used because it does not have an unambiguous meaning in the past literature.

In the second part of this lecture I shall give my idea of what is a reasonable problem in finite elasticity, and I shall also discuss questions of uniqueness, existence, and stability.

2. **Mechanical preliminaries.**[1] Continuum mechanics deals with mechanical interactions between deforming bodies. A reasonable mathematical model for a *body* $\mathscr{B}$ is a set whose elements X are called *material* points. A body is endowed with a structure defined by a class of *configurations* $\boldsymbol{\varkappa}$, which are mappings of $\mathscr{B}$ onto regions in Euclidean point-space $\mathscr{E}$. Any two configurations $\boldsymbol{\gamma}$ and $\boldsymbol{\varkappa}$ are connected by a *deformation* $\boldsymbol{\lambda} = \boldsymbol{\varkappa} \circ \boldsymbol{\gamma}^{-1}$, which is a C^2-diffeomorphism of a region in space onto another. The gradient $\nabla\boldsymbol{\lambda}(X)$ of a deformation is an invertible tensor (the term tensor is used here as a synonym for a linear transformation of the three-dimensional space $\mathscr{V}$ of spatial vectors).

[1] For more detailed treatments of portions of the subject matter of this and the following two sections, see [**1**], [**2**], [**3**], [**4**], [**5**].

Two configurations $\varkappa$ and $\hat{\varkappa}$ are said to be equivalent at $X \in \mathscr{B}$ if the gradient of the deformation from $\varkappa$ to $\hat{\varkappa}$, evaluated at $\varkappa(X)$, is the identity tensor. The resulting equivalence classes $\mathbf{K}$ are called *local configurations* at X.

A *motion* of a body is a one-parameter family of configurations. To describe a motion, it is often useful to employ an arbitrary but fixed *reference configuration* $\varkappa$. A motion is then determined by its *deformation function* $\boldsymbol{\chi}$ whose value

$$\mathbf{x} = \boldsymbol{\chi}(\mathbf{X}, t) \tag{2.1}$$

is the place in the configuration at time t of that material point which is located at $\mathbf{X}$ in the reference configuration. We assume that $\boldsymbol{\chi}$ is of class C^2. Then the *deformation-gradient*

$$\mathbf{F} = \mathbf{F}(\mathbf{X}, t) = \nabla_{\mathbf{X}}\boldsymbol{\chi}(\mathbf{X}, t) \tag{2.2}$$

exists and is of class C^1. If the reference configuration $\varkappa$ is changed to $\hat{\varkappa}$ then $\mathbf{F}$ transforms into

$$\hat{\mathbf{F}} = \mathbf{F}\mathbf{G}^{-1}, \tag{2.3}$$

where $\mathbf{G}$ is the gradient of the deformation from $\varkappa$ to $\hat{\varkappa}$. It is easily seen that $\mathbf{G}$ depends only on the local configurations corresponding to $\varkappa$ and $\hat{\varkappa}$ at the material point under consideration.

A *dynamical process* for a body $\mathscr{B}$ is determined by the prescription of a motion of $\mathscr{B}$ and of a system of forces for $\mathscr{B}$ at each time. The forces acting by contact between the parts of the body are determined by the *Cauchy-stress tensor* $\mathbf{T} = \mathbf{T}(X, t)$. The force $\mathbf{c}$ acting across an oriented surface $\mathscr{S}$ in $\mathscr{B}$ is given by

$$\mathbf{c} = \int_{\mathscr{S}} \mathbf{T}\mathbf{n}\, da, \tag{2.4}$$

where $\mathbf{n}$ is the unit normal to $\mathscr{S}$ and da the element of surface area of $\mathscr{S}$ in the configuration at time t. The force (2.4) can also be expressed by a surface integral extended over $\mathscr{S}$ in the reference configuration:

$$\mathbf{c} = \int_{\mathscr{S}} \mathbf{T}_R\mathbf{n}_R\, da_R, \tag{2.5}$$

where $\mathbf{n}_R$ is the unit normal to $\mathscr{S}$ and da_R the element of surface area in the *reference configuration.* The tensor $\mathbf{T}_R$ is called the *first Piola-Kirchhoff* stress tensor. The laws of transformation of surface integrals imply that

$$\mathbf{T}_R = |\det \mathbf{F}|(\mathbf{F}^{-1}\mathbf{T})^T, \tag{2.6}$$

where the superscript T denotes transposition.

We assume that only three kinds of mechanical interactions are present: (i) contact forces acting between the parts of the body, (ii) contact forces exerted on the boundary of the body, (iii) body forces exerted over a distance on the body by the outside world.

It is a consequence of the law of balance of moments that the Cauchy-stress $\mathbf{T}$ must be a symmetric tensor. Hence, by (2.6), the Piola-Kirchhoff stress must satisfy

$$\mathbf{T}_R\mathbf{F}^T = \mathbf{F}\mathbf{T}_R^T. \tag{2.7}$$

The law of balance of forces (including inertial forces) implies that Cauchy's law of motion

$$\operatorname{Div} \mathbf{T}_R = \rho_R(\ddot{\boldsymbol{\chi}} - \mathbf{g}) \tag{2.8}$$

must be satisfied, where ρ_R is the mass density in the reference configuration, $\mathbf{g}$ is the external body force per unit mass, $\ddot{\boldsymbol{\chi}}$ is the second time-derivative of the deformation function (2.1), and Div denotes the divergence operator with respect to the place $\mathbf{X}$ in the reference configuration.

3. **The concept of elasticity.** The material at a material point X in a body is said to be *elastic* if for all possible dynamical processes the present stress $\mathbf{T}$ at X is determined by the present local configuration $\mathbf{M}$ at X:

$$\mathbf{T} = \mathfrak{t}(\mathbf{M}). \tag{3.1}$$

If we choose a fixed reference configuration $\varkappa$, the relation (3.1) is equivalent to the *stress relation*

$$\mathbf{T}_R = \mathfrak{h}(\mathbf{F}), \tag{3.2}$$

where $\mathbf{F}$ is the present deformation gradient at X and $\mathbf{T}_R$ the present Piola-Kirchhoff stress at X. The function $\mathfrak{h}$, whose domain is a suitable subset of the space $\mathscr{L}$ of all tensors and whose range is another subset of $\mathscr{L}$, is called the *response function* of the material at X with respect to the reference configuration $\varkappa$.

A body is said to be elastic if the material at *all* of its points X is elastic. In general, the response function will vary with the material point X. Sometimes it is possible to choose the reference configuration $\varkappa$ such that the response function $\mathfrak{h}$ is the same for all X. In this case, the elastic body and the reference configuration $\varkappa$ are called *homogeneous*.

It is evident that the response function $\mathfrak{h}$ at a given material point is not altered if the reference configuration $\varkappa$ is replaced by another one equivalent to $\varkappa$ at X. In other words, the response function $\mathfrak{h}$, for a given material, depends only on the *local* reference configuration $\mathbf{K}$ at X. Sometimes it is possible to assign to each material point X a local reference configuration $\mathbf{K}_X$ such that the response function $\mathfrak{h}$ at X with respect to $\mathbf{K}_X$ is the same for all X. If this is the case, the body is called *materially uniform* and the correspondence $X \to \mathbf{K}_X$ is called a *uniform reference*. Every homogeneous body is materially uniform, but a materially uniform body need not be homogeneous because the local reference configurations need not "fit together" to define a global reference configuration.[2]

[2] A detailed analysis of the possible deviations from homogeneity in materially uniform bodies will be given in a forthcoming paper [4]. Physicists ascribe certain such deviations to the presence of "continuous distributions of dislocations" in the body.

A response function $\mathfrak{h}$ cannot be entirely arbitrary. First, since $\mathbf{T}_R = \mathfrak{h}(\mathbf{F})$ is subject to (2.7), $\mathfrak{h}$ must satisfy the identity

$$\mathfrak{h}(\mathbf{F})\mathbf{F}^T = \mathbf{F}\mathfrak{h}(\mathbf{F})^T. \tag{3.3}$$

Second, the *principle of material objectivity* must be satisfied. The physical meaning of this principle is that the behavior of a material should be independent of the observer. In the case of elasticity, the principle leads to the requirement that $\mathfrak{h}$ must satisfy the identity

$$\mathbf{Q}\mathfrak{h}(\mathbf{F}) = \mathfrak{h}(\mathbf{QF}), \tag{3.4}$$

which must be valid for all $\mathbf{F}$ in the domain of $\mathfrak{h}$ and for all orthogonal tensors $\mathbf{Q}$.

The identities (3.3) and (3.4) may be used to derive various "reduced forms" of the stress relation (3.2) involving various kinds of "strain tensors." I believe that use of such reduced forms only makes the theory unnecessarily opaque.

4. **Isotropic materials, elastic fluids, hyper-elastic materials.** The symmetries of an elastic material are described by its *isotropy group* $\mathscr{G}$, which consists of all unimodular tensors $\mathbf{H}$ such that

$$\mathfrak{h}(\mathbf{FH})\mathbf{H}^T = \mathfrak{h}(\mathbf{F}) \tag{4.1}$$

holds identically for $\mathbf{F}$ in the domain of $\mathfrak{h}$. The isotropy group $\mathscr{G}$ depends, of course, on the choice of the local reference configuration, but it can easily be shown that a change of local reference configuration merely transforms $\mathscr{G}$ into one of its conjugates within the unimodular group $\mathscr{U}$.

Of particular interest is the case when, for a suitable local reference configuration, the isotropy group $\mathscr{G}$ contains the orthogonal group $\mathscr{O}$. In this case, $\mathfrak{h}$ satisfies the identity

$$\mathfrak{h}(\mathbf{FQ}) = \mathfrak{h}(\mathbf{F})\mathbf{Q} \tag{4.2}$$

for all orthogonal tensors $\mathbf{Q}$ and all $\mathbf{F}$ in the domain of $\mathfrak{h}$. The materials for which $\mathscr{G}$ contains $\mathscr{O}$ are called *isotropic*.

An *elastic fluid* is defined by the property that its isotropy group coincides with the full unimodular group: $\mathscr{G} = \mathscr{U}$. For fluids, it can be shown that the stress relation (3.1) is equivalent to

$$\mathbf{T} = -p(\rho)\mathbf{1}, \tag{4.3}$$

where $p(\rho)$, the *pressure*, is a function of the density ρ.

Thermodynamic consideration of various kinds can be used to show that it is often reasonable to assume that the response function $\mathfrak{h}$ has a potential, i.e., that there exist a scalar-valued *stored-energy function* $\sigma(\mathbf{F})$ such that

$$\mathfrak{h}(\mathbf{F}) = \boldsymbol{\nabla}\sigma(\mathbf{F}), \tag{4.4}$$

where $\boldsymbol{\nabla}$ denotes the gradient operator in the nine-dimensional space $\mathscr{L}$ of all tensors. When a stored-energy function exists the material is called *hyper-elastic*.

5. **The differential equations.** Assume that $\mathscr{B}$ is a homogeneous elastic body and that a homogeneous reference configuration is employed. Then (3.2) holds with a response function $\mathfrak{h}$ that is independent of X. Substitution of (3.2) into Cauchy's law of motion (2.8) gives the *differential equation for homogeneous elastic bodies*:

$$\text{Div}\,\mathfrak{h}\,(\nabla\boldsymbol{\chi}) = \rho_R(\ddot{\boldsymbol{\chi}} - \mathbf{g}). \tag{5.1}$$

If $\mathbf{g} = \mathbf{g}(\mathbf{x}, X, t)$ is a given function, then (5.1) is a quasi-linear second order partial differential equation for the deformation function $\mathbf{x} = \boldsymbol{\chi}(X, t)$.

If we use independent coordinates X^α and $x^k = \chi^k(X^\alpha, t)$ for the places $\mathbf{X}$ and $\mathbf{x}$ in the reference configuration and in the configuration at time t, the equation (5.1) corresponds to the system

$$H_{k\ m}^{\ \alpha\ \beta}\chi^m{}_{|\alpha\beta} = \rho_R(\ddot{\chi}_k - g_k), \tag{5.2}$$

where

$$H_{k\ m}^{\ \alpha\ \beta} = \frac{\partial \mathfrak{h}_k{}^\alpha(\mathbf{F})}{\partial F^m{}_\beta}, \qquad F^m{}_\beta = \chi^m{}_{,\beta}, \tag{5.3}$$

$$\chi^m{}_{|\alpha\beta} = \chi^m{}_{,\alpha\beta} + \begin{Bmatrix} m \\ s\ \ r \end{Bmatrix} \chi^s{}_{,\alpha}\chi^r{}_{,\beta} - \begin{Bmatrix} \sigma \\ \beta\ \ \alpha \end{Bmatrix} \chi^m{}_{,\sigma}. \tag{5.4}$$

In these formulas partial derivatives with respect to the coordinates X^α are indicated by commas. The Christoffel-symbols

$$\begin{Bmatrix} m \\ s\ \ r \end{Bmatrix} \quad \text{and} \quad \begin{Bmatrix} \sigma \\ \beta\ \ \alpha \end{Bmatrix}$$

are taken with respect to the coordinates x^k and X^α, respectively. Note that the

$$\begin{Bmatrix} m \\ s\ \ r \end{Bmatrix}$$

may depend on the unknown functions χ^k.

For hyper-elastic materials (5.3) becomes

$$H_{k\ m}^{\ \alpha\ \beta} = \frac{\partial^2 \sigma}{\partial F^k{}_\alpha\, \partial F^m{}_\beta}, \qquad F^k{}_\alpha = \chi^k{}_{,\alpha} \tag{5.5}$$

and we have

$$H_{k\ m}^{\ \alpha\ \beta} = H_{m\ k}^{\ \beta\ \alpha}. \tag{5.6}$$

The differential equations of the classical theory of *infinitesimal elasticity* result from (5.2) if the $H_{k\ m}^{\ \alpha\ \beta}$ are evaluated at $\mathbf{F} = \mathbf{1}$ instead of at $\mathbf{F} = \nabla\boldsymbol{\chi}$.

Since elastic fluids are special elastic materials, the theory of the differential equation (5.1) contains the classical theory of barotropic flows of compressible perfect fluids (cf. [**6**, Chapter C]) as a special case. For such fluids, however, it is convenient to reduce (5.1) to the equivalent system of differential equations

$$\begin{aligned} \text{grad}\, p(\rho) + \rho(\dot{\mathbf{v}} - \mathbf{g}) &= \mathbf{0}, \\ \dot{\rho} + \rho\, \text{div}\, \mathbf{v} &= 0 \end{aligned} \tag{5.7}$$

for the unknown density $\rho = \rho(\mathbf{x}, t)$ and velocity $\mathbf{v} = \mathbf{v}(\mathbf{x}, t)$ as functions of the time t and the place $\mathbf{x}$ at time t. If (5.7) has been solved, the deformation function $\boldsymbol{\chi}$ is obtained by integrating the ordinary vector-differential equation

$$\dot{\boldsymbol{\chi}} = \mathbf{v}(\boldsymbol{\chi}, t). \tag{5.8}$$

If $\mathscr{B}$ is materially uniform but not homogeneous, it can be shown that (5.2) and (5.4) must be replaced by[3]

$$H_{k\ m}^{\ \alpha\ \beta}\chi^{m}{}_{|\alpha\beta} - \mathfrak{h}_{k}{}^{\alpha}S_{\alpha\sigma}{}^{\sigma} = \rho_R(\ddot{x}_k - g_k), \tag{5.9}$$

$$\chi^{m}{}_{|\alpha\beta} = \chi^{m}{}_{,\alpha\beta} + \left\{ {m \atop s\ r} \right\} \chi^{s}{}_{,\alpha}\chi^{r}{}_{,\beta} - \Gamma_{\beta\alpha}{}^{\sigma}\chi^{m}{}_{,\sigma}, \tag{5.10}$$

where X^{α} are arbitrary coordinates for the body-manifold, where $\Gamma_{\beta\alpha}{}^{\sigma}$ are the corresponding components of a certain affine connection in $\mathscr{B}$ and where

$$S_{\alpha\beta}{}^{\sigma} = \Gamma_{[\beta\alpha]}{}^{\sigma} \tag{5.11}$$

are the components of the torsion-tensor of the connection. The affine connection $\boldsymbol{\Gamma}$ is determined by the uniform reference $X \rightarrow \mathbf{K}_X$ with respect to which $\mathfrak{h}$ is the response function.

6. **Boundary value problems.** Posing a problem in finite elasticity is to ask for a solution $\boldsymbol{\chi}$ of (5.1) which satisfies a given set of initial and boundary conditions.

A *boundary condition of place* is the prescription, for each time, of the configuration of the boundary surface $\partial\mathscr{B}$:

$$\boldsymbol{\chi}(\mathbf{X}, t) = \boldsymbol{\chi}_b(\mathbf{X}, t). \tag{6.1}$$

Here, $\boldsymbol{\chi}_b(\mathbf{X}, t)$ is a given function defined for $\mathbf{X} \in \boldsymbol{\varkappa}(\partial\mathscr{B})$ and all $t \geqq 0$.

If we wish to prescribe the forces acting on the boundary $\partial\mathscr{B}$, difficulties arise because the configuration at time t of $\partial\mathscr{B}$ depends on the unknown solution. A rather general *boundary condition of surface action* may be described as follows: Let Σ be the set of all surfaces that can be obtained by deforming the boundary $\partial\mathscr{B}$ from its reference configuration. Let $\mathfrak{M}$ be a mapping which assign to every $\mathscr{S} \in \Sigma$ a vector field

$$\mathbf{t}_R = \mathfrak{M}(\mathscr{S}), \tag{6.2}$$

whose values

$$\mathbf{t}_R(\mathbf{X}, t) = \mathbf{T}_R(\mathbf{X}, t)\mathbf{n}_R \tag{6.3}$$

give the surface traction to be applied should the boundary $\partial\mathscr{B}$ assume the configuration $\mathscr{S}$ at time t. The mapping $\mathfrak{M}$ describes a sort of a priori strategy which tells us what force to apply for every conceivable motion of the body. In other words, the mapping $\mathfrak{M}$ is a description of the action of the environment on the body under all conceivable circumstances.

---

[3] The details of the derivation of (5.5) and (5.6) will be given in [4].

If we assume that the traction field $\mathbf{t}_R$ is independent of $\mathscr{S}$, i.e., if the mapping $\mathfrak{M}$ is constant, we obtain a *boundary condition of fixed traction.* In this case, the surface traction *per unit area in the reference configuration* is held constant in magnitude and direction no matter how the body may deform.

Another special boundary condition is a *boundary condition of pressure.* Here, it is assumed that the traction acting on a point of $\mathscr{S}$ is normal to $\mathscr{S}$ and depends, say, on the position of the point or on the volume of the region bounded by $\mathscr{S}$.

Since we can expect that the behavior of such diverse real materials as air and rubber is governed by particular differential equations of finite elasticity, it is clear that not all kinds of boundary conditions can be appropriate to all kinds of elastic bodies.

7. **Inequalities.** One can expect that the nature of the solutions of the differential equation (5.1) is strongly connected with the nature of the quadratic form

$$\Omega_{\mathbf{F}}\,[\mathbf{L}] = \operatorname{tr}\{(\mathbf{LF})^T\, \nabla\mathfrak{h}\mathbf{F}\,[\mathbf{LF}]\}, \tag{7.1}$$

on the space of all tensors $\mathbf{L} \in \mathscr{L}$. Here, $\nabla\mathfrak{h}(\mathbf{F})$ denotes the gradient of $\mathfrak{h}$ at $\mathbf{F}$ in the space $\mathscr{L}$, which is a linear transformation on $\mathscr{L}$, and $\nabla\mathfrak{h}(\mathbf{F})[\mathbf{L}]$ denotes the value of this gradient for $\mathbf{L} \in \mathscr{L}$.

It is not reasonable to assume that $\Omega_{\mathbf{F}}$ is positive definite for all $\mathbf{F}$. Differentiation of (3.4) with respect to $\mathbf{Q}$ leads to

$$\Omega_{\mathbf{F}}[\mathbf{W}] = -|\det \mathbf{F}|\, \operatorname{tr}\,(\mathbf{W}^2\mathbf{T}) \tag{7.2}$$

for all skew tensors $\mathbf{W}$. It can be shown that (7.2) can be positive for all skew $\mathbf{W} \neq \mathbf{0}$ only if the sum of any two principal stresses, i.e., proper values of the Cauchy-Stress $\mathbf{T}$, is positive. Thus if $\Omega_{\mathbf{F}}$ were positive definite, zero stress or uniform compression could never occur.

The requirement of *strong ellipticity* for the operator Div $\mathfrak{h}(\mathbf{F})$ is that for all $\mathbf{F}$

$$\Omega_{\mathbf{F}}[\boldsymbol{\lambda} \otimes \boldsymbol{\mu}] > 0 \tag{7.3}$$

whenever $\boldsymbol{\lambda} \otimes \boldsymbol{\mu} \neq 0$.

The *C-N^+ condition* is the requirement that for all $\mathbf{F}$

$$\Omega_{\mathbf{F}}[\mathbf{D}] > 0 \tag{7.4}$$

for all symmetric tensors $\mathbf{D}$. The physical significance of the conditions (7.3) and (7.4) has been studied extensively in the literature ([7], [8], [9], [10], [5]).

8. **Uniqueness and existence.** I am not aware of any investigations concerning the existence or uniqueness of solutions of (5.1) which satisfy given initial and boundary conditions.

Some information is available for problems of *statics*, in which the body forces and the boundary values as well as the solutions are assumed to be independent of time. Both intuition and certain known exact solutions suggest that *global* uniqueness cannot be expected to obtain. The inversion of a hemispherical shell of rubber is perhaps the best example which shows that a boundary value of zero traction can be compatible with two nontrivially distinct solutions. However, it is often reasonable to expect *local* uniqueness, i.e., it is reasonable to expect that in a certain neighborhood of a given solution there is no other solution satisfying the same boundary conditions and coinciding with the given solution at some point.

A local existence and uniqueness theorem was proved by Stoppelli [**11**] (see also the expositions in [**1**, §46], and in [**12**, Chapter V, § 1–5]). He considers a body having a homogeneous *natural state*, i.e., a reference configuration such that the corresponding response function $\mathfrak{h}$ satisfies $\mathfrak{h}(\mathbf{1}) = \mathbf{0}$, and he assumes that (7.4) holds for $\mathbf{F} = \mathbf{1}$. Let a system of loads $\mathbf{t}_R = \varepsilon\bar{\mathbf{t}}_R$, $\mathbf{g} = \varepsilon\bar{\mathbf{g}}$ be given such that there is no axis of equilibrium. Stoppelli then shows that for sufficiently small ε the loads give rise to one and only one solution which has a prescribed value at some point and which lies in a certain neighborhood of the identity deformation, provided suitable smoothness conditions are satisfied. Stoppelli's proof is based on the inverse function theorem in a Banach space and on uniqueness and existence theorems for the linear equations of infinitesimal elasticity.

9. **Stability.** For hyper-elastic bodies it is often possible to reduce statical boundary value problems to variational problems. For example, if the body forces are zero, the boundary value problem of fixed traction corresponds to the variational integral

$$J(\boldsymbol{\chi}) = \int_{\mathscr{B}} \sigma(\mathbf{F})\, dv_R - \int_{\partial\mathscr{B}} \mathbf{u}\cdot\mathbf{t}_R\, da_R, \tag{9.1}$$

where $\mathbf{u} = \mathbf{u}(\mathbf{X}) = \boldsymbol{\chi}(\mathbf{X}) - \mathbf{X}$. A *stable* solution $\boldsymbol{\chi}$ is a deformation which minimizes the integral (9.1). It is easily seen that a minimizing deformation $\boldsymbol{\chi}$ must satisfy the differential equations and the boundary conditions. By considering the second variation one can prove that, in order that $\boldsymbol{\chi}$ be a stable solution, it is necessary that the inequality

$$\Omega_{\mathbf{F}}[\boldsymbol{\lambda} \otimes \boldsymbol{\mu}] \geqq 0 \tag{9.2}$$

hold for all vectors $\boldsymbol{\lambda}$, $\boldsymbol{\mu}$ and all $\mathbf{F}$ such that $\mathbf{F} = \nabla\boldsymbol{\chi}(\mathbf{X})$ for some $\mathbf{X} \in \boldsymbol{\varkappa}(\mathscr{B})$.

The condition (9.2) is also necessary for stability of deformations with mixed boundary values of fixed traction and of place (a proof is given in [**1**, §89]). For the boundary value problem of place, the condition goes back to Hadamard [**13**].

I am not aware of any work presenting significant *sufficient* conditions for the existence of stable solutions.

References

1. C. Truesdell and W. Noll, *The non-linear field theories of mechanics*, Handbuch der Physik, Vol. III/3, Springer, Berlin, 1965.

2. W. Noll, *A mathematical theory of the mechanical behavior of continuous media*, Arch. Rational Mech. Anal. **2** (1958), 197–226.

3. C. Truesdell and R. Toupin, *The classical field theories*, Handbuch der Physik, Vol. III/1, Springer, Berlin, 1960.

4. W. Noll, *Materially uniform simple bodies with inhomogeneities*, Arch. Rational Mech. Anal. (to appear).

5. B. D. Coleman and W. Noll, *Material symmetry and thermostatic inequalities in finite elastic deformations*, Arch. Rational Mech. Anal. **15** (1964), 87–111.

6. J. Serrin, *Mathematical principles of classical fluid mechanics*, Handbuch der Physik, Vol. VIII/1, Springer, Berlin, 1959.

7. B. D. Coleman and W. Noll, *On the thermostatics of continuous media*, Arch. Rational Mech. Anal. **4** (1959), 97–128.

8. R. A. Toupin and B. Bernstein, *Sound waves in deformed perfectly elastic materials. Acousto-elastic effect*, J. Acoust. Soc. Amer. **33** (1961), 216–225.

9. M. Hayes and R. S. Rivlin, *Propagation of a plane wave in an isotropic elastic material subject to pure homogeneous deformation*, Arch. Rational Mech. Anal. **8** (1961), 15–22.

10. C. Truesdell and R. A. Toupin, *Static grounds for inequalities in finite elastic strain*, Arch. Rational Mech. Anal. **12** (1963), 1–33.

11. F. Stoppelli, *Un teorema di esistenza e di unicità relativo alle equazioni dell' elastostatica isoterma per deformazioni finiti*, Ricerche Mat. **3** (1954), 247–267.

12. S. Grioli, *Some recent results in the theory of elasticity*, Ergebnisse Angew. Math. No. 7, Springer, Berlin, 1962.

13. J. Hadamard, *Leçons sur la propagation des ondes et les équations de l'hydrodynamique*, Hermann, Paris, 1903.

CARNEGIE INSTITUTE OF TECHNOLOGY,
PITTSBURGH, PENNSYLVANIA

A PRIORI ESTIMATES APPLIED TO NONLINEAR SHELL THEORY

BY

FRITZ JOHN

In the theory of thin shells one describes the state of a thin layer of elastic material in terms of functions of two independent variables. One tries to characterize those functions by a system of partial differential equations and boundary conditions obtained by some limiting process from the relations for elastic solids.[1] Leaving aside the more delicate question of the boundary conditions, I am concerned here with the partial differential equations that hold in the interior of the shell. Usually their derivation is based on certain ad hoc assumptions ("Kirchhoff hypotheses") on the relative orders of magnitude of various quantities. Mainly one assumes that the transverse stresses are negligible in size compared to the longitudinal ones and that the longitudinal stresses vary essentially linearly along a normal fiber of the shell. Similar statements for the tangential derivatives of the stresses are implied. Related is the assertion that the surfaces parallel to the middle surface in its undeformed state and their common normals are transformed into surfaces and lines forming approximately right angles with each other.

It is the purpose of the present talk to *prove*[2] these hypotheses or rather to give an estimate for their degree of correctness, solely under the assumptions that

(a) the shell is sufficiently thin,

(b) the stresses are sufficiently small,

(c) the edge of the shell is sufficiently far away.

Nothing will have to be postulated about the derivatives of the stresses or about the size of the displacements. I restrict myself here to shells which in the unstrained natural state are in equilibrium with external forces acting only along the lateral surface ("edge"). It is assumed that we are dealing with a homogeneous isotropic perfectly elastic material whose physical properties are completely described by a strain energy density function W. The Kirchhoff hypotheses turn out to be correct to the extent that the quantity

$$\theta = \mathrm{Max}\left(\frac{h}{D}, \sqrt{\varepsilon}, \sqrt{\frac{h}{R}}\right) \tag{1}$$

[1] See [1], [2], [3], [6], [7].

[2] The proof will only be sketched here. The detailed proof (following closely the author's treatment of nonlinear plate theory [5]) will appear in the Communications on Pure and Applied Mathematics, Vol. 18, March, 1965.

is small. Here ε is the maximum strain anywhere in the shell, D is the distance from the edge, and R is a typical length associated with the *undeformed* middle surface (essentially the least radius of curvature, but defined more precisely below). The quantity

$$\lambda = \frac{h}{\theta} = \mathrm{Min}\left(D, \frac{h}{\sqrt{\varepsilon}}, \sqrt{(hR)}\right) \tag{2}$$

will be seen to represent a lower bound for the *wave lengths* of the stresses and strains of the deformed shell.

While, by hypothesis, the stresses are of order $E\varepsilon$ (where E is Young's modulus) we shall find that the transverse shear stress is of order $E\varepsilon\theta$ and the transverse normal stress even of order $E\varepsilon\theta^2$. Along a normal fiber of the shell the longitudinal stress will vary linearly within an error of order of magnitude $E\varepsilon\theta^2$. Here the term "order" indicates a concrete estimate involving constants depending exclusively on the choice of the energy function W.

These results will follow by applying standard techniques from the theory of elliptic partial differential equations for estimating the derivatives of a solution in terms of the maximum of the solution. However, the details of applying those techniques in the present situation are troublesome because of the nonlinearity of the equations and of the lack of symmetry in the equations and in the boundary conditions. It is possible, however, not only to verify the Kirchhoff hypotheses in the form stated above but also to estimate all the terms occurring in the various three-dimensional equations. One can then derive approximate two-dimensional equations with concrete estimates for the errors. While these results do not yield error estimates for the *solutions* of the equations they enable us to decide if two sets of interior shell equations are equally accurate. It is conceivable that the arguments used here might work in other cases where results are usually established by formal expansions.

For a precise formulation of our results and some indications of the proofs it is necessary to give the basic differential equations for three-dimensional perfectly elastic media,[3] and then to specialize to the geometric situation typical for shells.

The differential equations for elastic solids. Our elastic shell will be considered in two states: "unstrained," with particles having cartesian coordinates X^i, and "strained" with cartesian coordinates x^i for the same particles. To the individual particles are assigned *material* coordinates U^i, so that both the X^i and x^i are functions of the U^i. To the line elements dS (unstrained) and ds (strained) in the two states there correspond metric tensors G_{ik} and g_{ik} defined by

$$dS^2 = G_{ik}dU^idU^k, \qquad ds^2 = g_{ik}dU^idU^k.$$

The *principal strains* σ_j can be defined as the roots σ of the equation

$$\det\left(g_{ik} - (1 + 2\sigma)G_{ik}\right) = 0.$$

[3] See Truesdell [8].

For our material the energy density function W is a symmetric function of the σ_j. For a known W the *stress–strain relations* take the form

(3) $$t^{ik} = t^{ki} = 2\sqrt{\left(\frac{\det(G_{rs})}{\det(g_{rs})}\right)}\frac{\partial W}{\partial g_{ik}}.$$

Here the t^{ik} are the contravariant components of the Cauchy stress tensor referred to the coordinates U^i. In addition to the stress–strain relations we have the *equilibrium equations*

(4) $$t^{ik}_{;k} = 0$$

(where ";" denotes covariant differentiation with respect to the metric tensor $ds^2 = g_{ik}dU^idU^k$) and the *compatibility equations*

(5) $$0 = \tfrac{1}{2}(g_{hk,ij} + g_{ij,hk} - g_{hj,ik} - g_{ik,hj}) + g_{ab}\begin{Bmatrix} b \\ h \quad k\end{Bmatrix}\begin{Bmatrix} a \\ i \quad j\end{Bmatrix} - g_{ab}\begin{Bmatrix} b \\ h \quad j\end{Bmatrix}\begin{Bmatrix} a \\ i \quad k\end{Bmatrix}$$

(where "," denotes partial differentiation, and the Christoffel symbols are formed with respect to the metric $g_{ik}dUdU^k$). The compatibility equations express the vanishing of the Riemann curvature tensor for the Euclidean metric ds^2.

Expressing the g_{ik} in terms of the deformation gradients:

$$g_{ik} = x^j_{,i}x^j_{,k}$$

one could obtain from (3) and (4) a system of three nonlinear second order differential equations for the x^i as functions of the U^k. In our case, however, it is best to work exclusively with the stresses and strains and not with the displacements, since the only boundary conditions stated (vanishing of the tractions on the faces of the shell) involve the stresses, and the only a priori bound (maximum strain $= \varepsilon$) concerns the strains. For the purpose of obtaining estimates it is better to write the equations in a form that is as close as possible to the linear equations with constant coefficients of the classical theory rather than to achieve invariance under coordinate transformations.

In order to make stresses t^{ik} and strain energy W dimensionless we divide by Young's modulus E (or equivalently choose a system of units in which E has the value 1). To lowest order the only material constant is then Poisson's ratio ν, which we assume to have some value between 0 and 1/2. We call η^{ik} the deviation of the metric tensor G_{ik} for the unstrained line element from the cartesian form:

(6) $$G_{ik} = \delta^i_k + \eta^{ik}.$$

(Here δ^i_k is the Kronecker delta, and no distinction is made at present between superscripts and subscripts.) The stress–strain relations (1) can be given the form

(7) $$\tfrac{1}{2}(g_{ik} - G_{ik}) = (1 + \nu)t^{ik} - \nu t^{rr}\delta^i_k + F(\eta, t)(tt + \eta t).$$

Here the right-hand side is the same as in the classical formulae expressing strain in terms of stress except for the error term $F(\eta, t)(tt + \eta t)$ which makes up for the facts that the U^i are not cartesian coordinates, the stress–strain relations not strictly linear, and that covariant and contravariant components are mixed up. The form of the error term is meant to indicate symbolically that it is a sum of terms of the form

$$F_{ikabcdefgh}(\eta, t)(t^{ab}t^{cd} + \eta^{ef}t^{gh})$$

where the coefficients

$$F_{ikabcdefgh}(\eta, t)$$

are functions of the t^{ik}, η^{rs} which are completely determined by the choice of the strain energy function W, and which are regular for all sufficiently small t^{ik}, η^{rs} ("sufficiently small" only depending on W, and the degree of "regularity" only on the regularity of W). In other words, for a concretely given W (which we always assume to be as regular as may be needed) the coefficients are *universal* functions. In what follows we are led to other such universal functions, which we shall always denote by the same letter F.

The equations of equilibrium (4) then take the familiar looking form

$$(8) \qquad t^{ik}_{,k} = A^i = F(\eta, t)(\eta' t + \eta t' + tt')$$

where η' stands for the system of first derivatives $\eta^{ik}_{,r}$ and similarly t' for the $t^{ik}_{,r}$. Finally we obtain from the compatibility equations (5) an analogue of the Beltrami-Michell equations

$$(9) \qquad t^{ik}_{,rr} + \frac{1}{1+\nu} t^{rr}_{,ik} = B^{ik} = F(\eta, t)(\eta'\eta' t + \eta'' t + t'\eta' + t't' + t''\eta + tt'').$$

Of course writing the equations in this form is of advantage only in circumstances where the terms on the right-hand sides can be shown to be relatively small.

Geometry of the shell. We assume that our shell in the *unstrained state* is bounded by two parallel surfaces Σ_h, Σ_{-h} of constant distance h from a "middle surface" Σ_0, and by a "lateral" surface B. Let, for simplicity, B consist of normals of Σ_0.

We assume that the material coordinates U^i of a particle are "normal coordinates" with respect to the surface Σ_0 of the particle in the unstrained state. That means that U^1, U^2 are curvilinear coordinates on Σ_0, and are constant for the particles lying in the unstrained state along a normal of Σ_0, with U^3 denoting the normal distance from Σ_0. The faces $\Sigma_{\pm h}$ of the shell are then given by $U^3 = \pm h$, and the middle surface Σ_0 by $U^3 = 0$. In these normal coordinates the boundary condition that there is no load on the faces becomes simply

$$(10) \qquad t^{i3} = 0 \quad \text{for } U^3 = \pm h.$$

Moreover the components of the metric tensor $dS^2 = G_{ik}dU^i dU^k$ become

$$(11) \qquad G_{\alpha\beta} = E_{\alpha\beta} - 2L_{\alpha\beta}U^3 + M_{\alpha\beta}U^3U^3, \quad G_{\alpha 3} = 0, \quad G_{33} = 1$$

where $E_{\alpha\beta}$, $L_{\alpha\beta}$, $M_{\alpha\beta}$ are respectively the coefficients of the first, second, and third fundamental forms of the undeformed middle surface Σ_0 referred to parameters U^α.[4]

[4] Roman indices are to range over the values 1, 2, 3, Greek ones only over 1, 2.

For the purpose of getting estimates we have to make use of special systems of normal coordinates, though the results, when written invariantly, will then be valid more generally. Given a point P of the undeformed middle surface Σ_0 we say that a cartesian coordinate system X^1, X^2, X^3 is *based* on P when its origin is at P and its X^1X^2-plane is the tangent plane of Σ_0 at P. A system of cartesian coordinates X^i based on P defines a normal coordinate system U^i (at least locally) if we take as parameters U^1, U^2 of a point of Σ_0 simply its cartesian coordinates X^1, X^2 and extend this system into space as before: the U^α to be constant along normals and U^3 to be the distance from Σ_0. The resulting normal system of material coordinates U^i will be said to be "based on P."

In a cartesian X^i-system based on P the surface Σ_0 will have an equation of the form $X^3 = f(X^1, X^2)$ where f and its first derivatives vanish at the origin. Let $f^{(k)}$ denote a derivative of order k of f at the origin. We call R a "typical length" for the undeformed middle surface Σ_0 if the inequalities

$$|f^{(k)}| \leqq (k-1)!R^{1-k} \tag{12}$$

hold for $k = 2, \cdots, K$ and any X^i-system based on a point P of Σ_0. Here the maximum order K for which the inequalities (12) are required to hold depends on the number of stress derivatives one intends to estimate. In particular (12) for $k = 2$ implies that the principal curvatures at any point of Σ_0 do not exceed $1/R$ in absolute value. We make the assumption that $2h < R$.

Let ε be the maximum strain (i.e., maximum $|\sigma_j|$ anywhere in the shell), where $\varepsilon < 1/2$. Let P be a point of Σ_0 of distance D from the lateral surface, where $D > 2h$. We define the ratio θ and the length $\lambda = h/\theta$ by (1), (2). We use normal coordinates U^i based on P. In a neighborhood

$$U^\alpha U^\alpha < \tfrac{1}{4}\lambda^2, \qquad |U^3| \leqq h \tag{13}$$

of the shell we then have for the deviation η^{ik} of the metric tensor G_{ik} from unity the estimates

$$\eta = O\left(\frac{h}{R}\right), \quad \eta' = O\left(\frac{1}{R}\right), \quad \eta'' = O\left(\frac{1}{R^2}\right), \quad \cdots, \tag{14}$$

as a consequence of (11) and the definitions of R and λ. This leads by (7) to the estimate

$$t^{ik} = O(\varepsilon) \tag{15}$$

for the stress components in the region (13).[5]

Estimating the stress derivatives. If u is a solution of a linear homogeneous elliptic differential equation in a region C and if one knows that $|u| \leqq M$ in C one would expect to have for the kth order derivatives $u^{(k)}$ of u at a point Q an estimate of the form $|u^{(k)}| \leqq \gamma_k M/a^k$. Here the constant γ_k would depend on the differential equation, while the "wave-length" a could depend on the location of Q. In

[5] Here and in what follows we write $a = O(b)$ for the statement that there exists a constant γ, only depending on the choice of the energy function W, such that $|a| \leqq \gamma b$.

the absence of boundary conditions we can take for a the distance of Q from the boundary Γ of C; the estimates for the derivatives of u are then of value only deep in the interior of C. If, however, u satisfies suitable homogeneous boundary conditions on a portion Γ' of Γ we can extend our estimates to the case where Q is on or near Γ', taking for a the distance of Q from the boundary set $\Gamma - \Gamma'$.

Estimates of this type are obtained generally by first deriving integral estimates for u and a number of its derivatives, and then applying a lemma of Sobolev to obtain pointwise estimates for a somewhat lower number of derivatives. The integral estimates commonly represent some form of energy integral inequality which follows either by integration by parts or by Fourier transformation.

If we try to apply this simple procedure to the task of estimating the derivatives of the stress components in a shell we encounter a number of complications. We have to work with the nine nonlinear differential equations (8), (9) for what are essentially only six unknown functions t^{ik}. (There are, of course, dependencies between the differential equations.) Nowhere in the shell are we more than a distance h away from the boundary. Since estimates in terms of negative powers of h are unfavorable for small h we have to make use of the boundary conditions (10) which hold on the faces of the shell. We have the difficulty that those boundary conditions involve only three of the stress components. The steps by which these obstacles can be overcome and the general procedure still carried out can only be indicated here.[6]

We make use of normal coordinates U^i based on a point P of Σ_0. In order to get rid of the effect of the lateral boundary B where boundary conditions are lacking, we introduce the "cut off" function ϕ which shall agree with the expression

$$(1 - 4U^\alpha U^\alpha/\lambda^2)^2$$

for $1 - 4U^\alpha U^\alpha/\lambda^2 > 0$ and be zero elsewhere. The starting point for all the integral estimates is an identity that follows by integration by parts and uses only the boundary conditions (10):

$$\iiint\limits_{|U^3|<h} \phi\phi t^{3k}_{,i\alpha} t^{3k}_{,i\alpha}\, dU^1 dU^2 dU^3 = \iiint\limits_{|U^3|<h} \phi\phi\left(B^{3k} t^{3k}_{,\alpha\alpha} - \frac{1}{1+\nu} A^3_{,\alpha} t^{ii}_{,3\alpha}\right) dU^1 dU^2 dU^3$$

(15)
$$= + \iiint\limits_{|U^3|<h} 2\phi\phi_{,\beta}\left(\frac{1}{1+\nu} t^{ii}_{,\alpha} t^{3\beta}_{,\alpha 3} + B^{3k} t^{3k}_{,\beta} - t^{3k}_{,\alpha} t^{3k}_{,\beta\alpha}\right) dU^1 dU^2 dU^3.$$ [7]

From this identity combined with the differential equations (8), (9) we obtain estimates for the *norms* of the second derivatives of the stress components. Here the norm of a function v is defined by

$$\|v\| = \iiint\limits_{|U^3|<h} |v|^2\, dU^1 dU^2 dU^3.$$

[6] A more systematic approach could, perhaps, be based on the work of Agmon-Douglis-Nirenberg **[4]**.

[7] We write $\phi\phi$ for ϕ^2 in order to avoid confusion between exponents and superscripts.

One has to make use of the possibility of estimating the norm of a first derivative or of the square of a first derivative in terms of the maximum of the function and of the norms of the second derivatives. In addition one has to be able to estimate norms of mixed derivatives of a function in terms of pure derivatives, without making use of boundary conditions. This amounts to an inequality of the type of Korn's inequalities:

$$\|\phi v_{,3\alpha}\| = O\left(\frac{1}{\lambda h}\|v\| + \frac{\lambda}{h}\|\phi v_{,\alpha\alpha}\| + \frac{h}{\lambda}\|\phi v_{,33}\|\right).$$

One concludes that for θ less than a constant (depending only on the choice of W) we have

$$\|\phi t^{ik}_{,\alpha\beta}\|,\ \|\phi t^{\alpha\beta}_{,33}\|,\ \|\phi t^{3k}_{,3\alpha}\|,\ \|\phi t^{33}_{,33}\| = O\left(\frac{\varepsilon}{\lambda^2}\|\phi\|\right)$$

while

$$\|\phi t^{\alpha\beta}_{,3\gamma}\|,\ \|\phi t^{3\alpha}_{,33}\| = O\left(\frac{\varepsilon}{\lambda h}\|\phi\|\right).$$

In order to get analogous pointwise estimates for the second derivatives we have to estimate the norms of the third and fourth derivatives and apply Sobolev's lemma. For the slab $|U^3| < h$ this can be given the form

$$\frac{h^{1/2}}{\lambda}|\phi v| = O\left(\|\phi v_{,\alpha\alpha}\| + \frac{h^2}{\lambda^2}\|\phi v_{,33}\| + \frac{1}{\lambda^2}\|v\|\right).$$

(Actually, because of the nonlinearity of the differential equation, we have to use this lemma already in deriving estimates for the norms of the higher order derivatives.) It follows then that in the region (13) about the point P

$$t^{ik}_{,\alpha\beta},\ t^{\alpha\beta}_{,33},\ t^{3k}_{,3\alpha},\ t^{33}_{,33} = O(\varepsilon/\lambda^2), \tag{16a}$$

$$t^{\alpha\beta}_{,3\gamma},\ t^{3\alpha}_{,33} = O(\varepsilon/\lambda h); \tag{16b}$$

more generally any kth order derivative of a stress component can be estimated by $O(\varepsilon/\lambda^{k-1}h)$, and even by $O(\varepsilon/\lambda^k)$ if no differentiations with respect to U^3 are involved.

With the help of the boundary conditions (10) we find immediately from (16a, b) that

$$\begin{gathered} t^{\alpha 3} = O(\varepsilon h/\lambda) = O(\theta\varepsilon), \qquad t^{33} = O(\varepsilon h^2/\lambda^2) = O(\theta^2\varepsilon), \\ t^{\alpha\beta} = \tau^{\alpha\beta} + U^3\sigma^{\alpha\beta} + O(\theta^2\varepsilon) \end{gathered} \tag{17}$$

where $\tau^{\alpha\beta}$, $\eta^{\alpha\beta}$ are respectively the values of $t^{\alpha\beta}$, $t^{\alpha\beta}_{,3}$ for $U^3 = 0$. More precisely, using (8), (9) one gets for the $t^{\alpha 3}$ the quadratic approximation

$$t^{\alpha 3} = \tfrac{1}{2}(h^2 - (U^3)^2)\sigma^{\alpha\beta}_{,\beta} + O(\theta^3\varepsilon).$$

These statements imply the Kirchhoff hypotheses for small θ.

Interior shell equations. These are two obvious ways in which we can obtain from the differential equations (8), (9) and boundary conditions (10) equations for functions of two independent variables. We can either specify U^3 to have the value zero (corresponding to the undeformed middle surface) or, we can integrate with respect to U^3 between the limits $-h$ and $+h$ (which corresponds to forming some kind of "resultant" over a normal fiber). Either procedure leads to exact equations for certain quantities which depend on the two independent variables U^1, U^2. In order to obtain a system of as many equations as unknown functions it appears necessary to add relations which are only true approximately, with an error that can be estimated from (16a, b). Such relations might, e.g., compare the value of a quantity for $U^3 = 0$ with its average for all U^3 between $-h$ and $+h$. Clearly there is no obvious unique way of selecting relations.

Among the quantities that suggest themselves for consideration there are on the one hand the coefficients $e_{\alpha\beta}$ and $l_{\alpha\beta}$ of the first and second fundamental forms of the *deformed* middle surface, on the other hand the coefficients $\tau^{\alpha\beta}$ and $\sigma^{\alpha\beta}$ of the linear terms in the expansion (17) of the stresses along a normal fiber. The $e_{\alpha\beta}$, $l_{\alpha\beta}$ as functions of U^1, U^2 determine the *deformed* middle surface within rigid motion, and hence also determine the displacements $x^i - X^i$ of the middle surface. Actually finding the x^i from the $e_{\alpha\beta}$, $l_{\alpha\beta}$ amounts to solving a system of ordinary differential equations (the Gauss differentiation formulae which express the derivatives of the fundamental vectors with respect to the U^α). The $e_{\alpha\beta}$, $l_{\alpha\beta}$ are connected with each other by the three Gauss-Codazzi equations. We can pass from $e_{\alpha\beta}$, $l_{\alpha\beta}$ to the quantities $\tau^{\alpha\beta}$, $\eta^{\alpha\beta}$ that determine the stresses to first approximation by the constituent equations (7). Still using a system of normal coordinates based on P these yield

(18a) $$\tfrac{1}{2}(e_{\alpha\beta} - E_{\alpha\beta}) = (1+\nu)\tau_{\alpha\beta} - \nu\tau^\gamma_\gamma E_{\alpha\beta} + O(\theta^2\varepsilon),$$

(18b) $$L_{\alpha\beta} - l_{\alpha\beta} = (1+\nu)\sigma_{\alpha\beta} - \nu\sigma^\gamma_\gamma E_{\alpha\beta} + O(\theta^2\varepsilon/h).$$

The form given here to the relations (18a, b) can be interpreted as invariant under arbitrary changes of the parameters U^1, U^2, and hence valid in an arbitrary system of coordinates normal to the surface Σ_0. We have to agree that indices are shifted with respect to the metric $E_{\alpha\beta}dU^\alpha dU^\beta$ of the undeformed middle surface Σ_0, and that $|\sigma| = O(c)$, where an equation of the type $\sigma_{\alpha\beta} = O(c)$ for a tensor $\sigma_{\alpha\beta}$ stands for the statement that the "length" $|\sigma|$ is defined as the square root of the sum of products of covariant and contravariant components.

The vanishing of the resultants of the stresses over a normal fiber gives three additional relations between the $\tau^{\alpha\beta}$ and $\sigma^{\alpha\beta}$. (Here it does not matter greatly if we integrate over normals in the deformed or undeformed state.) In this way we obtain six approximate equations for the six quantities $\tau^{\alpha\beta}$ and $w_{\alpha\beta} = l_{\alpha\beta} - L_{\alpha\beta}$ (which are symmetric in α, β), with concrete estimates for the error terms. We write these equations in invariant form, using a vertical bar to indicate covariant differentiation with respect to the known metric $E_{\alpha\beta}dU^\alpha dU^\beta$ of Σ_0:

(19a)
$$\tau^{\alpha\beta}_{|\beta} = O(\theta^2\varepsilon/\lambda),$$

(19b)
$$w_{\alpha\beta|\gamma} - w_{\alpha\gamma|\beta} = O(\theta^2\varepsilon/\lambda h),$$

(19c)
$$2\tau^{\alpha|\beta}_{\alpha|\beta} + \delta^{\alpha\beta}_{\gamma\mu}(2L^{\gamma}_{\alpha}w^{\mu}_{\beta} + w^{\gamma}_{\alpha}w^{\mu}_{\beta}) = O(\theta^2\varepsilon/\lambda^2),$$

(19d)
$$\frac{h^2}{3(1-\nu^2)}\, w^{\alpha|\beta}_{\alpha|\beta} - \tau^{\alpha\beta}(L_{\alpha\beta} + w_{\alpha\beta}) = O(\theta^2\varepsilon h/\lambda^2).$$ [8]

In the special case of a *plate* ($L_{\alpha\beta} = 0$) equations (19a, b, c, d) become the equations of v. Karman and Föppl, on neglecting the error terms on the right-hand side; on the basis of (19b) we can then identify the "curvature changes" $w_{\alpha\beta}$ with the second derivatives $w_{,\alpha\beta}$ of a function w, which in suitable local coordinates can be interpreted as the transverse displacement of the middle plane.

A more refined investigation is needed to estimate the error of approximation in the solutions of equations (19a, b, c, d) when the right-hand sides are actually replaced by zero.[9]

Bibliography

1. V. V. Novozhilov, *The theory of thin shells*, edited by J. R. M. Radok, translated by P. G. Lowe, Noordhoff, Groningen, 1959.

2. P. M. Naghdi, *Foundations of elastic shell theory*, Appl. Mech. Ser. 131, ONR Tech. Rep. No. 15, Univ. of California, Berkeley, Calif., 1962.

3. W. Z. Chien, *The intrinsic theory of thin shells and plates*, Quart. Appl. Math. **1** (1943), 297–327; **2** (1944), 43–59, 120–135.

4. S. Agmon, A. Douglis, and L. Nirenberg, *Estimates near the boundary for solutions of elliptic partial differential equations satisfying general boundary conditions*. I, Comm. Pure Appl. Math. **12** (1959), 623–727; II, **17** (1964), 35–92.

5. F. John, *Estimates for the error in the equations of non-linear plate theory*, IMM-NYU 308, New York Univ., Courant Institute of Mathematical Sciences, New York, 1963.

6. A. L. Goldenveizer, *Theory of elastic thin shells*, Pergamon, 1961.

7. W. T. Koiter, *La théorie générale des coques minces élastiques*, Séminaire de Méchanique de la Faculté des Sciences de Poitiers, Conférence faite les 10 et 11 Avril 1961.

8. C. Truesdell, *The mechanical foundations of elasticity and fluid dynamics*, J. Rational Mech. Anal. **1** (1952), 125–300.

9. P. Fife, *Non-linear deflection of thin elastic plates under tension*, Comm. Pure Appl. Math. **14** (1961), 81–112.

Courant Institute of Mathematical Sciences,
New York University,
New York, New York

[8] See Koiter [7] for analogous equations.

[9] Boundary layer phenomena would have to be taken into account, as in the work of Fife [9] on plates.

ASYMPTOTIC DESCRIPTION OF A FREE BOUNDARY AT THE POINT OF SEPARATION

BY

P. R. GARABEDIAN

1. **General method of difference-differential equations.** In hydrodynamic problems involving free boundaries it is important to know the asymptotic behavior of the flow near the point where the free boundary meets the fixed boundary. The mistakes that are often made in writing down an asymptotic expansion for the free boundary at the point of separation can lead to erroneous physical conclusions or to significant errors in numerical calculations of the flow. The general theory of asymptotic expansion for solutions of boundary value problems at the confluence of analytic boundary conditions [**5**] suggests how to handle the difficulties at a point of separation. In simplified terms, the suggestion is to insert fractional powers and logarithms into the asymptotic expansion. This is exemplified by the behavior of conformal maps at a corner or of the solution of Dirichlet's problem at a discontinuity of the data.

Typical of the phenomena with which we are concerned is a shock wave in steady transonic flow that is attached to a profile at right angles. The pressure jump across the shock appears in practice to be smaller than that predicted by the shock conditions when the curvature of the shock and the pressure gradient behind it become infinite at the point of attachment. A second example, drawn from magnetohydrodynamics, is that of an axially symmetric cusped figure of equilibrium for a perfectly conducting fluid contained by a strong magnetic field. It is important to determine the asymptotic shape of the cusps at the free surface of the fluid because particles tend to escape through them. Dowd [**2**] has shown that near the axis of symmetry in a meridian plane the equation of the point cusps may be expressed in the form

$$\bar{z} = z + \frac{aiz^{3/2}}{\log z} + \cdots, \tag{1}$$

where z is a suitable complex variable. Further physical models to which his analysis applies are those of the solitary wave and of advanced stages of Taylor instability resulting from an implosion [**4**]. Here, however, we intend to illustrate our general approach to the problem by discussing the splash caused by the water entry of a wedge.

Our method for studying the solution of a free boundary problem at the point of separation is to reflect it across both the free boundary condition and the fixed boundary condition. This leads to a difference-differential equation suggesting how to expand the answer in a multiple series. That the series represents a valid asymptotic expansion of the solution is in turn established by transforming the difference-differential equation into an integral equation. The general procedure, which stems from work of Lewy [**5**], takes an especially elegant form in the case of the water entry problem. In particular, the difference-differential equation describing the splash near the wedge is simple enough so that explicit solutions can be found under certain physically unrealistic assumptions [**3**].

2. **Example of the splash in water entry.** We shall consider the plane similarity flow of an incompressible fluid resulting from the vertical entry of an infinite wedge into a half-space of water. The free surface of the water can be described by a complex-valued function $z = z(\sigma, t)$ which indicates the position at time $t > 0$ of a particle that was σ units from the vertex of the wedge at the initial instant of impact $t = 0$. If the origin is located at the vertex of the wedge, then the similarity of the flow and the fact that particles originally on the free surface stay there yield the relation

$$\lambda z(\sigma, t) = z(\lambda\sigma, \lambda t) \tag{2}$$

asserting that z is homogeneous of degree one. We wish to derive a free boundary condition for the complex potential ζ of the flow from this statement and from the knowledge that the pressure must be constant at the surface of the water.

Differentiating (2) we find that

$$z = \sigma z_\sigma + t z_t \tag{3}$$

and

$$\sigma z_{\sigma t} + t z_{tt} = 0. \tag{4}$$

Because the pressure gradient has the direction of the normal at the free boundary C, the acceleration z_{tt} there is perpendicular to the tangent z_σ. Consequently

$$\frac{\partial}{\partial t}|z_\sigma|^2 = 2\,\mathrm{Re}\,\{\bar{z}_\sigma z_{\sigma t}\} = -\frac{2t}{\sigma}\,\mathrm{Re}\,\{\bar{z}_\sigma z_{tt}\} = 0, \tag{5}$$

which shows that the parameter σ is identical with the arc length s along C. This means that the distance between any two particles along the free surface does not change with time. Putting $t = 1$ with no loss of generality, we may reformulate the free boundary condition (3) in terms of the complex potential ζ to obtain

$$\bar{\zeta}' = z - s z_s, \tag{6}$$

since $\bar{\zeta}' = z_t$. The geometrical significance of (6) is that the hodograph transformation $\overline{\zeta'(z)}$ maps the free boundary curve C onto its involute so that points correspond in the obvious way.

The model of water entry that we have described was first introduced by Wagner [**6**]. In an attempt to solve the problem he investigated the analytic function

$$W = \int \sqrt{\zeta''}\,dz. \tag{7}$$

Differentiation of (6) with respect to the arc length s along C gives

$$\zeta'' z_s = \bar{z}_s - \bar{z}_s - s\bar{z}_{ss} = is\kappa\bar{z}_s, \tag{8}$$

where κ denotes the curvature of C. Therefore

$$W = \sqrt{i}\int \sqrt{(s\kappa)}\, ds \tag{9}$$

on C, which shows that W maps the region occupied by water in the right half of the z-plane onto an isosceles triangle in the W-plane bounded by a vertical line, a horizontal line, and a line inclined at 45°. If Wagner had succeeded in finding another conformal mapping of the flow onto a known region he would have been able to solve the water entry problem in closed form.

Our analysis of the free boundary condition (6) depends on considering the analytic function $w = w(z)$ that has on C the boundary values

$$w \equiv s. \tag{10}$$

From (8) we conclude that w can be continued analytically throughout the flow region as a solution of the ordinary differential equation

$$\zeta'' = -ww''. \tag{11}$$

It is our intention to study the asymptotic behavior of C at a point z_0 where it meets the wall of the wedge by deriving a difference-differential equation for the auxiliary function w.

It is convenient to choose coordinates in the z-plane so that the real axis passes through z_0. Now let us map the splash region between C and the part of the real axis near z_0 onto an infinite strip in the ϕ-plane in such a way that $\operatorname{Im}\{\phi\} = 0$ on C and $\operatorname{Im}\{\phi\} = 1$ at the wedge. One mapping of the desired kind is defined by the formula

$$W = \frac{4\sqrt{i}}{\pi} e^{-\pi\phi/4}. \tag{12}$$

Our difference-differential equation will express values of w and its derivatives at $\phi + i$ in terms of corresponding values at $\phi - i$.

Two of the boundary conditions to be imposed on w and z assert that $w(\phi)$ and $z(\phi + i)$ are real functions of ϕ. The Schwarz reflection principle therefore shows that the boundary condition (10), which is equivalent to

$$|dw|^2 = |dz|^2, \tag{13}$$

may be recast in the form

$$\dot{w}(\phi)^2 = \dot{z}(\phi)\dot{z}(\phi + 2i), \tag{14}$$

where the dot indicates differentiation with respect to ϕ. Finally, we obtain the fourth condition

$$ie^{-\pi\phi/2} = \dot{W}^2 = \zeta''\dot{z}^2 = -ww''\dot{z}^2 \tag{15}$$

by differentiating (12), squaring the result, and then eliminating W in favor of w by means of (7) and (11).

It is helpful to make use of the abbreviated notation

$$(16)\quad z = z(\phi), \qquad z_- = z(\phi - i), \qquad z_+ = z(\phi + i), \qquad z_{++} = z(\phi + 2i),$$

together with similar specifications of w_- and w_+. Then (15) combines with (14) to give

$$(17)\qquad ie^{-\pi\phi/2} = -w\frac{d}{d\phi}\left(\frac{\dot{w}}{\dot{z}}\right)\dot{z} = -w\dot{z}\frac{d}{d\phi}\sqrt{\frac{\dot{z}_{++}}{\dot{z}}},$$

or

$$(18)\qquad ie^{-\pi\phi/2} = \frac{w\dot{w}}{2}\left(\frac{\ddot{z}}{\dot{z}} - \frac{\ddot{z}_{++}}{\dot{z}_{++}}\right).$$

On the other hand, taking the logarithmic derivative of (14) we have

$$(19)\qquad 2\frac{\ddot{w}}{\dot{w}} = \frac{\ddot{z}}{\dot{z}} + \frac{\ddot{z}_{++}}{\dot{z}_{++}}.$$

Hence

$$(20)\qquad \frac{\ddot{z}}{\dot{z}} = \frac{\ddot{w}}{\dot{w}} + \frac{ie^{-\pi\phi/2}}{w\dot{w}}$$

and

$$(21)\qquad \frac{\ddot{z}_{++}}{\dot{z}_{++}} = \frac{\ddot{w}}{\dot{w}} - \frac{ie^{-\pi\phi/2}}{w\dot{w}}.$$

Replacing ϕ by $\phi + i$ in (20) and replacing ϕ by $\phi - i$ in (21), we eliminate z to establish the difference-differential equation

$$(22)\qquad \frac{\ddot{w}_+}{\dot{w}_+} + \frac{e^{-\pi\phi/2}}{w_+\dot{w}_+} = \frac{\ddot{w}_-}{\dot{w}_-} + \frac{e^{-\pi\phi/2}}{w_-\dot{w}_-}$$

for w alone.

In order to convert (22) into an integral equation, let us consider the function

$$(23)\qquad g(\phi) = \frac{1}{2\pi i}\int_0^\infty f(\psi)\log\left(e^{-\pi\phi} - e^{-\pi\psi}\right)d\psi,$$

where

$$(24)\qquad f(\psi) = e^{-\pi\psi/2}\left[\frac{1}{w(\psi + i)\dot{w}(\psi + i)} - \frac{1}{w(\psi - i)\dot{w}(\psi - i)}\right].$$

An examination of the argument of the logarithm shows that

$$(25)\qquad g_+ - g_- = -\int_\phi^\infty f(\psi)\,d\psi,$$

whence

$$(26)\qquad \dot{g}_+ - \dot{g}_- = e^{-\pi\phi/2}\left[\frac{1}{w_+\dot{w}_+} - \frac{1}{w_-\dot{w}_-}\right].$$

Consequently

$$\frac{\ddot{w}_+}{\dot{w}_+} + \dot{g}_+ = \frac{\ddot{w}_-}{\dot{w}_-} + \dot{g}_- \tag{27}$$

is a single-valued analytic function of the complex variable $\lambda = e^{-\pi\phi}$ in some neighborhood of the origin. From Taylor's theorem we therefore obtain the integral equation

$$\frac{\ddot{w}}{\dot{w}} = \sum_{n=0}^{\infty} a_n e^{-n\pi\phi} - \frac{1}{2\pi i}\frac{d}{d\phi}\int_0^{\infty} e^{-\pi\psi/2}\left[\frac{1}{w_+\dot{w}_+} - \frac{1}{w_-\dot{w}_-}\right]\log\left(e^{-\pi\phi} - e^{-\pi\psi}\right) d\psi \tag{28}$$

for w, where the power series on the right represents an arbitrary periodic function occurring in the solution of the difference-differential equation (22).

The method of successive approximations can be applied to (28) to yield an asymptotic expansion for w. Postponing that analysis until the next section, we digress for a moment to discuss finding closed solutions of the difference-differential equation (22). Observe that any solution of the simpler equation

$$w_+^2 = w_-^2 \tag{29}$$

also solves (22). Since the general solution of (29) may be expressed in the form

$$w = \sqrt{(\textstyle\sum b_n e^{-n\pi\phi})}, \tag{30}$$

we can obtain in this way certain explicit similarity flows obeying the free boundary condition (6) which, however, have been discovered earlier [3] from an investigation of the ordinary differential equation (11) alone. It would be of interest to determine further special solutions of the water entry problem through ingenious manipulation of (22), but we have as yet had little success in doing so.

Finally, we should like to mention a difference-differential equation analogous to (22) which may be used to study the steady motion of a solitary wave. Let ζ be the complex potential of such a flow. Our technique of reflection across the free boundary condition and across the fixed boundary condition shows that the mapping z from the ζ-plane to the physical plane satisfies a difference-differential equation of the form

$$i + \dot{z}_+\dot{z}_-[z_+ - z_- - 2iy_0] = 0, \qquad y_0 > 0. \tag{31}$$

It is an intriguing problem to look for explicit solutions of this equation that represent solitary waves.

3. **Dobrovolskaya's conjecture.** We now take up the question of the asymptotic shape of the free boundary curve C near the point z_0 where it separates from the wedge. In particular, we are interested in estimating the angle α between the free surface and the wedge wall at z_0. Both Dobrovolskaya [1] and the author [3] have conjectured that this angle α cannot vanish. We shall prove the conjecture here by using the integral equation (28) to find an asymptotic expansion of the

auxiliary function $w = w(\phi)$ valid for large ϕ. A similar expansion of z then follows by substitution into the relation (20).

If $\alpha = 0$, then w must exhibit slower than exponential decay as $\phi \to +\infty$. Consequently the integral on the right in (28) approaches zero at an exponential rate, and we may write

$$\frac{\ddot{w}}{\dot{w}} \sim a_0 = -\varepsilon. \tag{32}$$

Integrating, we obtain the asymptotic formula

$$w \sim Ae^{-\varepsilon\phi}, \tag{33}$$

where A and ε are positive constants. That $\varepsilon \neq 0$ follows from the fact that otherwise (28) would give $\dot{w} \neq 0$ at infinity, which is in contradiction with our knowledge that z_0 has to be finite because the distance between surface particles does not change with time. Clearly $\alpha = \varepsilon$, and therefore we have established Dobrovolskaya's theorem $\alpha \neq 0$ stating that the free boundary curve C and the wedge wall do not form a cusp together at the point of separation z_0.

We have seen that if the integral on the right in (28) decays exponentially as $\phi \to +\infty$, then (33) holds. Moreover, (33) is consistent with the exponential decay of the integral when ε lies in the range

$$0 < \varepsilon < \frac{\pi}{4}. \tag{34}$$

On the other hand, for $\varepsilon > \pi/4$ the integral becomes infinite and it is the terms involving $e^{-\pi\phi/2}/(w\dot{w})$ rather than the terms involving $\ddot{w}/\dot{w}$ that dominate in the difference-differential equation (22). For $\varepsilon > \pi/4$ we are therefore led to replace (28) by the alternate integral equation

$$\frac{e^{-\pi\phi}}{w\dot{w}} = \sum c_n e^{-n\pi\phi} + \frac{1}{2\pi i}\frac{d}{d\phi}\int_0^\infty e^{-\pi\psi/2}\left[\frac{\ddot{w}_+}{\dot{w}_+} - \frac{\ddot{w}_-}{\dot{w}_-}\right]\log(e^{-\pi\phi} - e^{-\pi\psi})\,d\psi \tag{35}$$

based on (22).

From (35) we obtain

$$w \sim Be^{-m\pi\phi/2}, \tag{36}$$

where m is some positive integer and B is a positive constant. Thus if $\varepsilon > \pi/4$ then either $\alpha = \pi/2$ or $\alpha = \pi$. The latter two cases are excluded, however, because the geometry of the conformal mapping by the Wagner function (7) implies that the free boundary curve C is convex. Thus $\alpha = \pi$ is obviously impossible. Also, if $\alpha = \pi/2$ observe that the point on the involute of C corresponding to infinity is located outside the wedge, which brings us to the absurd conclusion that the velocity of the flow at infinity is not vertical. It follows that the splash angle α must be restricted to the interval

$$0 < \alpha \leqq \frac{\pi}{4}. \tag{37}$$

Note that this result depends on our knowledge of the geometry of the Wagner function W in the large.

Further analysis of the integral equation (28) suggests that when ε/π is an irrational number the auxiliary function w ought to have an asymptotic expansion of the form

$$w \sim e^{-\varepsilon\phi} \sum_{m,n=0}^{\infty} A_{mn} e^{-m(\pi/4-\varepsilon)\phi - n\pi\phi}. \tag{38}$$

A similar representation is valid for z, too, because of (20). If, on the other hand, ε/π is rational, then powers of ϕ or $\log \phi$ may enter the expansions of w and z, which become much more complicated multiple series.

References

1. Z. N. Dobrovolskaya, *On the nature of the contact between the free boundary of a fluid and the rigid boundary in the problem of entry of a wedge*, Dokl. Akad. Nauk SSSR **153** (1963), 783–786.

2. R. E. Dowd, *Asymptotic description of the cusps of a hydromagnetic figure of equilibrium*, N.Y.U. Rep. No. N.Y.O.-10,435, New York Univ., New York, February, 1964.

3. P. R. Garabedian, *Oblique water entry of a wedge*, Comm. Pure Appl. Math. **6** (1953), 157–165.

4. ———, *On steady state bubbles generated by Taylor instability*, Proc. Roy. Soc. London Ser. A **241** (1957), 423–431.

5. H. Lewy, *Developments at the confluence of analytic boundary conditions*, Univ. California Publ. Math. **1** (1950), 247–280.

6. H. Wagner, *Über Stoss- und Gleitvorgänge an den Oberflächen von Flüssigkeiten*, Z. Angew. Math. Mech. **12** (1932), 193–215.

Courant Institute of Mathematical Sciences,
New York University,
New York, New York

III. VISCOUS FLUIDS, MAGNETOHYDRODYNAMICS

STATIONARY SOLUTIONS OF THE NAVIER-STOKES EQUATIONS

BY

ROBERT FINN

TABLE OF CONTENTS

1. **Preliminary remarks.** There is a considerable, if largely indirect, evidence to support the use of the equations

$$\rho \frac{\partial \mathbf{w}}{\partial t} - \mu \Delta \mathbf{w} + \rho \mathbf{w} \cdot \nabla \mathbf{w} + \nabla p = \mathbf{f}(x, t), \qquad \nabla \cdot \mathbf{w} = 0 \tag{1}$$

to describe the motions of a viscous, incompressible fluid. The symbols in (1) denote the following physical quantities: $t \sim$ time; $x = (x_1, x_2, x_3) \sim$ position vector; $\mathbf{w} = \mathbf{w}(x, t) \sim$ velocity of fluid particle in position x at time t; $p = p(x, t) \sim$ pressure; $\rho \sim$ density; $\mu \sim$ viscosity coefficient; $\mathbf{f} \sim$ external force density. The first of the equations (1) expresses the equilibrium of the forces acting on the fluid at the point (x, t), the second is the equation of conservation of mass, under the assumption $\rho \equiv$ const.

The system (1) was proposed by Navier [1] in 1822; an improved and clarified derivation appears in the work of de Saint Venant [2] and of Stokes [3]. In addition to Newton's laws, Cauchy's stress principle, and some continuity requirements, the underlying assumption required in the derivation is the relation

$$\mathbf{T} = -p\mathbf{I} + 2\mu \mathbf{D} \tag{2}$$

between the stress tensor $\mathbf{T}$ and the deformation tensor $\mathbf{D} = \frac{1}{2}(\partial w_i/\partial x_j + \partial w_j/\partial x_i)$. The assumption is an arbitrary one and would ordinarily be expected to hold at best in an asymptotic sense for small $\mathbf{D}$. Nevertheless the equations (1) have been successfully applied to cases in which the deformations are large relative to the pressures.

The present report is concerned with those cases for which, in a suitable Galilean reference frame[1] there holds $\partial \mathbf{w}/\partial t \equiv 0$ in (x, t). Such solutions of (1) are called *stationary solutions*. Their study presents characteristic difficulties which impose on the resulting theory a structure different from that appropriate to the original system (1). Examples of stationary solutions are the steady flow of fluid in a tube, and the steady motion of a rigid body in a fluid at rest at infinity (stationary with respect to a coordinate frame fixed in the body). The principal purpose of this report is expository, to bring the interested reader up to date with current developments; however, I have taken the opportunity to give strengthened versions and improved demonstrations of various results (principally my own) which appear in the literature.

The equations for stationary solutions may be written, after a relabeling of the pressure and external force,

$$\nu \Delta \mathbf{w} - \mathbf{w} \cdot \nabla \mathbf{w} - \nabla p = -\mathbf{f}(x), \qquad \nabla \cdot \mathbf{w} = 0, \tag{3}$$

where $\nu = \mu/\rho$. In much of what follows, it will be convenient to assume $\nu = 1$. This can always be achieved, in any given flow, by a similarity transformation.

[1] The system (1) is invariant under Galilean transformations.

Corresponding to a given constant velocity $\mathbf{w}_0$ (in general, velocity at infinity), the perturbations from the uniform flow $\mathbf{w} \equiv \mathbf{w}_0$ may be studied by introducing the change of variables $\mathbf{w} - \mathbf{w}_0 = \lambda\mathbf{u}$, where $\mathbf{u}$ is to satisfy fixed boundary conditions, for small λ. The parameter λ is essentially the "Reynolds number" of the flow, measured relative to the velocity $\mathbf{w}_0$. In terms of $\mathbf{u}(x)$, the system (3) becomes, after another relabeling,

$$\begin{aligned} \Delta\mathbf{u} - \mathbf{w}_0\cdot\nabla\mathbf{u} - \nabla p &= -\mathbf{f}(x) + \lambda\mathbf{u}\cdot\nabla\mathbf{u}, \\ \nabla\cdot\mathbf{u} &= 0. \end{aligned} \tag{4}$$

Letting $\lambda \to 0$ in (4) leads to the Oseen linearization [4]

$$\begin{aligned} \Delta\mathbf{u} - \mathbf{w}_0\cdot\nabla\mathbf{u} - \nabla p &= -\mathbf{f}(x), \\ \nabla\cdot\mathbf{u} &= 0. \end{aligned} \tag{5}$$

In the particular case $\mathbf{w}_0 = 0$ we obtain the Stokes equations

$$\begin{aligned} \Delta\mathbf{u} - \nabla p &= -\mathbf{f}(x), \\ \nabla\cdot\mathbf{u} &= 0 \end{aligned} \tag{6}$$

for flows with infinitesimally small velocity.

All equations (3), (4), (5), (6) become simplified if the external field is derivable from a potential Φ, for then the term $-\mathbf{f}(x) = \nabla\Phi$ can be absorbed into the pressure term. Throughout this report, I shall refer to this situation by a subscript "zero"; thus $(\ )_0$ means $(\ )$ with $\mathbf{f}(x) \equiv 0$.

In addition to the symbols already introduced, the following notation will be used:

Σ	closed surface.
$\mathscr{G}, \mathscr{E}$	regions interior and exterior to Σ.
$(\mathbf{u}, \mathbf{v})$	$\int \mathbf{u}\cdot\mathbf{v}\, dx$ (extended over some given region).
$[\mathbf{u}, \mathbf{v}]$	$\int \nabla\mathbf{u}\cdot\nabla\mathbf{v}\, dx$.
$\Vert\mathbf{u}\Vert$	$(\int \vert\nabla\mathbf{u}\vert^2\, dx)^{1/2}$.
$\{\mathbf{u}, \mathbf{v}, \mathbf{w}\}$	$\int \mathbf{u}\cdot\mathbf{v}\cdot\nabla\mathbf{w}\, dx$.
$C^{r+\alpha}$	functions, having derivatives up to rth order, Hölder continuous with exponent α in a given region.
$C_0^{r+\alpha}$	as above, but with compact support in the region.
$\mathscr{J}$	solenoidal (i.e., divergence free) vector fields of class C_0^∞ in a given region.
$\mathscr{H}$	Hilbert space, obtained by completion of $\mathscr{J}$ with respect to the norm $\Vert\ \Vert$, in a bounded region.
$\mathbf{E}, \mathscr{E}$	fundamental solution tensors associated with systems (5) and (6); defined in §§2.8, 3.1.

$\mathbf{E}^\gamma$, $\mathscr{E}^\gamma$	truncated tensors, see §2.8.
$\mathbf{G}$, $\mathscr{G}$	Green's tensors for (5) and (6).
Tw	stress tensor, $(\mathbf{Tw})_{ij} = -p\delta_{ij} + (\partial w_i/\partial x_j + \partial w_j/\partial x_i)$, according to (2).
Dw = **def w**	deformation tensor, $(\mathbf{def\ w})_{ij} = \frac{1}{2}(\partial w_i/\partial x_j + \partial w_j/\partial x_i)$.
D	class of solutions in $\mathscr{E}$, having finite Dirichlet integral.
PR	physically reasonable solutions in $\mathscr{E}$, see §3.3.

All results described in this report for an interior region hold as well for $n = 2$ and for $n = 3$ dimensions. In the case of an exterior region, it will be assumed, except where otherwise specified, that $n = 3$. The case $n = 2$ is considerably the more difficult in an exterior region, and little information about it is available. The formal reason for this arises from the "Stokes paradox," that if $n = 2$ there exists no bounded solution of $(6)_0$ in $\mathscr{E}$ for which $\mathbf{w}(x) = 0$ on Σ, and $\mathbf{w}(x) \not\equiv 0$ in $\mathscr{E}$.

2. **The interior problem.** Aside from the situations in which explicit solutions can be found, the most accessible problem from a mathematical point of view is that of finding a solution of (3) in a finite region $\mathscr{G}$, such that $\mathbf{w}$ achieves prescribed values $\mathbf{w}^*$ on the bounding surface (or curve) Σ. Physically the most natural requirement is the condition of adherence, $\mathbf{w}^* \equiv 0$; however, other conditions can be realized, e.g., one may consider a region bounded by a flexible belt moving on a fixed path, or a device in which fluid is removed or added along Σ at prescribed rates. In any event, the case of general data $\mathbf{w}^*$ possesses an evident mathematical interest. It should be noted that, as physical experience suggests, the pressure p cannot be prescribed on Σ, but is rather determined (up to an additive constant) by the field $\mathbf{w}(x)$ (and hence by $\mathbf{w}^*$). From a formal point of view, this reflects the fact that the system (3), while of elliptic type, is not strongly elliptic (cf. [**5**]). The data $\mathbf{w}^*$ cannot be prescribed arbitrarily, as the last of the equations (3) imposes the restriction

$$\oint_\Sigma \mathbf{w}^* \cdot \mathbf{n}\, d\sigma = 0 \tag{7}$$

on any solution. (7) is the formal expression of the assumed incompressibility of the fluid.

2.1. Linearized theory. The first studies of the interior boundary value problem for (3) are due to Lichtenstein [**6**] and to Odqvist [**7**], and are based on potential-theoretic methods. The paper of Odqvist has been of central importance for the later historical development. Odqvist bases his study on the linearized system $(6)_0$ for which he develops a "hydrodynamical potential theory" analogous to the classical potential theory of harmonic functions. Although this material is complicated in detail, it exhibits in its underlying structure a considerable elegance and conceptual appeal. Consider, for definiteness, the case of dimension $n = 3$. As in potential theory, the development is based on the properties of the *fundamental solution tensor* $\mathbf{E}(x - y)$ and *pressure vector* $\mathbf{P}(x - y)$ with components

(8)
$$E_{ij}(x - y) \equiv -\frac{1}{8\pi}\left[\frac{\delta_{ij}}{r_{xy}} + \frac{(x_i - y_i)(x_j - y_j)}{r_{xy}^3}\right],$$
$$P_i(x - y) \equiv -\frac{1}{4\pi}\frac{x_i - y_i}{r_{xy}^3}.$$

Here $x = (x_1, x_2, x_3)$, $r_{xy}^2 = \Sigma(x_i - y_i)^2$.

For each fixed i, the vector $\{E_{ij}(x - y)\}$ and scalar $P_i(x - y)$ define a solution of $(6)_0$ as function of x or of y for all $x \neq y$. Further, for any vector $\mathbf{f} = \{f_j(x)\}$ defined in $\mathscr{G}$, the vector

(9)
$$\mathbf{W}(x) = -\int_{\mathscr{G}} \mathbf{E}(x - y)\cdot\mathbf{f}(y)\,dy$$

and scalar

(10)
$$P(x) = -\int_{\mathscr{G}} \mathbf{P}(x - y)\cdot\mathbf{f}(y)\,dy$$

define a solution of the inhomogeneous equations (6) in $\mathscr{G}$. One has also the following identities, for arbitrary vector fields $\mathbf{u}(x)$, $\mathbf{v}(x)$, and scalars $p(x)$, $q(x)$, in which physically significant quantities appear in a natural way. Introducing the *stress tensor*

$$\mathbf{Tu} = \{(\mathbf{Tu})_{ij}\} = -p\delta_{ij} + \left(\frac{\partial u_i}{\partial x_j} + \frac{\partial u_j}{\partial x_i}\right)$$

and the *deformation tensor*

$$\mathbf{def\ u} = \left\{\frac{1}{2}\left(\frac{\partial u_i}{\partial x_j} + \frac{\partial u_j}{\partial x_i}\right)\right\}$$

one finds the relations

(11)
$$\int_{\mathscr{G}} \mathbf{v}\cdot(\Delta\mathbf{u} - \nabla p)\,dy + 2\int_{\mathscr{G}} (\mathbf{def\ u})\cdot(\mathbf{def\ v})\,dy = \oint_{\Sigma} \mathbf{v}\cdot\mathbf{Tu}\,d\boldsymbol{\sigma},$$

(12)
$$\int_{\mathscr{G}} [\mathbf{u}\cdot(\Delta\mathbf{v} - \nabla q) - \mathbf{v}\cdot(\Delta\mathbf{u} - \nabla p)]\,dy = \oint_{\Sigma} (\mathbf{u}\cdot\mathbf{Tv} - \mathbf{v}\cdot\mathbf{Tu})\,d\boldsymbol{\sigma}.$$

In (11), (12), $d\boldsymbol{\sigma}$ is understood as surface element multiplied by a unit normal vector.

From these relations and from the properties of $\mathbf{E}(x - y)$, one obtains the representation

(13)
$$\mathbf{w}(x) = \oint_{\Sigma} (\mathbf{w}\cdot\mathbf{TE} - \mathbf{E}\cdot\mathbf{Tw})\,d\boldsymbol{\sigma} - \int_{\mathscr{G}} \mathbf{E}\cdot\mathbf{f}\,dy,$$
$$p(x) = \oint_{\Sigma} (\mathbf{w}\cdot\mathbf{TP} - \mathbf{P}\cdot\mathbf{Tw})\,d\boldsymbol{\sigma} - \int_{\mathscr{G}} \mathbf{P}\cdot\mathbf{f}\,dy$$

for any solution of (6) in $\mathscr{G}$ which is smooth up to Σ. Here the "pressure" to be used in forming the expression **TP** may be chosen to be an arbitrary constant.

The particular form of the fundamental solution tensor and of the identities (11), (12), (13) permit the development of an analogue of those parts of classical potential theory which do not depend on the maximum principle. Odqvist exploited this situation by constructing hydrodynamical surface potentials of simple and double layer. The solution of the "Dirichlet problem," for which

$$\mathbf{w}(x) = \mathbf{w}^* \quad \text{on } \Sigma \tag{14}$$

is then sought as the potential of a hydrodynamical double layer. The corresponding jump relations then lead, as in classical potential theory, to an integral equation, of the form

$$w_i^* = \varphi_i + \oint_\Sigma K_{ij}\varphi_j \, d\sigma \tag{15}$$

for the $\{\varphi_j\}$ (essentially the double layer density).

Odqvist now poses an exterior "Neumann problem": to find a solution of $(6)_0$ in the exterior $\mathscr{E}$ of Σ which vanishes at infinity and which yields prescribed force density on Σ,

$$(\mathbf{Tw}^*)_{ij}n_j = \mathscr{F}_i^* \quad \text{on } \Sigma. \tag{16}$$

Representation of the solution as a simple layer leads to the equation

$$\mathscr{F}_i^* = \psi_i + \oint_\Sigma K_{ji}\psi_j \, d\sigma, \tag{17}$$

which is the adjoint of (15).

A solution of (15) can be found for exactly those data $\mathbf{w}^*$ which are orthogonal to the solutions of the homogeneous system $(17)_0$. Let $\boldsymbol{\psi}$ be such a solution of $(17)_0$, and let $\mathbf{V}$ be the flow in $\mathscr{E}$ arising from a simple layer on Σ with density $\boldsymbol{\psi}$. The identity (11) yields, since $(\mathbf{TV})\cdot\mathbf{n} = 0$ on the outer surface $\Sigma^{(+)}$,

$$\int_{\mathscr{E}} (\mathbf{def}\, \mathbf{V})^2 \, dx = 0$$

from which follows that $\mathbf{V}$ is a rigid motion. But $\mathbf{V} \to 0$ at ∞, hence $\mathbf{V} \equiv 0$ in $\mathscr{E}$.

Because of the continuity of simple layer potentials, $\mathbf{V} \equiv 0$ also on the inner bounding surface $\Sigma^{(-)}$ of Σ. Using (11) one then finds $\mathbf{V} \equiv 0$ in $\mathscr{G}$, hence the associated pressure $P \equiv \text{const}$ in $\mathscr{G}$. But from the assumed representation,

$$P(x) \equiv \text{const} = \oint_\Sigma \boldsymbol{\psi}\cdot\nabla\left(\frac{1}{r_{xy}}\right) d\sigma_y,$$

an equation for which the only solution is $\boldsymbol{\psi} = c\mathbf{n}$ for some constant c. It follows that *a solution of* $(6)_0$ *exists in* $\mathscr{G}$, *achieving data* $\mathbf{w}^*$ *on* Σ, *if and only if* (7) *holds.*

Consider now the interior "Neumann problem," to find a solution in $\mathscr{G}$ satisfying (16) on Σ. The integral equation is

$$\mathscr{F}_i^* = \varphi_i - \oint_\Sigma K_{ji}\varphi_j \, d\sigma \tag{18}$$

and its adjoint, corresponding to the exterior "Dirichlet problem," is

$$w_i^* = \psi_i - \oint_\Sigma K_{ij}\psi_j \, d\sigma. \tag{19}$$

Odqvist found explicitly six independent solutions $\{\boldsymbol{\psi}_i\} = \{\psi_{ij}\}$ of the homogeneous system $(19)_0$ and showed that no others exist. The orthogonality condition then yields the result: *A solution exists in* $\mathscr{G}$ *with prescribed force density* $\mathscr{F}_i^*$ *on* Σ *if and only if all resultant forces and moments on* Σ *vanish.* (The necessity of these conditions can be shown from (11).)

The simple layer potentials $\{\mathbf{V}_i\}$ in $\mathscr{G}$ corresponding to the solutions $\{\boldsymbol{\psi}_j\}$ of the homogeneous system $(19)_0$ yield the six independent rigid body motions in $\mathscr{G}$. These potentials are continuous across Σ and vanish at infinity. Hence *the densities* $\{\boldsymbol{\psi}_j\}$ *determine the most general steady motion of a rigid body in a fluid at rest at infinity.*

Next, consider the exterior "Dirichlet problem." A solution exists as a double layer potential exactly for those data $\mathbf{w}^*$ such that

$$\oint_\Sigma \mathbf{w}^* \cdot \boldsymbol{\psi}_i \, d\sigma = 0$$

for each of the above $\boldsymbol{\psi}_j$. Suppose $\oint_\Sigma \mathbf{w}^* \cdot \boldsymbol{\psi}_i \, d\sigma \neq 0$ for some i, and let $\mathbf{V}_i$ be the simple layer potential on Σ with density $\boldsymbol{\psi}_i$. By the jump relations, $2\boldsymbol{\psi}_i = \mathbf{TV}_i$ on $\Sigma^{(+)}$, hence using (11),

$$2 \oint_\Sigma \mathbf{V}_i \cdot \boldsymbol{\psi}_i \, d\sigma = \oint_\Sigma \mathbf{V}_i \cdot \mathbf{TV}_i \, d\sigma = \int_{\mathscr{E}} (\mathbf{def}\, \mathbf{V}_i)^2 \, dx \neq 0.$$

Hence by adjoining to $\mathbf{w}^*$ a linear combination of rigid body motions, one obtains data which can be extended to a solution by a double layer potential. A similar discussion applies to the exterior "Neumann problem," and we obtain: *There exists a solution of* $(6)_0$ *in* $\mathscr{E}$ *which vanishes at infinity and which assumes arbitrary prescribed data or yields arbitrary prescribed force density on* Σ. *The solution appears in general as a sum of simple and double layer potentials over* Σ.

Note that for the exterior problem no restriction need be imposed on the prescribed data.

In later applications it will be necessary to have solutions which tend to a given rigid motion at infinity. Because of the linearity of (6), it is necessary only to superpose the given motion on the data considered above.

The identities (13) lead immediately to the uniqueness of the above solutions in the class of all solutions representable as potentials over Σ. The solution is in fact unique in a much broader class **[8]**.

As already mentioned, the exterior problem is not in general solvable in dimension $n = 2$ for a solution which vanishes at infinity. It is then necessary to impose the restriction that the resultant force on Σ vanish **[7]**, **[8]**, **[33]**. The conditions for solvability of the interior problem remain however unchanged **[7]**.

The existence of a solution to the "Dirichlet problem" yields the existence of a Green's tensor $\mathbf{G}(x, y)$ in $\mathscr{G}$, which as function of y admits a fundamental singularity (8) at x and vanishes on Σ. Again using potential-theoretic methods, Odqvist established properties of $\mathbf{G}(x, y)$ which are basic in much of the present theory. One has, for $\mathbf{G}(x, y) = \{G_{ij}\}$ and corresponding "pressure" $\mathbf{P}(x, y)$,

$$
\begin{aligned}
|\mathbf{G}(x, y)| &< \frac{C}{r_{xy}}, \\
|\mathbf{G}(x, y) - \mathbf{G}(x', y)| &< C\frac{r_{xx'}^{1-\varepsilon}}{r_0^2}, \\
|\nabla \mathbf{G}(x, y)| &< C r_{xy}^{-2}; \qquad |\mathbf{P}(x, y)| < C r_{xy}^{-2}, \\
|\nabla(\mathbf{G}(x, y) - \mathbf{G}(x', y))| &< C\frac{r_{xx'}^{1-\varepsilon}}{r_0^3}, \\
|\mathbf{P}(x, y) - \mathbf{P}(x', y)| &< C\frac{r_{xx'}^{1-\varepsilon}}{r_0^3}
\end{aligned}
\tag{20}
$$

for some constant $C(\varepsilon)$ and any $\varepsilon > 0$. Also $\mathbf{G}(x, y)$ has the symmetry property, $G_{ij}(x, y) = G_{ji}(y, x)$.

The Green's tensor permits the solution of the Dirichlet problem for the inhomogeneous system (6). One need only add $-\int_{\mathscr{G}} \mathbf{G}(x, y)\mathbf{f}(y)\, dy$ to the solution obtained above. It leads also to a priori Hölder estimates on any solution, depending only on Σ and on the smoothness of $\mathbf{f}(x)$ and of $\mathbf{w}^*$.

2.2 The nonlinear problem; solution of Odqvist. For an interior region $\mathscr{G}$ bounded by a smooth surface (or curve) Σ, write

$$\mathbf{u}(x) = \mathbf{u}_0(x) + \sum_{1}^{\infty} \mathbf{u}_j(x)\lambda^j \tag{21}$$

where $\mathbf{u}_0(x)$ is the solution of (6) assuming prescribed data $\mathbf{w}^*$ on Σ. Formal substitution into

$$\mathbf{u}(x) = \mathbf{u}_0(x) + \lambda \int_{\mathscr{G}} \mathbf{G}\cdot\mathbf{u}\cdot\nabla\mathbf{u}\, dy \tag{22}$$

leads to a series of recursion formulas for the $\{\mathbf{u}_j(x)\}$. The estimates (20) of Odqvist imply the uniform convergence of (21) to a solution of (4) (with $\mathbf{w}_0 = 0$) which achieves the prescribed data $\mathbf{w}^*$ on Σ, provided λ is sufficiently small (Odqvist [7]).[2] This is the result suggested by physical experience.

2.3. Leray's observation. Leray [**9**] discovered the property of solutions of (3), that *there exists a bound on Dirichlet integral in $\mathscr{G}$, depending only on Σ, on $\mathbf{w}^*$ and on ν, but otherwise independent of the particular solution considered.* (It had

[2] If the data $\mathbf{w}^*$ are sufficiently small, then (21) will converge for $\lambda = 1$; thus the solution of the original equation (3) exists for prescribed data $\mathbf{w}^*$ provided they are small.

long been expected, although not definitely established, that multiple solutions could in some cases exist for small ν.) Leray gave two demonstrations of this basic property of the equations (3), one of which leads to an explicit estimate. The reasoning was later clarified by E. Hopf in an elegant paper **[10]** in which he extended the result to time dependent motions and to the case of moving boundaries. (This last result may be significant for the problem of obtaining stationary solutions of the exterior problem as a limit of time dependent motions, cf. the discussion in §6.) Hopf's demonstration depends on the following lemma:

Let $\mathbf{w}^*$ *be prescribed data on* Σ, *satisfying* (7), *and let* $\boldsymbol{\eta}(x)$ *be any vector field in* $\mathscr{G}$, *for which* $\boldsymbol{\eta} = 0$ *on* Σ. *Let* $\varepsilon > 0$ *be prescribed. Then there is a solenoidal extension* $\mathbf{v}(x)$ *of* $\mathbf{w}^*$ *into* $\mathscr{G}$, *such that* $|\{\mathbf{v}, \boldsymbol{\eta}, \boldsymbol{\eta}\}_{\mathscr{G}}| < \varepsilon\|\boldsymbol{\eta}\|^2$.

The idea of the proof is to introduce first an arbitrary solenoidal extension in the form[3] curl $\boldsymbol{\psi}(x)$, and then a smooth function $h(s; \delta)$ corresponding to prescribed $\delta > 0$, which satisfies the conditions: $h(0; \delta) = 1$; $h_s(0; \delta) = 0$; $h(\delta; \delta) = h_s(\delta; \delta) = 0$; $|h(s)| + |h'(s)| < \varepsilon s^{-1}$ on the interval $0 \leqq s \leqq \delta$. Choosing δ so that the neighborhood $\mathscr{A}_\delta$ of width δ at Σ is simply covered by the normals to Σ, and letting s denote arc length along the normals, the lemma follows by choosing $\mathbf{v}(x) = \operatorname{curl} h(s)\boldsymbol{\psi}(x)$, and noting that $\int_{\mathscr{A}_\delta} \boldsymbol{\eta}^2/s^2\, dx < C \int_{\mathscr{A}_\delta} |\nabla\boldsymbol{\eta}|^2$ for some constant C.

A construction of $h(s)$ which is more geometrical (but not otherwise better) than that of Hopf is given in my paper **[11**, p. 209]. The reader may wish to supply his own construction, as an exercise.

To apply the lemma to stationary flows in $\mathscr{G}$, we may assume the equations written in the form (4) with $\mathbf{w}_0 = 0$. Writing $\boldsymbol{\eta}(x) = \mathbf{u}(x) - \mathbf{v}(x)$, (4) becomes

$$\Delta\boldsymbol{\eta} - \lambda\boldsymbol{\eta}\cdot\nabla\boldsymbol{\eta} - \nabla p = -\mathbf{f} - \Delta\mathbf{v} + \lambda\boldsymbol{\eta}\cdot\nabla\mathbf{v} + \lambda\mathbf{v}\cdot\nabla\boldsymbol{\eta} + \lambda\mathbf{v}\cdot\nabla\mathbf{v},$$
$$\nabla\cdot\boldsymbol{\eta} = 0.$$

Multiply the first equation by $\boldsymbol{\eta}$ and integrate over $\mathscr{G}$. Since $\boldsymbol{\eta} = 0$ on Σ and $\mathbf{v} = 0$ outside $\mathscr{A}_\delta$, we find

$$\begin{aligned}(23)\qquad &\int_{\mathscr{G}} |\nabla\boldsymbol{\eta}|^2\, dx \\ &= \int_{\mathscr{G}} \boldsymbol{\eta}\cdot\mathbf{f}\, dx - \int_{\mathscr{A}_\delta} \nabla\boldsymbol{\eta}\cdot\nabla\mathbf{v}\, dx + \lambda\int_{\mathscr{A}_\delta} \mathbf{v}\cdot\mathbf{v}\cdot\nabla\boldsymbol{\eta}\, dx + \lambda\int_{\mathscr{A}_\delta} \mathbf{v}\cdot\boldsymbol{\eta}\cdot\nabla\boldsymbol{\eta}\, dx\end{aligned}$$

from which Leray's estimate follows from Schwarz' inequality, Poincaré's inequality $(\boldsymbol{\eta}, \boldsymbol{\eta}) < \text{const}\cdot\|\boldsymbol{\eta}\|^2$, and by appropriate choice of ε.

2.4. Leray's existence theorem. From the a priori estimate on Dirichlet integral, Leray concluded that *for any prescribed data* w^* *satisfying* (7), *there exists at least one solution of* (3) *in* $\mathscr{G}$. This remarkable result could not have been predicted from any known experimental observations, nor is it in any way obvious

[3] Such a field can be obtained, for example, by an integration of the solution of the linearized equations $(6)_0$. More direct constructions appear in the references **[11]**, **[12]**, **[13]**.

from the mathematical structure of the equations. The demonstration is most perspicuously presented in the language of the Leray-Schauder fixed point theorem [**14**], although this apparatus was not available to Leray at the time of his original writing.[4]

One considers the integral equation, corresponding to (4) with $\mathbf{w}_0 = 0$,

$$\mathbf{u}(x) = \mathscr{T}(\mathbf{u}; \lambda) = \mathbf{u}_0(x) - \lambda \int_{\mathscr{G}} \mathbf{G}(x, y) \cdot \mathbf{u}(y) \cdot \nabla \mathbf{u}(y)\, dy \tag{24}$$

in the class of solenoidal fields $\mathbf{u}(x)$ which together with their first derivatives are Hölder continuous in $\mathscr{G} + \Sigma$. Here

$$\mathbf{u}_0(x) = \oint_{\Sigma} \mathbf{w}^* \cdot \mathbf{TG}\, d\sigma - \int_{\mathscr{G}} \mathbf{G} \cdot \mathbf{f}\, dy \tag{25}$$

is the solution of the linearized system (6) with the same data. A solution of (24) is sought for some given λ, say $\lambda = 1$.

For any fixed Hölder exponent α, the Odqvist estimates (20) yield immediately the complete continuity of $\mathscr{T}(\mathbf{u}; \lambda)$ in the corresponding Hölder norm. Further, $\mathscr{T}(\mathbf{u}; 0)$ maps the entire function space to the single point $\mathbf{u}_0$. Thus, the transformation $\mathbf{\Phi}(\mathbf{u}) = \mathbf{u} - \mathscr{T}(\mathbf{u}; 0)$ is a uniform translation, hence the degree[5] of the (unique) solution of $\mathbf{\Phi}(\mathbf{w}) = 0$ is one. Finally, for $0 \leqq \lambda \leqq 1$, all solutions of (24) remain uniformly bounded in norm. This may be seen as follows:[6] an integration by parts yields

$$\int_{\mathscr{G}} \mathbf{G} \cdot \mathbf{u} \cdot \nabla \mathbf{u}\, dy = - \int_{\mathscr{G}} \mathbf{u} \cdot \mathbf{u} \cdot \nabla \mathbf{G}\, dy.$$

Hence if $\mathbf{u}(x)$ satisfies (24), then by (20)

$$|\mathbf{u}(x)| < C + C \int_{\mathscr{G}} \frac{|\mathbf{u}(y)|^2}{r_{xy}^2}\, dy$$

for some constant C. But

$$\int_{\mathscr{G}} \frac{|\mathbf{u}|^2}{r^2}\, dy < C \int_{\mathscr{G}} |\nabla \mathbf{u}|^2\, dy + C \tag{26}$$

(essentially Poincaré's inequality). Hence Leray's bound on Dirichlet integral implies an inequality

$$|\mathbf{u}(x)| < C.$$

The equation (24) then implies a Hölder bound on $\mathbf{u}(x)$ for any exponent $\alpha < 1$. Placing this back into the equation permits differentiation under the sign, and leads, using (20), to the desired Hölder bound on $\nabla \mathbf{w}(x)$.

---

[4] Actually the somewhat simpler theorem of Schauder suffices; cf. Schaeffer [**15**].

[5] In general terms, the degree is the number of times a neighborhood of a point is covered by its inverse image; cf. the discussion in [**14**].

[6] The following demonstration differs in detail from those appearing in the literature.

Thus any possible solution of (24) is bounded in norm, uniformly in λ. It follows that the degree of the mapping does not change in the range $0 \leqq \lambda \leqq 1$. But for $\lambda = 0$ the degree differs from zero. Hence the degree does not vanish when $\lambda = 1$, which implies the existence of a solution.

The method is easily adapted to the two-dimensional case, $n = 2$; however, if $n > 3$ there appear to be serious difficulties.

2.5. Ladyzhenskaia's contribution. An interesting variant of Leray's existence theorem was obtained by Ladyzhenskaia **[16]**, **[13]**, who used the methods of functional analysis.

A field $\mathbf{w}(x)$ is said to be a *generalized solution* of (3) in $\mathscr{G}$, with boundary data $\mathbf{w}^*$, if, for any smooth solenoidal field $\mathbf{a}(x)$ in $\mathscr{G}$ with $\mathbf{a}(x) = \mathbf{w}^*$ on Σ, the field $\mathbf{u}(x) = \mathbf{w}(x) - \mathbf{a}(x) \in \mathscr{H}$, and if

$$\text{(27)} \qquad \int_{\mathscr{G}} \{\nu\nabla(\mathbf{u} + \mathbf{a})\cdot - (\mathbf{u} + \mathbf{a})\cdot(\mathbf{u} + \mathbf{a})\cdot\}\nabla\mathbf{\Phi}(x)\, dx = -\int_{\mathscr{G}} \mathbf{f}\cdot\mathbf{\Phi}\, dx$$

for every "test function" $\mathbf{\Phi}(x) \in \mathscr{H}$.

Evidently the right-hand side of (27) is, under modest assumptions on $\mathbf{f}$, a bounded linear functional of $\mathbf{\Phi}$ in $\mathscr{H}$. Hence we may write

$$\int_{\mathscr{G}} \mathbf{f}\cdot\mathbf{\Phi}\, dx = [\mathbf{F}, \mathbf{\Phi}]$$

for some $\mathbf{F}(x) \in \mathscr{H}$, by the Riesz representation theorem. For fixed $\mathbf{u} \in \mathscr{H}$, all terms on the left in (27) are also linear functionals of $\mathbf{\Phi}$. This is evident for all except the one in which $\mathbf{u}$ appears quadradically. But

$$\left(\int_{\mathscr{G}} \mathbf{u}\cdot\mathbf{u}\cdot\nabla\mathbf{\Phi}\, dx\right)^2 \leqq \int_{\mathscr{G}} \mathbf{u}^4\, dx \int_{\mathscr{G}} |\nabla\mathbf{\Phi}|^2\, dx$$

and by the Sobolev imbedding theorems (cf. [**13**, p. 11 and p. 13]),

$$\text{(28)} \qquad \int_{\mathscr{G}} \mathbf{u}^4\, dx \leqq \left(\int_{\mathscr{G}} |\nabla\mathbf{u}|^2\, dx\right)^2$$

from which the assertion follows. Thus there is an operator $\mathbf{Au}$ such that

$$\int_{\mathscr{G}} [-\nu\mathbf{a}\cdot + (\mathbf{u} + \mathbf{a})\cdot(\mathbf{u} + \mathbf{a})\cdot]\nabla\mathbf{\Phi}\, dx = [\mathbf{Au}, \mathbf{\Phi}].$$

The problem is thus reduced to a study of the nonlinear functional equation

$$\text{(29)} \qquad \mathbf{u} - \lambda(\mathbf{Au} + \mathbf{F}) = 0$$

in the space $\mathscr{H}$, for the value $\lambda = \nu^{-1}$.

By Leray's theorem on boundedness of Dirichlet integral (§2.3) all possible solutions of (29) are bounded in $\mathscr{H}$. Further, the operator $\mathbf{A}$ is completely continuous in dimension $n \leqq 3$. For by the Rellich choice theorem **[17]** a bounded set in $\mathscr{H}$ admits a subsequence which converges strongly in L_2. The Sobolev inequality [**13**, p. 11]

$$\int_{\mathscr{G}} \mathbf{u}^4\,dx \leqq 4\left(\int_{\mathscr{G}} \mathbf{u}^2\,dx\right)^{1/2}\left(\int_{\mathscr{G}} |\nabla\mathbf{u}|^2\,dx\right)^{3/2} \tag{30}$$

then implies that the subsequence converges strongly also in L_4. For such a sequence one finds, for any $\mathbf{\Phi} \in \mathscr{H}$,

$$[\mathbf{Au}_m - \mathbf{Au}_n, \mathbf{\Phi}] \leqq C\|\mathbf{v}_m - \mathbf{v}_n\|_{L_4}\|\mathbf{\Phi}\|_{\mathscr{H}}$$

for some constant $C(\mathscr{G})$. Setting $\mathbf{\Phi} = \mathbf{Au}_m - \mathbf{Au}_n$ yields the assertion. Hence, the Leray-Schauder fixed point theorem implies, as in §2.4, the existence of a solution of (29) in $\mathscr{H}$, that is, of a generalized solution of the boundary value problem for (3).

REMARKS. 1. For the Dirichlet problem in a bounded region, the above method offers an evident conceptual advantage over Leray's original demonstration (§2.4), as the existence of a generalized solution $\mathbf{w}(x)$ is shown directly, without recourse to difficult estimates on the Green's tensor for $(6)_0$. There is a further advantage in that the method permits discussion of the physically important case in which Σ has isolated discontinuities (such as edges). See §8 below. The regularity of $\mathbf{w}(x)$ interior to $\mathscr{G}$ is not hard to prove (§2.8 below); however, the continuity of $\mathbf{w}(x)$ up to Σ has not yet been shown without the Odqvist estimates (20).

2. In her paper [**16**] (see also [**13**, pp. 100–104]) Ladyzhenskaia offers an alternative proof of boundedness of the solutions in $\mathscr{H}$. This proof does not seem correct as stated; however, the demonstration outlined above (§2.3) suffices for the purpose.

2.6. SHINBROT'S CONTRIBUTION. In dimension $n > 3$, Ladyzhenskaia's method fails, as the operator $\mathbf{Au}$ can no longer be shown to be completely continuous in $\mathscr{H}$. Shinbrot [**18**] has extended the result to $n = 4$ by showing that a weaker property of $\mathbf{Au}$ suffices. His reasoning is based on the following fixed point theorem: *Let* $\mathbf{H}$ *be an operator on the separable Hilbert space* $\mathscr{H}$, *continuous in the weak topology on* $\mathscr{H}$. *If there is a positive constant r such that*

$$\mathrm{Re}\,(\mathbf{Hx}, \mathbf{x}) \leqq \|\mathbf{x}\|^2$$

for all $\mathbf{x}$ *on the surface* $S_r: \|\mathbf{x}\| = r$, *then* $\mathbf{H}$ *has a fixed point in the ball* $B_r: \|\mathbf{x}\| \leqq r$.

The following corollary is immediate: *Let* $\mathbf{Q}$ *be an operator on* $\mathscr{H}$, *continuous in the weak topology. Then, zero is in the range of* $\mathbf{Q}$ *if* $(\mathbf{Qx}, \mathbf{x})$ *is of one sign on some sphere* S_r.

In the present case, set $\mathbf{Qu} \equiv \mathbf{Au} + \mathbf{u}$. According to the lemma of §2.3, the field $\mathbf{a}(x)$ can be chosen so that if $\mathbf{u} \in \mathscr{H}$, then $|\{\mathbf{a}, \mathbf{u}, \mathbf{u}\}_{\mathscr{G}}| \leqq \varepsilon\|\mathbf{u}\|_{\mathscr{G}}^2$ for any prescribed $\varepsilon > 0$. By choosing $\varepsilon < 1$, one then obtains $[\mathbf{Qu}, \mathbf{u}] > 0$ on a sufficiently large sphere. Further, if $\mathbf{u}$ is bounded in $\mathscr{H}$, then by (28) $\mathbf{u}$ is bounded in L_4. The Rellich theorem implies that if $\mathbf{u}_n \to \mathbf{u}$ weakly in $\mathscr{H}$, then (for a subsequence)

$\mathbf{u}_n \to \mathbf{u}$ strongly in L_2, hence $\mathbf{u}_n \to \mathbf{u}$ almost everywhere in $\mathscr{G}$. Hence $\{\mathbf{u}_n, \mathbf{u}_n, \mathbf{\Phi}\} \to \{\mathbf{u}, \mathbf{u}, \mathbf{\Phi}\}$ for any $\mathbf{\Phi} \in \mathscr{H}$. The corresponding property is evident for all other terms in $\mathbf{Q}$, which implies continuity in the weak topology. Shinbrot then concludes from his corollary the existence of $\mathbf{u}(x) \in \mathscr{H}$ such that $\mathbf{Qu} = 0$. The function $\mathbf{w}(x) = \mathbf{u}(x) + \mathbf{a}(x)$ is the desired generalized solution.

Still another demonstration in the case $n = 4$, along similar lines, has been obtained in unpublished work of Leray and Lions [**19**], using the theory of monotone operators.

2.7. Fujita's contribution. Another modification of Leray's approach is due to H. Fujita [**20**], who demonstrated the existence of stationary solutions by Galerkin's method. The method had previously been used for the study of time dependent motion by E. Hopf [**21**] and by Kiselev and Ladyzhenskaia [**22**], but its application to the present problem requires somewhat different technique. The idea is to seek first an "approximate solution" in the manifold $\mathscr{M}(N)$ spanned by the first N of a complete set $\{\boldsymbol{\psi}^j\}$ of solenoidal vector functions over $\mathscr{G}$. This is a finite dimensional problem; its solution, if properly effected, leads to a priori bounds which permit the limiting transition as $N \to \infty$. The method as presented in [**20**] fails in dimension $n > 4$; however, the very slight modification given below permits the demonstration of existence of a generalized solution for any finite n.

A solenoidal field $\mathbf{w}(x)$ will be called a generalized solution of (3) if (α) there exists a smooth solenoidal field $\mathbf{a}(x)$ in $\mathscr{G}$ such that $\mathbf{a}(x) = \mathbf{w}^*$ on Σ and $\mathbf{w}(x) - \mathbf{a}(x) = \mathbf{u}(x) \in \mathscr{H}$ in $\mathscr{G}$, and (β) the equation

$$(31) \qquad \int_{\mathscr{G}} \{\nu \nabla \mathbf{w} \cdot - \mathbf{w} \cdot \mathbf{w} \cdot\} \nabla \mathbf{\Phi}\, dx = \int_{\mathscr{G}} \mathbf{f} \cdot \mathbf{\Phi}\, dx$$

is satisfied for every solenoidal field $\mathbf{\Phi}(x) \in \mathscr{J}$ in $\mathscr{G}$. Note that this definition differs from the one given in §2.5 in that (31) is now required to hold only for $\mathbf{\Phi}(x) \in \mathscr{J}$, rather than for all $\mathbf{\Phi}(x) \in \mathscr{H}$. Sobolev's inequalities imply that the two definitions are equivalent if $n \leqq 4$; if $n > 4$ the equivalence fails, as the integral of the nonlinear term is no longer known to exist for all $\mathbf{w}$, $\mathbf{\Phi} \in \mathscr{H}$.

It is not hard to show the existence of a family $\{\boldsymbol{\psi}^j(x)\}$ of vector functions in $\mathscr{J}$ which are complete in $\mathscr{H}$ and which have the additional property that any function in $\mathscr{J}$ can be approximated uniformly together with its first derivatives in $\mathscr{G}$ by linear combinations of the $\{\boldsymbol{\psi}^j\}$. We may assume the $\{\boldsymbol{\psi}^i\}$ satisfy $(\boldsymbol{\psi}^i, \boldsymbol{\psi}^j) = \delta_{ij}$.

An "approximate solution"

$$(32) \qquad \mathbf{w}_N = \mathbf{a} + \mathbf{u}_N = \mathbf{a} + \sum_1^N \alpha_i \boldsymbol{\psi}^i$$

is to be determined by the conditions

$$(33) \qquad \nu[\mathbf{w}_N, \boldsymbol{\psi}^i] + \{\boldsymbol{\psi}^i, \mathbf{w}_N, \mathbf{w}_N\} = (\boldsymbol{\psi}^i, \mathbf{f})$$

for each $i = 1, \cdots, N$. Substitution of (32) into (33) yields a system

$$(34) \qquad T(\alpha)\alpha = \eta$$

of N equations in N unknowns $(\alpha_1, \cdots, \alpha_N) = \alpha$. Here $T(\alpha)$ denotes an $N \times N$ matrix whose elements are

$$T_{ij}(\alpha) = [\boldsymbol{\psi}^i, \boldsymbol{\psi}^j] + \{\boldsymbol{\psi}^i, \mathbf{a}, \boldsymbol{\psi}^j\} + \{\boldsymbol{\psi}^i, \boldsymbol{\psi}^j, \mathbf{a}\} + \left\{\boldsymbol{\psi}^i, \sum_1^N \alpha_k \boldsymbol{\psi}^k, \boldsymbol{\psi}^j\right\}$$

and $\eta = (\eta_1, \cdots, \eta_N)$ is known.

Let $\mathbf{v} = \sum_1^N \beta_i \boldsymbol{\psi}^i$ be arbitrary in $\mathscr{M}(N)$. One finds

$$\beta \cdot T(\alpha)\beta = \nu \|\mathbf{v}\|^2_{\mathscr{H}} - \{\mathbf{a}, \mathbf{v}, \mathbf{v}\}, \tag{35}$$

all other terms vanishing when the integrations are carried out. By the lemma of §2.3, we may choose $\mathbf{a}(x)$ so that

$$\beta \cdot T(\alpha)\beta \geqq \tfrac{1}{2}\nu \|\mathbf{v}\|^2_{\mathscr{H}}.$$

Then, since $|\beta| = (\mathbf{v}, \mathbf{v})^{1/2} \leqq C\|\mathbf{v}\|$ for some $C(\mathscr{G})$, we obtain the inequality, uniform in α,

$$|T(\alpha)\beta| \geqq \frac{\nu}{2C^2} |\beta|. \tag{36}$$

From (36) follows that T^{-1} exists, and $|T^{-1}| \leqq 2C^2/\nu$. The equation (34) can therefore be written

$$\alpha = T^{-1}(\alpha)\eta = F(\alpha) \tag{37}$$

and since η is fixed, $F(\alpha) \leqq 2C^2|\eta|/\nu = \delta$. In particular, the closed sphere $|\alpha| \leqq \delta$ is mapped by F into itself. Brouwer's fixed point theorem then implies the existence of a solution of (37), that is, of an "approximate solution" $\mathbf{w}_N(x) = \mathbf{a}(x) + \mathbf{u}_N(x)$, with $\mathbf{u}_N(x) \in \mathscr{M}(N)$.

We now wish to let $N \to \infty$. The functions $\{\mathbf{u}_N\}$ remain bounded in $\mathscr{H}$, as one sees by replacing $\boldsymbol{\psi}^i$ in (33) by $\mathbf{u}_N(x) = \sum_1^N \alpha_i \boldsymbol{\psi}^i$ and again applying the lemma of §2.3. Thus, by the Rellich choice theorem, a subsequence will converge strongly in $L_2(\mathscr{G})$ and weakly in $\mathscr{H}(\mathscr{G})$ to a limit $\mathbf{u}(x) \in \mathscr{H}$. Let $\mathbf{w}(x) = \mathbf{u}(x) + \mathbf{a}(x)$, let $\boldsymbol{\phi}(x) \in \mathscr{J}$. By the choice of $\{\boldsymbol{\psi}^j\}$, for any $\varepsilon > 0$ there is an $r(\varepsilon)$ and a $\boldsymbol{\phi}^r \in \mathscr{M}(r)$ such that $|\boldsymbol{\phi}(x) - \boldsymbol{\phi}^r(x)| < \varepsilon$ uniformly in $\mathscr{G}$. Keeping r fixed and letting $N \to \infty$, we find (since $\mathbf{w}_N$ is an approximate solution with respect to test functions in $\mathscr{M}(r)$ whenever $N \geqq r$)

$$\nu[\mathbf{w}, \boldsymbol{\phi}^r] + \{\boldsymbol{\phi}^r, \mathbf{w}, \mathbf{w}\} = (\boldsymbol{\phi}^r, \mathbf{f}). \tag{38}$$

Letting $r \to \infty$ in (38) shows that $\mathbf{w}(x)$ is a generalized solution in the indicated sense.

REMARKS. 1. Besides yielding a solution in any dimension n, Fujita's method leads to a somewhat more natural construction of a solution in an exterior domain than do the preceding methods; see §3.5.

2. Note that, as is the case with Leray's original paper, the Sobolev imbedding theorems are not needed in this demonstration.

2.8. REGULARITY OF GENERALIZED SOLUTIONS. *If* $n = 2$ *or* 3, *and if* $\mathbf{f}(x) \in C^{r+\alpha}$, $r \geqq 0$, *then the generalized solution* $\mathbf{w}(x) \in C^{r+2+\alpha}$, $p(x) \in C^{r+1+\alpha}$, *and* $\mathbf{w}(x)$ *is a strict solution of* (3).

The proof consists in showing that $\mathbf{w}(x)$ admits an integral representation such as (24), from which the result follows as in §2.4. We may assume $\nu = 1$. In discussing *interior* regularity it is however unnecessary to introduce a Green's tensor, as a suitable representation can be obtained with a *truncated fundamental solution tensor*. The following demonstration follows Fujita [20] in the case $n = 3$.

The fundamental solution (8) can be represented in the form

$$E_{ij} = \left(\delta_{ij}\Delta - \frac{\partial^2}{\partial x_i\, \partial x_j}\right)\Phi; \qquad P_i = -\frac{\partial}{\partial x_i}\Delta\Phi \tag{39}$$

where $\Phi(x - y) = -|x - y|/8\pi$ (Oseen [4]).

Let $\eta(r) \in C^\infty$, and

$$\eta(r) = \begin{cases} 1, & 0 \leqq r \leqq 1, \\ 0, & r \geqq 2. \end{cases}$$

Choose $\gamma > 0$, set $\Phi^\gamma = \eta(|x - y|/\gamma)\Phi(x - y)$. The truncated tensor $\mathbf{E}^\gamma$, $\mathbf{P}^\gamma$ is defined by (39) with Φ replaced by Φ^γ. Clearly, $\mathbf{E}^\gamma, \mathbf{P}^\gamma \equiv \mathbf{E}, \mathbf{P}$ if $|x - y| < \gamma$, while $\mathbf{E}^\gamma, \mathbf{P}^\gamma \equiv 0$ if $|x - y| > 2\gamma$.

Let $\boldsymbol{\psi} \in C_0^\infty(\mathscr{G})$, define $\mathbf{E}^\gamma\boldsymbol{\psi}$, $\mathbf{P}^\gamma\boldsymbol{\psi}$ by

$$\boldsymbol{\phi}(x) = \int_{\mathscr{G}} \mathbf{E}^\gamma(x - y)\cdot\boldsymbol{\psi}(y)\, dy = \mathbf{E}^\gamma\boldsymbol{\psi},$$

$$\pi(x) = \int_{\mathscr{G}} \mathbf{P}^\gamma(x - y)\cdot\boldsymbol{\psi}(y)\, dy = \mathbf{P}^\gamma\boldsymbol{\psi}.$$

Then if γ is sufficiently small, there will hold $\boldsymbol{\phi}(x), \pi(x) \in \mathscr{J}(\mathscr{G})$. Further,

$$\Delta\boldsymbol{\phi} - \nabla\pi = \boldsymbol{\psi} + \mathbf{H}^\gamma\boldsymbol{\psi}$$

where $\mathbf{H}^\gamma(x - y) \in C^\infty$ and has the same support as $\mathbf{E}^\gamma$. Using $\boldsymbol{\phi}(x)$ as a test function for the weak equation (31) and applying the relations (11), (12) leads to

$$(\boldsymbol{\psi}, \mathbf{w}) = (\boldsymbol{\psi}, \mathbf{E}^\gamma\mathbf{w}\cdot\nabla\mathbf{w} - \mathbf{E}^\gamma\mathbf{f} + \mathbf{H}^\gamma\mathbf{w}).$$

Since this holds for *arbitrary* (not necessarily solenoidal) $\boldsymbol{\psi}(x)$ whose support has distance $\geqq 2\gamma$ from Σ, we conclude

$$\mathbf{w}(x) = \int_{\mathscr{G}} \mathbf{E}^\gamma\cdot\mathbf{w}\cdot\nabla\mathbf{w}\, dy - \int_{\mathscr{G}} \mathbf{E}^\gamma\cdot\mathbf{f}\, dy + \int_{\mathscr{G}} \mathbf{H}^\gamma\cdot\mathbf{w}\, dy \tag{40}$$

for almost all x of distance $\geqq 2\gamma$ from Σ.

If $\mathbf{f} \in C^{0+\alpha}$, the remainder of the proof follows the discussion in §2.4. If $\mathbf{f}$ has better regularity properties, correspondingly improved properties of $\mathbf{w}(x)$ are obtained by repeated use of the representation (40); cf. Fujita [20, p. 79].

If Σ and $\mathbf{w}^*$ are smooth, then the solution $\mathbf{w}(x)$ is correspondingly smooth up to Σ and achieves the prescribed data. This can be proved, as in §2.4, with the aid of Odqvist's estimates (20) for the Green's tensor. No other demonstrations have been given.

Note that the method yields as a corollary the following a priori estimate: *If* $\mathbf{w}(x)$ *is a solution and* $|\mathbf{w}| < M$ *in* $\mathcal{G}$, *then all derivatives of* $\mathbf{w}$ *are bounded in* $\mathcal{G}$, *depending only on* M, *on* $\mathbf{f}$, *and on distance to* Σ.[7]

The above results hold without change if $n = 2$; however, if $n > 3$ nothing is known about regularity of generalized solutions.

2.9. UNIQUENESS; VELTE'S RESULT. *If* ν *is sufficiently large* (*depending on* $\mathbf{w}^*$ *and on* $\mathcal{G}$), *the solution is unique.* This is easily proved by a standard reasoning (see, e.g., [**11**, p. 241]), and I shall not repeat the details here.[8] It has long been thought that as ν decreases the solution will bifurcate and that multiple solutions will appear. Such multiplicities have been indicated by linearizations in special cases, and also observed experimentally (e.g., Taylor instability [**23**, p. 502]). Recently W. Velte in a striking paper [**24**] has proved the existence of multiple solutions for a system of equations closely related to (3).

The problem considered is that of stationary flow in a horizontal cylinder of circular (or square) cross section, with flow components w (along the tube), u, v independent of the coordinate z directed along the tube. The fluid is under the influence of gravity, and the surface of the tube is subject to an externally applied temperature, depending only on y (height). If Θ denotes normalized temperature, and $F(x, y)$ the stream function, $F_y = u$, $F_x = -v$, the flow is described by the system

$$\Delta\Delta F = \frac{\partial(\Delta F, F)}{\partial(x, y)} + Gr\,\frac{\partial\Theta}{\partial x},$$

$$(41)\qquad (Pr)^{-1}\Delta\Theta = \frac{\partial(\Theta, F)}{\partial(x, y)},$$

$$\Delta w = \frac{\partial(w, F)}{\partial(x, y)} + \frac{\partial p}{\partial x}$$

which is equivalent to the Navier-Stokes equations for this case if $\Theta = \text{const.}$ Here Gr, Pr are constants depending on physical parameters.

Let $\mathbf{T}(\mathbf{u})$ denote a completely continuous operator in a Banach space, and let $\mathbf{u}_0$ be an *isolated solution* of the functional equation

$$(42)\qquad \mathbf{\Phi}(\mathbf{u}) = \mathbf{u} - \mathbf{T}(\mathbf{u}) = 0.$$

The *index* of the solution $\mathbf{u}_0$ is defined as the degree (at 0) of the restriction of $\mathbf{\Phi}(\mathbf{u})$ to a neighborhood of $\mathbf{u}_0$ containing no other solutions of (42) (see footnote 5).

---

[7] It suffices to know that $\mathbf{w}(x)$ is bounded in $L_{6+\varepsilon}$ for some $\varepsilon > 0$. A problem suggested by physical intuition is to bound the derivatives of $\mathbf{w}(x)$ in terms of the kinetic energy of disturbance from the rest position, that is, in terms of $\int_{\mathcal{G}} |\mathbf{w}|^2\,dx$. This result is easily proved if $n = 2$, but if $n \geq 3$ no information is available. The problem is intimately connected with an essential difficulty which has occurred in attempts to prove an existence theorem "in the large" for time dependent motions.

[8] *Added in proof.* After this paper was submitted I learned of a recent work by L. E. Payne in which an explicit sufficiency criterion for uniqueness is given (Univ. of Maryland Tech. Note BN-374, 1964).

Suppose $\mathbf{T}(\mathbf{u})$ admits a Frechet differential $\mathbf{A}(\mathbf{u}_0; \mathbf{v})$ at $\mathbf{u} = \mathbf{u}_0$; that is, suppose there is a linear homogeneous operator $\mathbf{A}(\mathbf{u}_0; \mathbf{v})$ such that

$$\mathbf{T}(\mathbf{u}_0 + \mathbf{v}) - \mathbf{T}(\mathbf{u}_0) = \mathbf{A}(\mathbf{u}_0; \mathbf{v}) + \mathbf{R}(\mathbf{u}_0; \mathbf{v})$$

where $\|\mathbf{R}(\mathbf{u}_0; \mathbf{v})\|/\|\mathbf{v}\| \to 0$ as $\|\mathbf{v}\| \to 0$. Suppose further that the linear mapping $\mathbf{w} = \mathbf{v} - \mathbf{A}(\mathbf{u}_0; \mathbf{v})$ is 1-1. Then if $\mathbf{u}_0$ satisfies (42), it is necessarily an isolated solution; further, its index is either $+1$ or -1, and is equal to the index of the solution $\mathbf{v} = 0$ of the linear mapping.

In the present case, if the prescribed temperature $\Theta^* = 1 - y$, then (41) admits the solution $F_0 \equiv 0$, $\Theta_0 \equiv 1 - y$, and $w_0 \equiv$ Poiseuille flow, for any values of the parameters Pr, Gr.

Writing $F = F_0 + f(x, y)$, $\Theta = \Theta_0 + \theta(x, y)$, one is led to the system

$$\begin{aligned} \Delta\Delta f &= \frac{\partial(\Delta f, f)}{\partial(x, y)} + Pr\, Gr\, \theta_x, \\ \Delta\theta &= Pr \frac{\partial(\theta, f)}{\partial(x, y)} + f_x, \\ \theta &= f = 0 \quad \text{on } \Sigma \end{aligned} \tag{43}$$

for a nonlinear perturbation (θ, f). If on the left side of (43) θ and f are replaced by quantities θ', f', also to vanish on Σ, then (43) defines a mapping $\mathbf{T}$ from (θ, f) to (θ', f'). A perturbed stationary solution of (41) will exist if and only if $\mathbf{T}$ admits a nonzero fixed point, i.e., if and only if there is a solution of the functional equation

$$\mathbf{\Phi}(\mathbf{u}) \equiv \mathbf{u} - \mathbf{T}(\mathbf{u}) = 0, \qquad \mathbf{u} = (\theta, f)$$

with $\mathbf{u} \not\equiv 0$.

Linearizing (43) leads to the system

$$\begin{aligned} \Delta\Delta f &= \lambda\theta_x, \\ \Delta\theta &= f_x, \qquad \lambda = Pr\, Gr, \\ \theta &= f = 0 \quad \text{on } \Sigma \end{aligned} \tag{44}$$

which permits, as above, the definition of a mapping

$$\mathbf{A}(\mathbf{u}; \lambda){:}\quad (\theta, f) \to (\theta'', f'').$$

$\mathbf{A}(\mathbf{u}; \lambda)$ *is the Frechet differential of* $\mathbf{T}(\mathbf{u})$ *at the point* $\mathbf{u} = (\theta, f) = 0$.

Velte shows that the eigenvalues $\{\lambda_\nu\}$ of $\mathbf{A}(\mathbf{u}; \lambda)$ are positive and discrete, furthermore the smallest eigenvalue λ_1 is, for a circular or square cross section, simple. If λ is not an eigenvalue, then $\mathbf{u} = 0$ is by the above remarks a solution of (42) with index equal to that of $\mathbf{u} - \mathbf{A}(\mathbf{u}; \lambda)$. This latter mapping evidently has index $+1$ if $\lambda < \lambda_0$. To study what happens as λ increases past λ_0, set $\theta = \lambda^{-1/2}\varphi$ in (44), leading to the equations

$$\begin{aligned} \Delta\Delta f'' &= \lambda^{1/2}\varphi_x, \\ \Delta\varphi'' &= \lambda^{1/2} f_x, \\ \varphi'' &= f'' = 0 \quad \text{on } \Sigma \end{aligned} \tag{45}$$

and a new transformation

$$\bar{\mathbf{A}}(\bar{\mathbf{u}}; \lambda) = \lambda^{1/2}\bar{\mathbf{A}}(\bar{\mathbf{u}}; 1)$$

of $\bar{\mathbf{u}} = (\varphi, f)$. Evidently the eigenvalues for $\mathbf{A}$ and for $\bar{\mathbf{A}}$ coincide, and so do the indexes at the corresponding eigenfunctions. But $\bar{\mathbf{A}}$ is linear in $\bar{\mathbf{u}}$ and homogeneous in λ, hence the index of $\bar{\mathbf{u}} - \lambda^{1/2}\bar{\mathbf{A}}(\bar{\mathbf{u}}; 1)$ changes by the factor (-1) as λ crosses the (simple) eigenvalue λ_1. This is therefore the case also for $\mathbf{u} - \mathbf{A}(\mathbf{u}; \lambda)$, hence also for $\mathbf{\Phi}(\mathbf{u})$ at the (isolated) solution $\mathbf{u} = 0$.

On the other hand, Leray's bound on Dirichlet integral shows that the domain of $\mathbf{\Phi}(\mathbf{u})$ can be defined in such a way that as λ increases from 0 to $\lambda_1^+ > \lambda_1$, there will be no solutions on the boundary, and hence the degree at 0 does not change. The degree $= +1$ if $\lambda = 0$, hence it is $+1$ also at $\lambda = \lambda_1^+$. But the index of the isolated solution $\mathbf{u} = 0$ was just shown to be -1 if $\lambda_1 < \lambda_1^+ < \lambda_2$. Hence there must be other solutions $\mathbf{u} \not\equiv 0$ of (42), Q.E.D.

Velte showed also that all solutions converge together in norm as $\lambda_1^+ \to \lambda_1$.

3. **The exterior problem.** A whole new spectrum of difficulties appears if solutions of (3) are sought in the domain exterior to a bounded closed surface Σ. In this case one must impose a boundary condition at infinity; the one which arises naturally in physical considerations is the requirement $\mathbf{w} \to \mathbf{w}_0 \equiv$ const. On Σ, one prescribes again $\mathbf{w} = \mathbf{w}^*$ under the condition[9] (7).

In contrast to the interior problem, significant differences appear in the structure of the theory for $n = 2$ or $n = 3$, the two-dimensional theory being decidedly the more difficult. The difficulty is encountered immediately in the "Stokes paradox," [**25**], according to which the corresponding problem for the linearized system $(6)_0$ in general admits no solution if $n = 2$. A clarification of this behavior has been given by Chang and Finn [**8**]. The material that follows, except where specially noted, refers to the case $n = 3$. I shall assume throughout that $\nu = 1$. This can always be achieved by a similarity transformation.

Analogous to (39) we may introduce a fundamental tensor $\mathscr{E}(x - y)$ for the linearized system $(5)_0$ by the relations

$$\begin{aligned} \mathscr{E}_{ij} &= \left(\delta_{ij}\Delta - \frac{\partial^2}{\partial x_i \partial x_j}\right)\mathscr{O}, \\ \mathscr{P}_j &= -\frac{\partial}{\partial x_j}(\Delta - 2\mathbf{w}_0 \cdot \nabla)\mathscr{O}, \\ \mathscr{O} &= -\frac{1}{8\pi\sigma}\int_0^{\sigma s} \frac{1 - e^{-\alpha}}{\alpha}\, d\alpha, \\ \sigma &= \frac{|\mathbf{w}_0|}{2}; \qquad s = r_{xy} + \frac{\mathbf{w}_0 \cdot (y - x)}{|\mathbf{w}_0|} \end{aligned} \tag{46}$$

(Oseen [**4**, p. 31]). The local properties of $\mathscr{E}$ at the singular point are the same as those of $\mathbf{E}(x - y)$. There are however important differences in asymptotic behavior; these will be developed as needed in the context.

[9] It is not clear whether this condition is necessary. For small data in three dimensions it can be deleted (Finn [**11**, p. 228]).

We shall need also the truncated tensor $\mathscr{E}^\gamma(x-y)$. The definition is formally the same as that given for $\mathbf{E}^\gamma$ in §2.8.

3.1. SOLUTIONS WITH FINITE DIRICHLET INTEGRAL. Let $\mathscr{E}$ be the exterior of Σ and let[10] $\mathbf{f}(x) \in L_2(\mathscr{E})$. *Let* $\mathbf{w}(x)$ *be a solution of* (3) *in* $\mathscr{E}$ *such that*

$$\int_{\mathscr{E}} |\nabla \mathbf{w}|^2\,dx < \infty. \tag{47}$$

Then there is a vector $\mathbf{w}_0$ *such that* $\mathbf{w}(x) \to \mathbf{w}_0$ *as* $x \to \infty$.

The following demonstration simplifies considerably the ones I gave in **[27]** and in **[11]**. It is based, as were the others, on a lemma of Payne and Weinberger **[28]**: *Let* $\mathbf{w}(x)$ *be a continuous vector field on and exterior to a sphere* Σ_R, *and suppose* $|\nabla \mathbf{w}(x)| \in L_2$ *in the exterior* $\mathscr{E}_R$ *of* Σ_R. *Then there is a vector* $\mathbf{w}_0$ *such that*

$$\frac{1}{R}\oint_{\Sigma_R} |\mathbf{w}-\mathbf{w}_0|^2\,d\sigma \leqq \int_{\mathscr{E}_R} |\nabla \mathbf{w}|^2\,dx. \tag{48}$$

Given $\mathbf{w}(x)$ in the indicated class, choose $\mathbf{w}_0$ as in the lemma, and consider the identity

$$\int_{\mathscr{E}_R} |\mathbf{w}-\mathbf{w}_0|^2 \Delta \log r_{xy}\,dy = -\int_{\mathscr{E}_R} \nabla(\mathbf{w}-\mathbf{w}_0)^2 \cdot \nabla \log r_{xy}\,dy + \int_{\Sigma_R} |\mathbf{w}-\mathbf{w}_0|^2 \frac{\partial \log r_{xy}}{dn}\,d\sigma$$

for a point x such that $|x| \geqq 2R$. (The outer surface integral vanishes in the limit because of (48).) Applying (48) again and also the inequality $2ab \leqq \varepsilon a^2 + \varepsilon^{-1} b^2$ for any $\varepsilon > 0$, we are led to the estimate

$$\int_{\mathscr{E}_R} \frac{|\mathbf{w}-\mathbf{w}_0|^2}{r_{xy}^2}\,dy \leqq \kappa \int_{\mathscr{E}_R} |\nabla \mathbf{w}|^2\,dy \tag{49}$$

where we may choose $\kappa = (1+\sqrt{2})^2 < 6$.

Set $\mathbf{u}(x) = \mathbf{w}(x) - \mathbf{w}_0$, where $\mathbf{w}(x)$ is the indicated solution in $\mathscr{E}$, and $\mathbf{w}_0$ is chosen as above. For any fixed $\gamma < R$ (say, $\gamma = 1$) we may represent $\mathbf{u}(x)$ by the truncated tensor $\mathscr{E}^\gamma(x-y)$:

$$\mathbf{u}(x) = \int_V \mathscr{E}^\gamma \cdot \mathbf{u} \cdot \nabla \mathbf{u}\,dy - \int_V \mathscr{E}^\gamma \cdot \mathbf{f}\,dy + \int \mathscr{H}^\gamma \cdot \mathbf{u}\,dy \tag{50}$$

where V is a sphere of radius 2γ and $\mathscr{H}^\gamma \in C^\infty$ in V. There follows immediately, by Schwarz' inequality and by (49),

$$|\mathbf{u}(x)|^2 \leqq C \int_{\mathscr{E}_R} |\nabla \mathbf{w}|^2\,dy + C \int_V \mathbf{f}^2\,dy \tag{51}$$

for a fixed constant C, and hence $\mathbf{w}(x) \to \mathbf{w}_0$ as $x \to \infty$, which was to be proved.[11]

---

[10] It will be evident from the proof that the requirement on $\mathbf{f}(x)$ can be weakened in various ways.

[11] The demonstration could have been carried out with the simpler tensor $\mathbf{E}^\gamma$ defined in (39). It would then have been necessary to add an extra term in (50), and the resulting estimate (51) on decay of $\mathbf{u}(x)$ in terms of Dirichlet integral would have been somewhat weaker.

If $\mathbf{f}(x)$ is locally Hölder continuous, uniformly in $\mathscr{E}$, then the derivatives of $\mathbf{w}(x)$ up to second order tend to zero at infinity, and one concludes from the equation that $p = o(r)$. Actually, under a slightly stronger assumption on $\mathbf{f}(x)$, $p(x)$ tends to a limit, as follows by using this estimate in conjunction with the following considerations.

In the annular region $\mathscr{E}_R$ bounded by Σ and by a sphere Σ_R of (large) radius R, we have for the indicated solution $\mathbf{w}(x)$ in $\mathscr{E}$,

$$\mathbf{w}(x) = \mathbf{w}_0 + \oint_{\Sigma+\Sigma_R} [\mathbf{u}\cdot\mathbf{T}\mathscr{E} - \mathscr{E}\cdot\mathbf{Tu} + (\mathscr{E}\cdot\mathbf{u})\mathbf{w}_0]\, d\sigma + \int_{\mathscr{E}_R} \mathscr{E}\cdot\mathbf{u}\cdot\nabla\mathbf{u}\, dy + \int_{\mathscr{E}_R} \mathscr{E}\cdot\mathbf{f}\, dy. \tag{52}$$

Suppose $|x|^\beta\mathbf{f}(x) \in L_2(\mathscr{E})$ for some $\beta > \frac{1}{2}$, or else that $\mathbf{f}(x) = \mathbf{g}(x)\cdot\nabla\mathbf{g}(x)$, with $|\nabla\mathbf{g}| \in L_2(\mathscr{E})$ and $\mathbf{g}(x) \to 0$ as $x \to \infty$. Simple estimates show that the two volume integrals, extended over all of $\mathscr{E}$, converge absolutely and $\to 0$ as $x \to \infty$. A consequence of the former fact is that the outer surface integral tends to a finite limit,

$$\mathbf{F}(x) = \lim_{R\to\infty} \oint_{\Sigma_R} [\mathbf{u}\cdot\mathbf{T}\mathscr{E} - \mathscr{E}\cdot\mathbf{Tu} + (\mathscr{E}\cdot\mathbf{u})\mathbf{w}_0]\, d\sigma \tag{53}$$

as $R \to \infty$. The inner surface integral $\to 0$ as $x \to \infty$ since $\mathscr{E}$, $\mathbf{T}\mathscr{E}$ both $\to 0$. Thus, since $\mathbf{u}(x) \to 0$, we have $\mathbf{F}(x) \to 0$ as $x \to \infty$. Formal estimation of $\mathscr{E}$ and use of (48) shows that all terms in the outer integral vanish in the limit, with the possible exception of the one involving $\mathbf{Tu}$, for which only the estimate $|\mathbf{Tu}| = o(r)$ is known. However, the rate of decay of $\mathscr{E}(x)$ at infinity increases if it is differentiated. Although (53) cannot be differentiated under the sign, it is possible to take difference quotients, and these lead to the same rate of decay at infinity. For a sufficiently large N, if $\mathscr{E}(x)$ in (53) is replaced by the result $\delta^{(N)}\mathscr{E}$ of taking N fixed differences in arbitrary directions, one finds that the corresponding difference quotient $\delta^{(N)}\mathbf{F}(x) \equiv 0$ in x. One concludes that $\mathbf{F}(x)$ is a polynomial in x_1, x_2, x_3. But since $\lim_{x\to\infty} \mathbf{F}(x) = 0$, there must hold $\mathbf{F}(x) \equiv 0$ in $\mathscr{E}$.

Summarizing: *Let* $\mathbf{w}(x)$ *be a solution of* (3) *in* $\mathscr{E} + \Sigma$, *satisfying* (47). *Suppose either* (i) $x^\beta\mathbf{f}(x) \in L_2(\mathscr{E})$ *for some* $\beta > \frac{1}{2}$, *or* (ii) $\mathbf{f}(x) = \mathbf{g}(x)\cdot\nabla\mathbf{g}(x)$, *where* $|\nabla\mathbf{g}(x)| \in L_2$ *and* $\mathbf{g}(x) \to 0$ *as* $x \to \infty$ (see footnote 9). *Suppose further that* $\mathbf{f}(x)$ *is locally Hölder continuous, uniformly in* $\mathscr{E}$. *Then there is a constant vector* $\mathbf{w}_0$ *such that*

$$\mathbf{w}(x) = \mathbf{w}_0 + \oint_\Sigma [\mathbf{u}\cdot\mathbf{T}\mathscr{E} - \mathscr{E}\cdot\mathbf{Tu} + (\mathscr{E}\cdot\mathbf{u})\mathbf{w}_0]\, d\sigma + \int_{\mathscr{E}} \mathscr{E}\cdot(\mathbf{u}\cdot\nabla\mathbf{u} - \mathbf{f})\, dy \tag{54}$$

and $\mathbf{w} \to \mathbf{w}_0$ *at infinity* (Finn **[27]**, **[11]**). A similar representation can be found for the pressure $p(x)$, from which one concludes that $p(x) \to p_0$ at infinity.

3.2. SOLUTIONS CONTINUOUS AT INFINITY. *Suppose* $\mathbf{w}(x)$ *satisfies* (3) *for some* $\mathbf{f}(x) \in L_\beta(\mathscr{E})$, $\beta > 2$ (see footnote 9) *and suppose* $\mathbf{w}(x) \to \mathbf{w}_0$ *as* $x \to \infty$. *Then* $\nabla\mathbf{w}(x) \to 0$ *as* $x \to \infty$ (Finn **[12]**). Note that the assumption (47) is not used. My original proof was rather complicated; however, the result can be obtained easily from (50). It is only necessary to observe that

$$\int_V \mathscr{E}^\gamma \cdot \mathbf{u} \cdot \nabla \mathbf{u}\, dy = - \int_V \mathbf{u} \cdot \mathbf{u} \cdot \nabla \mathscr{E}^\gamma\, dy \tag{55}$$

on account of the solenoidal property of the entering vectors. Under appropriate additional assumptions on $\mathbf{f}(x)$, one can show that all derivatives of $\mathbf{w}(x)$ of arbitrary orders tend to zero.

Suppose, for simplicity, $\mathbf{f}(x) = 0$ (see footnote 9), and let

$$m(\rho) = \max_{|x| = \rho} |\mathbf{w}(x) - \mathbf{w}_0|.$$

Suppose $m(\rho) \to 0$, and that

$$\int^\infty \frac{m^2(\rho)}{\rho}\, d\rho < \infty. \tag{56}$$

Then $\mathbf{w}(x)$ *admits the representation* (54), *and an analogous formula holds for* $p(x)$ (Finn [**12**]). The idea of the proof is similar to that which led to (54), but there are differences in detail.

Other representations are also given in [**12**], which hold under still weaker hypotheses on the solution. A particular consequence is that whenever $\mathbf{w}(x) \to \mathbf{w}_0$, then $p(x) = O(\log r)$. It is an open question whether there exist solutions which are continuous at infinity, for which (47) does not hold.

3.3. SOLUTIONS OF CLASS *PR*. I shall assume in what follows that $\mathbf{f}(x)$ arises from a potential (see footnote 9). A solution $\mathbf{w}(x)$ in $\mathscr{E}$ will be said to be of class *PR* (physically reasonable) if there is an $\varepsilon > 0$ and a vector $\mathbf{w}_0$ such that $|\mathbf{w}(x) - \mathbf{w}_0| < Cr^{-1/2-\varepsilon}$ as $r \to \infty$. The behavior of any such solution is controlled at infinity by that of the fundamental tensor $\mathscr{E}(x - y)$ associated with the linearized system (5). *Precisely,*

$$\mathbf{w}(x) = \mathbf{w}_0 + \mathbf{a} \cdot \mathscr{E}(x) + b\nabla\left(\frac{1}{r}\right) + \text{smaller order terms} \tag{57}$$

for some constant vector $\mathbf{a}$ *and scalar* b, *and any* $\delta > 0$. *In particular, there is a paraboloidal "wake region" in the direction of* $\mathbf{w}_0$, *interior to which* $|\mathbf{w} - \mathbf{w}_0| = O(r^{-1})$. *Letting* φ *denote polar angle with respect to this direction, one has* $|\mathbf{w} - \mathbf{w}_0| = O(r^{-1-2\sigma})$ *on the surface* $|\varphi| = r^{-1/2+\sigma}$, $0 \leqq \sigma \leqq \frac{1}{2}$. *Outside any circular cone with axis* $\varphi = 0$, $|\mathbf{w} - \mathbf{w}_0| = O(r^{-2})$ (Finn [**12**], [**41**]). Similar estimates can be obtained for $\nabla\mathbf{w}$ and for $p(x)$. The proof uses potential-theoretic methods and requires a somewhat painstaking estimation of $\mathbf{w}(x)$, starting with a modified form of the representation (54).

This result leads to a series of consequences. For example (cf. Finn [**12**], [**41**]): *Let* $\mathbf{w}(x)$ *satisfy* $(3)_0$ *in* $\mathscr{E}$. *Suppose* $\mathbf{w}(x) = 0$ *on* Σ *and* $\mathbf{w}(x) \in PR$ *at infinity. Let* $\mathscr{F}$ *denote the force exerted on* Σ *by the flow. Then*

$$\mathbf{w}_0 \cdot \mathscr{F} = \int_{\mathscr{E}} (\mathbf{def}\ \mathbf{w})^2\, dx. \tag{58}$$

In particular, the component of $\mathscr{F}$ *in the direction of* $\mathbf{w}_0$ *is positive, that is, the fluid exerts a "drag" on* Σ, *unless* $\mathbf{w} \equiv 0$ *in* $\mathscr{E}$.

Let $\mathbf{w}(x)$ *satisfy* $(3)_0$ *in* $\mathscr{E}$. *Suppose* $\mathbf{w}(x) = 0$ *on* Σ, *and* $|\mathbf{w}(x) - \mathbf{w}_0| = o(r^{-1})$ *at infinity. Then* $\mathbf{w}(x) \equiv 0$ *in* $\mathscr{E}$.[12]

Let $\mathbf{w}(x)$ *satisfy* $(3)_0$ *throughout three-dimensional Euclidean space, and suppose* $\mathbf{w}(x) \in PR$ *at infinity. Then* $\mathbf{w}(x) \equiv \mathbf{w}_0$.

3.4. KINETIC ENERGY = INFINITY. *Suppose* $\mathbf{w}(x)$ *satisfies* $(3)_0$ *in* $\mathscr{E}$ *and remains bounded at infinity. Suppose* $\mathbf{w}(x) = 0$ *on* Σ. *Then the kinetic energy of disturbance from the uniform flow at infinity is infinite, that is,*

$$T \equiv \frac{1}{2}\int_{\mathscr{E}} |\mathbf{w} - \mathbf{w}_0|^2\, dx = \infty \tag{59}$$

for every possible choice of the constant $\mathbf{w}_0$ (Finn **[30]**).

The situation is in striking contrast to the behavior of potential flows, for which not only is $T < \infty$, but for which the flow is even characterized by minimizing T in a suitable class. The formal reason that (59) holds is that it is true for the fundamental tensor $\mathscr{E}(x)$ for any choice of $\mathbf{w}_0$. The rigorous justification of the result in the nonlinear case seems however to require a considerable technical effort. The one I have given uses the representation formula as point of departure and exploits the results of §3.3.

As an immediate corollary one obtains: *Let* $\mathbf{w}(x)$ *be a bounded solution of* $(3)_0$ *in all space, such that* $\int_{\mathscr{E}} |\mathbf{w} - \mathbf{w}_0|^2\, dx < \infty$ *for some* $\mathbf{w}_0$. *Then* $\mathbf{w}(x) \equiv \mathbf{w}_0$.

An analogous result in two dimensions was given by W. Wolibner **[31]**. Important extensions to compressible and time dependent motions have been obtained by A. Krzywicki **[32]**.

3.5. EXISTENCE IN THE CLASS D. By the class D will be meant solutions which satisfy (47) in $\mathscr{E}$. *If* $\mathbf{w}^*$ *satisfies* (7) *and if* $|x| f(x) \in L_2(\mathscr{E})$, *then for any prescribed* $\mathbf{w}_0$ *there is at least one solution* $\mathbf{w}(x)$ *of* (3) *in* $\mathscr{E}$ *such that,* (i) $\mathbf{w}(x) = \mathbf{w}^*(x)$ *on* Σ, (ii) $\mathbf{w}(x) \in D$, (iii) $\mathbf{w}(x) \to \mathbf{w}_0$ *at infinity.*

The existence of a solution satisfying (i) and (ii) was proved by Leray **[9]**, who obtained also (iii) if $\mathbf{w}_0 = 0$, and who proved the relation

$$\int_{\mathscr{E}} \frac{|\mathbf{w} - \mathbf{w}_0|^2}{r_{xy}^2}\, dx < \infty \tag{iii$'$}$$

for any $\mathbf{w}_0$. The result follows from the observation that if data $\mathbf{w}_R^* = \mathbf{w}_0$ (or more generally, any data imposed by a rigid motion) are prescribed on the outer bounding surface Σ_R of an annular domain $\mathscr{E}_R$ between Σ and Σ_R, then the method of §2.3 yields an a priori bound on Dirichlet integral independent of R. Thus, it is possible to consider solutions in an expanding sequence of bounded domains and pass to the limit. A similar procedure was adopted by Ladyzhenskaia **[16]**, **[13]** and by Finn **[11]**. The latter treatment differs somewhat in detail and offers improved a

[12] A theorem of this type was first proved by R. Berker **[29]**, under some additional hypotheses.

priori bounds on the solutions. The method of Fujita [20] avoids this seemingly artificial procedure, as the test functions have a fixed compact support for each N; hence the solution is obtained directly as with a finite region. In an exterior domain it is possible to relax somewhat the condition (7) (Finn [11, p. 228]); it is not known whether (7) can be discarded entirely in this case.

Whichever method one uses, one arrives at a solution $\mathbf{w}(x) \in D$ in $\mathscr{E}$ which satisfies (iii′). The proof of continuity at infinity can then be obtained by adapting the method of §3.1 to this situation.

3.6. Discussion. It is an intriguing question, to determine whether solutions of class D are also in class PR. Beyond the continuity of the solution and vanishing of its derivatives at infinity, no information has been obtained on asymptotic behavior of solutions of class D. It is not known whether the solutions exhibit the physically observed "wake region"; it is not even known whether they satisfy condition (56). The situation is particularly mystifying in view of the following elementary remark (Finn [11, p. 229]): *Let* $\mathbf{w}(x)$ *be any vector function satisfying* (47) *in* $\mathscr{E}$, *such that* $\mathbf{w}(x) \to \mathbf{w}_0$ *at infinity. Then on almost every ray from the origin, there is a constant* C, *such that* $|\mathbf{w}(x) - \mathbf{w}_0| < Cr^{-1/2}$.

One might expect that the additional property of $\mathbf{w}(x)$ being a solution of (3) would suffice to prove that $\mathbf{w}(x) \in PR$. As yet, it has not. Lest the reader be misled into believing the outcome to be evident, it must be pointed out that there is also evidence pointing the other way. In fact, as is shown in §3.3, every solution of class PR has the same asymptotic order of decay as the fundamental tensor $\mathscr{E}(x)$. In dimension $n = 2$, there exist (explicitly known) solutions of class D which decay more slowly than any prescribed power of r, and hence cannot belong to a corresponding class PR (Finn [11, p. 228]).[13]

Another question is that of uniqueness in the class D. No uniqueness theorem has been proved, even for small data (see footnote 13), the best result of this sort being that all solutions are uniformly close together if the data are small (Finn [11, p. 237]; see also §4 of the present paper).

The connection, if any, between physical reality and solutions of class D remains thus an obscure one.

3.7. Solutions of class PR; existence. For simplicity, assume that the external force field arises from a potential, so that it can be absorbed into the pressure term in (3) (see footnote 9). The representation (54) achieves a form in which no derivatives of $\mathbf{w}(x)$ appear in the boundary integral, if the tensor $\mathscr{E}(x - y)$ is replaced by the Green's tensor $\mathscr{G}(x, y)$ for the system (5) in $\mathscr{E}$. The existence of $\mathscr{G}(x, y)$ can be proved, for example, by Fujita's method (§2.7), and the representation formula (54), applied to the solutions of $(5)_0$ shows that all components of $\mathscr{G}(x, y)$ can be assumed to vanish at infinity.

[13] Ladyzhenskaia [13, p. xi] has given a more general form of this example which shows that if $n = 2$ solutions in PR need not be unique, at least if (7) is not imposed.

The form of the representation then yields $\mathbf{w}(x)$ as a solution of the linear system $(5)_0$, plus a nonlinear term in which the solution enters quadratically. If the nonlinear term can be shown to have the same order of decay as $\mathbf{w}(x) - \mathbf{w}_0$ at infinity, this term will map the class of such functions into itself. Because of the quadratic nature of the nonlinearity, if $\mathbf{u}(x) = \mathbf{w} - \mathbf{w}_0$ is small, this should all the more be the case for its image, thus yielding an a priori bound on the mapping. This is the motivating idea behind the following theorem: *If* $\mathbf{u}^* = \mathbf{w}^* - \mathbf{w}_0$, *together with its tangential derivatives on* Σ *up to third order, is sufficiently small, then there exists a solution* $\mathbf{w}(x) \in PR$ *of* (3) *in* $\mathscr{E}$, *such that* $\mathbf{w}(x) = \mathbf{w}^*$ *on* Σ, *and* $\mathbf{w}(x) \to \mathbf{w}_0$ *at infinity* (Finn [33], [**41**]).

In particular, if $\mathbf{w}^* = 0$, there exists a solution in PR for all sufficiently small $\mathbf{w}_0$.

As it turns out, the indicated property of the nonlinear term appearing in (54) is difficult to verify. However, this term can be transformed to a more accessible form. The integral equation considered is then

$$\mathbf{u}(x) = \oint_{\Sigma} \mathbf{u}^* \cdot \mathbf{T}\mathscr{G}\, d\sigma + \int_{\mathscr{E}} \mathbf{u}\cdot\mathbf{u}\cdot \nabla\mathscr{G}\, dy \tag{60}$$

for a solution of $(4)_0$ with $\lambda = 1$.

A solution $\mathbf{u}(x)$ is sought in the class of vector functions satisfying $|\mathbf{u}(x)| = O(r^{-1})$ at infinity. The crucial estimate on which the demonstration depends is

$$\int_{\mathscr{E}} r_{0y}^{-2} |\nabla\mathscr{G}(x, y; \mathbf{w}_0)|\, dy < C r_{0x}^{-1} \tag{61}$$

in $\mathscr{E}$, uniformly in any range $0 \leqq |\mathbf{w}_0| \leqq M < \infty$. Assuming (61), the solution is easily obtained by an explicit formal construction [33], [**41**].

The proof of (61) requires careful estimation of the Green's tensor in $\mathscr{E}$, followed by a painstaking evaluation of the integral. Cursory estimation of orders of magnitude unfortunately does not yield the result, and each step must be performed with care. Although I am now able to give a demonstration which considerably improves the one I originally found, it still would be desirable to find some other way to approach the problem, which (hopefully) would avoid use of the Green's tensor.

3.8. Solutions of class *PR*; uniqueness. *If the data* $\mathbf{u}^*$ *are sufficiently small on* Σ, *then the solution* $\mathbf{w}(x)$ *of the preceding section is unique among all solutions of class PR which achieve the same prescribed data on* Σ *and at infinity* (Finn [33]).

The proof follows standard lines, in that an application of the identity (11) to the equation satisfied by the difference $\boldsymbol{\eta}(x)$ of two solutions leads to an estimation of the Dirichlet integral of $\boldsymbol{\eta}(x)$, from which one concludes that this integral vanishes if one of the solutions is sufficiently small. The estimations are carried out with the aid of the results of §3.3 and the inequality (49).

The method yields, however, no information unless both solutions are known to be of class *PR*.

4. **Flows at low Reynolds' number.** In what sense do solutions of the linear equations $(5)_0$ or $(6)_0$ serve as approximations to those of the strict equations? This is a nonlinear perturbation problem; it turns out that in an interior region $\mathcal{G}$ the perturbation is nonsingular, and for small data (or, equivalently, for a solution $\mathbf{u}(x)$ of $(4)_0$ with fixed data and small λ) the solution of $(4)_0$ can be represented by a convergent expansion in powers of λ. This is precisely the method by which Odqvist proved his existence theorem for (3) (§2.2). A particular consequence is that if $\mathbf{u}(x; \lambda)$ is the solution of $(4)_0$ with data $\mathbf{w}^*$, and $\mathbf{U}(x)$ the solution of $(6)_0$ with the same data, then

$$|\mathbf{u}(x; \lambda) - \mathbf{U}(x)| < C\lambda \tag{62}$$

uniformly in $\mathcal{G}$, as $\lambda \to 0$.

In an exterior domain, there is a choice in the kind of perturbation or class of solutions which is studied, which affects considerably the result obtained. For example, one may vary the boundary data toward an unperturbed velocity at infinity $\mathbf{w}_0$. The perturbation is then effected by a family of solutions $\mathbf{u}(x; \lambda)$ of $(4)_0$ which achieve fixed boundary data and vanish at infinity, and for which $\lambda \to 0$. One may, however, choose to vary also the velocity $\mathbf{w}_0$. If this is done at a rate proportional to λ, one must then require $\mathbf{u}(x; \lambda) \to \mathbf{u}_0 \neq 0$ at infinity. In either case, the result will differ according to the class of solutions in which the perturbation is made. The following table summarizes what occurs under perturbations in the classes D and PR (Finn [**33**], [**41**]).

CASE	FLOW CLASS	LIMITING PERTURBATION	UNIFORM ESTIMATE IN $\mathcal{E}$
1	PR	zero	$\mathbf{u}(x; \lambda) = \mathbf{U}(x) + \sum_1^\infty \mathbf{u}_j(x)\lambda^j$ $\lvert\mathbf{u}(x; \lambda) - \mathbf{U}(x)\rvert < C\lambda r^{-1}$
2	PR	$\mathbf{u}_0 \neq 0$	$\lvert\mathbf{u}(x; \lambda) - \mathbf{U}(x)\rvert$ $< C \min \{\lambda \log \lambda, r^{-1} \log r\}$
3	D	zero	$\lvert\mathbf{u}(x; \lambda) - \mathbf{U}(x)\rvert < C\lambda$ $\lvert\nabla\mathbf{u}(x; \lambda) - \nabla\mathbf{U}(x)\rvert < C(\lambda^2 + \lambda r^{-1/2})$
4	D	$\mathbf{u}_0 \neq 0$	$\lvert\mathbf{u}(x; \lambda) - \mathbf{U}(x)\rvert < C(\lambda + \lambda^{1/2} r^{-1})$ $\lvert\nabla\mathbf{u}(x; \lambda) - \nabla\mathbf{U}(x)\rvert < C(\lambda^2 + \lambda r^{-1/2})$

Note that case 1 is the only one in which an asymptotic expansion is available. The expansion is the one which is used in the proof of existence for solutions $\mathbf{w}(x) \in PR$ in $\mathcal{E}$(§3.7). Case 2 illustrates the nonuniformity in the perturbation, which gives rise to Whitehead's paradox [**4**, p. 163] when $\mathbf{w}_0 = 0$. If $n = 2$, the corresponding nonuniformity leads to the more striking Stokes paradox.

To indicate the method of proof of these results, consider case 4. Letting $\boldsymbol{\eta} = \mathbf{u}(x; \lambda) - \mathbf{U}(x)$, we obtain the representation

$$\boldsymbol{\eta}(x; \lambda) = \oint_\Sigma \mathbf{u}^*(\mathbf{T}\mathscr{G} - \mathbf{T}\mathscr{G}_0)\, d\boldsymbol{\sigma} + \lambda \int_{\mathscr{E}} \mathscr{G}\cdot(\mathbf{u} - \mathbf{u}_0)\cdot \nabla\mathbf{u}\, dy \tag{63}$$

where $\mathscr{G}_0$ is the Green's tensor for $(5)_0$ in $\mathscr{E}$ and $\mathscr{G}$ the corresponding tensor with $\mathbf{w}_0$ replaced by $(\mathbf{w}_0 + \lambda\mathbf{u}_0)$. One demonstrates first the estimate

$$|\mathscr{G}(x, y)| < C\left(\frac{1}{r_{xy}} + \frac{1}{r_{0y}}\frac{1}{r_{0x}}\right)$$

for large x, from which, using (49) and the assumed uniform bound on Dirichlet integral, one is led to the desired estimate for the last term. It remains to estimate the difference in boundary behavior of $\mathscr{G}$ and of $\mathscr{G}_0$. To do so, observe first that if $x \in \Sigma$ the difference $\hat{\mathscr{G}}(x, y) = \mathscr{G} - \mathscr{G}_0$ has Dirichlet integral in y, extended outside a fixed neighborhood of Σ, bounded by const λ. Using the representation (40) (adapted to the linear equations) for spheres of fixed radius, centered at the points of some fixed sphere Σ_0 surrounding Σ, one finds an estimate $|\hat{\mathscr{G}}| < C\lambda^{1/2}$ for y on Σ_0, and a similar estimate for $|\mathbf{T}\hat{\mathscr{G}}|$. Now represent $\hat{\mathscr{G}}$ and the corresponding pressure $\hat{\mathscr{P}}$ in the region $\mathscr{E}_R$ between Σ_0 and Σ_R by means of the fundamental tensor $\mathscr{E}_0$ of $(5)_0$. After differentiation to form $\mathbf{T}\hat{\mathscr{G}}$ one may let $R \to \infty$, leading to the desired estimate $|\mathbf{T}\hat{\mathscr{G}}| < C\lambda^{1/2}r^{-1}$.

To estimate $|\nabla\boldsymbol{\eta}|$, represent $\boldsymbol{\eta}$ in an annular region between Σ and Σ_R by means of $\hat{\mathscr{G}}(x, y)$, differentiate under the sign and pass to the limit as $R \to \infty$, obtaining

$$\nabla\boldsymbol{\eta} = \lambda \int_{\mathscr{E}} \nabla\mathscr{G}\cdot(\mathbf{u} - \mathbf{u}_0)\cdot\nabla\mathbf{u}\, dy - \lambda \int_{\mathscr{E}} \nabla\mathscr{G}\cdot\mathbf{u}_0\cdot\nabla\mathbf{U}\, dy.$$

The second of these integrals is easily estimated, since the asymptotic behavior of $\mathbf{U}(x)$ is known explicitly. In the first integral one may write

$$|\mathbf{u} - \mathbf{u}_0| < |\mathbf{U} - \mathbf{u}_0| + C(\lambda + \lambda^{1/2}r^{-1})$$

because of what already has been proved. The known behavior of $\mathbf{U}(x)$, together with the Dirichlet bound on $|\nabla\mathbf{u}|$, yield the stated estimate (actually a stronger estimate could in principle be obtained).

Case 4 corresponds to Theorem 7.4 in **[11]**, in which I gave a similar estimate under the assumption $\mathbf{w}_0 = 0$ (the symbol $\mathbf{w}_0$ of that paper corresponds to $\mathbf{u}_0$ above).

5. **Flows at high Reynolds' number.** If $\nu \to 0$ in (3), a perturbation problem is encountered, which is singular in interior as well as in exterior regions. The singularity is of a type which arises in many classical problems, and leads to a lowering of the order of the equation (and hence, necessarily, to a relaxing of the boundary condition) in the limit. The profundity of the difficulty may be surmised from the result of Velte (§2.9), which leaves little doubt that multiple

solutions will appear in general situations, if ν is small.[14] Yet there are many important physical situations in which flows are observed, and for which the results of repeated experiments are in close agreement. What appears to happen is that as ν decreases, the flow behaves as a potential flow outside a thin "boundary layer" near Σ in which $\mathbf{w}$ changes rapidly from the adherence condition $\mathbf{w}^* \equiv 0$ on Σ to the tangential velocity of the potential flow, in which only the normal component of $\mathbf{w}$ vanishes on Σ. If ν decreases beyond a critical value ν_0, depending on the geometry, stationary flows are not observed, and experimentally reproducible results are no longer obtained, except in an average sense.

Equations to describe the flow in the "boundary layer" were proposed by L. Prandtl in 1904. They arise by neglecting terms which experiments indicate to be small relative to others in (3) near Σ. With reference to a rectilinear boundary in dimension $n = 2$, these equations take the form

$$\begin{aligned} Pu \equiv uu_x + vu_y + p_x - \nu u_{yy} &= 0, \\ u_x + v_y &= 0, \end{aligned} \tag{64}$$

which, in terms of the more intrinsic coordinates $\xi = x$, $\eta = \int^y u(x, t)\, dt$, become a single equation

$$uu_\xi + p_x - \nu u(uu_{\eta\eta} + u_\eta^2) \tag{65}$$

for u as function of ξ, η.

Equation (65) and its generalizations have been in recent years the object of considerable study from a mathematical point of view; general uniqueness theorems under physically natural conditions have been given by K. Nickel [**34**], [**35**], and a basic theorem of existence was established by O. A. Oleinik [**36**]. The natural conditions to impose are the values $u = 0$ on the boundary, $p_x(\xi, \eta)$ prescribed, $u(0, \eta)$ prescribed. In Oleinik's theorem p is assumed to be a function of x alone.

The following theorem was established by K. Nickel [**37**]. Consider a region $\mathcal{G}$ bounded by a rectangular boundary Σ, with vertices $A(O, -H)$, $B(O, H)$, $C(1, H)$, $D(1, -H)$, and a family of solutions $\bar{u}, \bar{v}, \bar{p}$ of the Navier-Stokes equations, depending on ν, such that $\lim_{\nu\to 0} \nu\bar{u}_{xx} = 0$, uniformly in $\mathcal{G}$. The family is to satisfy certain reasonable restrictions and regularity conditions, which I shall not repeat. *Let $u(\xi, \eta)$ be a solution of the Prandtl equation* (65), *determined by setting $u = \bar{u}$ on AB, BC, AD, and by choosing for p_x the values $\bar{p}_x$ at corresponding "stream coordinates"* (ξ, η). *Then*

$$\lim_{\nu\to\infty} (u(\xi, \eta) - \bar{u}(\xi, \eta)) = 0$$

uniformly in the image $\hat{\mathcal{G}}(\xi, \eta)$ of $\mathcal{G}$.

Nickel proves his result by writing the particular one of the Navier-Stokes equations in which u_{xx} appears, as the Prandtl equation plus an error term, which $\to 0$ in $\mathcal{G}$ and vanishes on AB, BC, AD. To this situation he applies a general

[14] I have been informed by Dr. Velte that he has proved the existence of bifurcations for solutions of the Navier-Stokes equations (3) describing the stationary flow of fluid between rotating concentric cylinders (the classical "Taylor instability").

comparison theorem for parabolic equations, the "Nagumo-Westphal lemma," which shows that the two solutions are uniformly close in $\hat{\mathscr{G}}$.

REMARK 1. Nickel states his conclusion in the form $\lim_{\nu\to 0} |u(x, y) - \bar{u}(x, y)| = 0$ in $\mathscr{G}$, but proves only the statement given above. The uniform convergence in $\mathscr{G}$ does not appear to follow from his assumptions. However, one may prove that neighboring points remain close together under the mapping, so that $|u - \bar{u}| \to 0$ throughout $\mathscr{G}$ provided the difference is taken at nearby "corresponding" points. This type of result suffices, for example, to demonstrate boundary-layer formation in the Navier-Stokes solution whenever this is the case for the Prandtl solution.

REMARK 2. Nickel's equation (11a) $u^2(\xi, \eta) \geqq A(H^2 - \eta^2)^{1/2}$ does not follow from his hypothesis (11). However, (11a) is easily verified directly in cases of principal interest, and can therefore be taken as hypothesis in place of (11).

The application of the result which first comes to mind is to the explicitly known Poiseuille flow in a channel. In this case, however, both solutions coincide, so no information is provided. One may also consider a rectilinear piece of a general curved channel; however, it seems unlikely that such solutions of (3) exhibit a boundary layer, so the significance of the theorem is still ambiguous in this case. A more interesting application is to a rectilinear piece Σ of a boundary immersed in a fluid which is in uniform motion parallel to Σ at infinity. This situation is accessible to the method, as no (essential) restriction is imposed by Nickel on the boundary data achieved by the two solutions on AB, BC, AD, further than they should agree. The result shows that *under certain qualitative assumptions as to the behavior of the solutions of the exterior problem for the Navier-Stokes equations, the x-components of these solutions are uniformly approximated as* $\nu \to 0$, *in any strip emanating orthogonally from a rectilinear boundary segment in the x-direction, by the corresponding solutions of the Prandtl equation.*

Thus, if the strict solution $\bar{\mathbf{w}}(x)$ of (3) exhibits on the entrance line, the velocity distribution corresponding to a "boundary-layer solution" of (65), and if, similarly, the pressure $\bar{p}$ is essentially that of the potential flow, one may conclude that the component $\bar{\mathbf{w}}_1$ exhibits a boundary-layer behavior near the entire rectilinear segment. However, it must be pointed out that there is an infinity of solutions of (3) in the rectangle $ABCD$, all with the same data on the segments AB, BC, BD where data for (65) are prescribed. Data on CD which do not lead out of the given class are still to some extent arbitrary, and affect the Prandtl solution through the changes in prescribed pressure. There is evidently a wide range of possibilities for the solutions $\bar{\mathbf{w}}$, and Nickel's theorem shows that the solutions of (65) must respond accordingly. It is not yet clear whether the requirement $\nu\bar{u}_{xx} \to 0$, together with Nickel's other hypotheses, will force the solutions to behave in the anticipated way.

Nickel's result has been sharpened by P. Fife, who considered the specific kind of situation expected in a boundary layer. Fife obtained for this case an estimate for the thickness of the region near Σ in which the solutions are close, and a proof of uniform convergence as function of (x, y) in this region. This estimate is better than the result expected intuitively in the case that a boundary layer appears. An abstract of his work appears in this volume.

6. **Stationary solutions as limits of nonstationary solutions.** Given prescribed boundary data $\mathbf{w}^*$ on Σ and an initial velocity configuration of the fluid, does the solution of the initial-boundary-value problem for the general Navier-Stokes system

$$\frac{\partial \mathbf{w}}{\partial t} - \Delta \mathbf{w} + \mathbf{w} \cdot \nabla \mathbf{w} + \nabla p = \mathbf{f}(x), \qquad \nabla \cdot \mathbf{w} = 0 \tag{1}$$

tend, as $t \to \infty$, to a stationary solution which equals $\mathbf{w}^*$ on Σ? The only case for which an answer has been given is that of a two-dimensional flow in a sufficiently small bounded region $\mathscr{G}$, with $\mathbf{w}^* \equiv 0$. It turns out that under these conditions the difference of the two solutions tends in $\mathscr{H}$ exponentially to zero (Ladyzhenskaia [**13**, p. 147]); it can be shown by known methods (cf. [**38**]) that if $\mathbf{f}(x)$ is reasonably smooth, the convergence will even be pointwise.

Certain other cases are easily studied; for example, the condition that $\mathscr{G}$ be small can be replaced by the condition that the stationary solution vanish. $\mathscr{G}$ is then required merely to be finite, and is otherwise arbitrary.

Thus, in particular, fluid in two-dimensional motion interior to a cylinder, under the influence of a conservative force field and satisfying an adherence condition on the boundary, will tend to rest position as $t \to \infty$.

Also, in three dimensions some results on convergence can be obtained for a bounded region.

For an exterior region, the situation seems decidedly more difficult. In this connection, the situation which arises in studying the stationary flow past a body may be worth discussing. Physically, one starts with the body at rest, and accelerates it until a given velocity is attained, after which the body may be kept in motion with the same velocity. The fluid presumably attains a steady motion after infinite time. The motion appears steady, however, only to an observer in a (Galilean) coordinate frame attached to the body. If one attaches this frame to the body throughout the process of acceleration, one is required to insert the negative of the acceleration into the equations of motion as a uniform force field throughout space, until the final velocity is reached. No methods seem currently available to study such a problem. Alternatively, one may arrange to have the reference frame move always with the prescribed velocity, $-\mathbf{w}_0$. Then, Σ will be in accelerated motion in this frame for a finite time interval. Basic a priori energy estimates which apply to such a problem have been obtained by E. Hopf [**10**], and a uniqueness theorem has been given by Sathers and Serrin (cf. [**39**, p. 94]).

7. **Other results.** 1. Boundaries Σ which admit local singularities, such as edges or conical points, are important physically. For example, one may seek the flow past a finite circular cylinder, or, in the limit of vanishing altitude, the flow past a circular disk. It is not hard to show the existence of solutions of such problems in the class D, if the boundary data are of simple form, such as the

(physically natural) condition $\mathbf{w}^* \equiv 0$. J. E. Edwards [**40**] has studied this question in generality and has shown the existence of solutions for essentially arbitrary piecewise smooth $\mathbf{w}^*$ on piecewise smooth boundaries. The principal difficulty which had to be overcome consists in the construction of a solenoidal comparison field, in order to obtain an a priori Dirichlet bound on the solutions of (3). By using Edwards' result, it is possible to prove existence of the Green's tensor $\mathcal{G}$ for the system (5) for nonsmooth boundaries; the properties of this tensor should lead to the existence of a solution of the exterior problem for (3) in the class *PR*, whenever $\mathbf{w}^* - \mathbf{w}_0$ is suitably small although this has not yet been done.

2. A corresponding class *PR* in dimension $n = 2$ has been introduced and studied by D. Smith, in work not yet published. Some of the results given in §3.3, notably the fact that the representation reproduces the expected global order of decay (in this case $r^{-1/2}$), carry over without much change. However, the method no longer suffices to characterize the wake region with precision, or to obtain the result (the essential content of the relation (58)) that no energy is dissipated or inserted into the flow at infinity.

3. The a priori bound on Dirichlet integral in an exterior domain, which leads to existence of solutions of class *D*, depends heavily on the assumption that the condition at infinity is the uniform motion $\mathbf{w} \equiv \mathbf{w}_0$. More generally, an analogous bound could have been obtained for the Dirichlet integral associated with the deviation of $\mathbf{w}(x)$ from the velocity field arising in a prescribed rigid motion. There are, however, natural problems in unbounded domains for which the condition at infinity differs from a rigid motion. One such is the question of the flow in an infinite tube. One may assume that if $|x| \geqq A > 0$, the tube is defined by the relation $y^2 + z^2 = 1$. In the interval $|x| < A$ the tube is smooth and joins smoothly to the given circular sections. Does there exist a flow with prescribed flux? Here the natural condition at infinity is that the flow should approach the classical Poiseuille solution. Under the assumption that the prescribed flux is sufficiently small, an affirmative answer was given by P. Patterson in an unpublished work; Patterson also obtained quantitative estimates on the rate of decay of the solution to the Poiseuille flow at infinity. In contrast to the situation with the exterior problem, however, an existence proof in a general case does not seem to be accessible to presently available methods (a demonstration by Ladyzhenskaia [**26**] contains an error). The principal technical difficulty appears to lie in the fact that terms which integrate to zero when the Dirichlet integral is estimated with boundary conditions at infinity corresponding to a rigid body motion, remain in the expressions in any other case, and contribute quantities which presumably can become arbitrarily large with increasing size of the region. The question as to the extent to which this situation is a reflection of physical reality becomes particularly puzzling, in view of the fact that in a tube of *arbitrary* uniform cross section, a strict solution of the Navier-Stokes equations, with adherence on the boundary, exists for any prescribed flux. Are such solutions mathematical curiosities without meaning? Evidently not entirely, for they are observed experimentally in tubes of finite length, or, what amounts to the same thing, in tubes of

any (fixed) length *if the flux is small.* If, for prescribed flux, the tube length is increased beyond a critical value, smooth solutions are not observed. In this sense, the physical meaning even of Patterson's solutions with small flux is somewhat ambiguous. This contrasts with the case of the exterior problem, in which the fact that smooth flows are observed if and only if the data are small appears to correspond with the fact that solutions of class PR have been shown to exist only for small data.

8. **Outlook.** It is apparent that less is known than is not. The connection between the classes D and PR should be clarified, especially for small data. It would be of particular interest to determine whether there are multiple solutions within the class D. It is not even known whether there exist nontrivial solutions of class D which vanish on Σ and at infinity. As to the class PR, besides the unsettled matter of existence in three dimensions for large data, there is the still more intriguing question of whether such solutions exist for $n = 2$, corresponding to the physically natural boundary data, or whether something analogous to the Stokes paradox governs the behavior at infinity even for the nonlinear case. As a consequence of the work of D. Smith (§7) it appears likely that solutions in $n = 2$ which are smooth at infinity will exist if $\mathbf{w}_0 \neq 0$ and if $|\mathbf{w}^* - \mathbf{w}_0|$ is suitably small. However, the case of most interest, $\mathbf{w}_0$ prescribed and $\mathbf{w}^* \equiv 0$, remains unsettled.

The relation between the Navier-Stokes equations and the Prandtl equations also needs clarification. The results of Nickel and of Fife are important first steps for the rigorous treatment of this problem, but they show only that one component of the Navier-Stokes solution is close to that of a Prandtl solution with corresponding data. As the example of Poisseuille flow indicates, the results as they stand do not yet prove even the existence of a boundary layer (although they are certainly suggestive).

Then there is the question of obtaining stationary solutions as limits of nonstationary ones. As is evident from §6, hardly a beginning has been made on this problem.

I hope the reader may find on perusing this report still other points of departure for new and fruitful investigations.

This work was supported in part by a grant from the Air Force Office of Scientific Research.

References

1. L. Navier, *Mémoire sur les lois du mouvement des fluides*, Mém. Acad. Roy. Sci. **6** (1822), 389.

2. B. de Saint-Venant, Comptes Rendus (Paris) **17** (1843), 1240.

3. G. G. Stokes, *On the theories of the internal friction of fluids in motion, etc.*, Math. and Phys. Papers **I** (1845), 75.

4. C. W. Oseen, *Neuere Methoden und Ergebnisse in der Hydrodynamik*, Akademische Verlagsgesellschaft m.b.H., Leipzig, 1927.

5. A. Douglis and L. Nirenberg, *Interior estimates for elliptic systems of partial differential equations*, Comm. Pure Appl. Math. **8** (1955), 503–538.

6. L. Lichtenstein, *Über einige Existenzprobleme der Hydrodynamik*, Math. Z. **32** (1930), 608–640.

7. F. K. G. Odqvist, *Die Randwertaufgaben der Hydrodynamik zäher Flüssigkeiten*, Norstedt and Söner, Stockholm, 1928; Math. Z. **32** (1930), 329–375.

8. I-Dee Chang and R. Finn, *On the solutions of a class of equations occurring in continuum mechanics, with application to the Stokes paradox*, Arch. Rational Mech. Anal. **7** (1961), 388–401.

9. J. Leray, *Étude de diverses équations intégrales non linéaires et de quelques problèmes que pose l'Hydrodynamique*, J. Math. Pures Appl. **9** (1933), 1–82; *Les problèmes non linéaires*, Enseignement Math. **35** (1936), 139–151.

10. E. Hopf, *Ein allgemeiner Endlichkeitssatz der Hydrodynamik*, Math. Ann. **117** (1940–41), 764–775.

11. R. Finn, *On the steady-state solutions of the Navier-Stokes equations.* III, Acta Math. **105** (1961), 197–244.

12. ———, *Estimates at infinity for stationary solutions of the Navier-Stokes equations*, Bull. Math. Soc. Sci. Math. Phys. R.P. Roumaine **3(51)** (1959), 387–418; Proc. Sympos. Pure Math. Vol. 4, pp. 143–148, Amer. Math. Soc., Providence, R.I., 1961.

13. O. A. Ladyzhenskaia, *The mathematical theory of viscous incompressible flow*, Gordon and Breach, New York, 1963.

14. J. Leray and J. Schauder, *Topologie et équations fonctionelles*, Ann. Sci. École Norm. Sup. **51** (1934), 45–78.

15. H. Schaefer, *Über die Methode der a-priori Schranken*, Math. Ann. **129** (1955), 415–416.

16. O. A. Ladyzhenskaia, *Investigation of the Navier-Stokes equations in the case of stationary motion of an incompressible fluid*, Uspehi Mat. Nauk **3** (1959), 75–97.

17. F. Rellich, *Ein Satz über mittlere Konvergenz*, Nachr. Akad. Wiss. Göttingen Math. Phys. Kl. II (1930), 30–35.

18. M. Shinbrot, *A fixed point theorem and some applications*, Arch. Rat. Mech. Anal. **17** (1964), 255–271.

19. J. Leray and J. L. Lions, *Quelques résultats de Visik sur les problèmes elliptiques non-linéaires par les méthodes de Minty-Browder*, Seminaire Collège de France (to appear).

20. H. Fujita, *On the existence and regularity of the steady-state solutions of the Navier-Stokes equations*, J. Fac. Sci. Univ. Tokyo Sect. I **9** (1961), 59–102.

21. E. Hopf, *Über die Anfangswertaufgabe für die hydrodynamischen Grundgleichungen*, Math. Nachr. **4** (1950–51), 213–231.

22. A. A. Kiselev, and O. A. Ladyzhenskaia, *On the existence and uniqueness of the solution of the nonstationary problem for a viscous incompressible fluid*, Izv. Akad. Nauk SSSR Ser. Mat. **21** (1957), 655–680.

23. N. J. Kotschin, I. A. Kibel and N. W. Rose, *Theoretische Hydromechanik.* II, Akademie-Verlag, Berlin, 1955.

24. W. Velte, *Stabilitätsverhalten und Verzweigung stationärer Lösungen der Navier-Stokesschen Gleichungen*, Arch. Rational Mech. Anal. **16** (1964), 97–125.

25. G. G. Stokes, *On the effect of the internal friction of fluids on the motion of pendulums*, Math. and Phys. Papers **3** (1851), 1.

26. O. A. Ladyzhenskaia, *Stationary motion of a viscous incompressible fluid in a pipe*, Dokl. Akad. Nauk SSSR **124** (1959), 551–553.

27. R. Finn, *On steady-state solutions of the Navier-Stokes partial differential equations*, Arch. Rational Mech. Anal. **3** (1959), 381–396.

28. L. E. Payne and H. F. Weinberger, *Note on a lemma of Finn and Gilbarg*, Acta Math. **98** (1957), 297–299.

29. R. Berker, *Sur les forces exercées par un fluide visqueux sur un obstacle*, Rend. Circ. Mat. Palermo **2** (1952), 260–280.

30. R. Finn, *An energy theorem for viscous fluid motions*, Arch. Rational Mech. Anal. **6** (1960), 371–381.

31. W. Wolibner, *Sur le mouvement plan du liquide visqueux, incompressible, entourant une courbe simple fermée*, Studia Math. **12** (1951), 279–285.

32. A. Krzywicki, *Sur le mouvement plan d'un liquide visqueux compressible*, Studia Math. **15** (1955), 114–122; **15** (1956), 174–181, 252–266; **16** (1957), 48–55.

33. R. Finn, *On the Stokes paradox and related questions*, Nonlinear problems, Univ. of Wisconsin Press, Madison, Wis., 1963.

34. K. Nickel, *Einige Eigenschaften von Lösungen der Prandtlschen Grenzschichtdifferentialgleichungen*, Arch. Rational Mech. Anal. **2** (1958).

35. ———, *Parabolic equations with applications to boundary layer theory*, Partial differential equations and continuum mechanics, Univ. of Wisconsin Press, Madison, Wis., 1961.

36. O. A. Oleinik, *The Prandtl system of equations in boundary layer theory*, Soviet Math. Dokl. **3** (1963), 583–586.

37. K. Nickel, *Die Prandtlschen Grenzschichtdifferentialgleichungen als asymptotischer Grenzfall der Navier-Stokesschen und der Eulerschen Differentialgleichungen*, Arch. Rational Mech. Anal. **13** (1963), 1–14.

38. J. Serrin, *On the interior regularity of weak solutions of the Navier-Stokes equations*, Arch. Rational Mech. Anal. **9** (1962), 187–195.

39. ———, *The initial value problem for the Navier-Stokes equations*, Nonlinear problems, Univ. of Wisconsin Press, Madison, Wis., 1963.

40. J. E. Edwards, *On the existence of solutions of the steady-state Navier-Stokes equations for a class of non-smooth boundary data*, Tech. Rep. No. 6-90-63-70, Lockheed Missiles and Space Co.; Sunnyvale, Calif., 1963.

41. R. Finn, *On the exterior stationary problem for the Navier-Stokes equations, and associated perturbation problems*, Arch. Rational Mech. Anal. (to appear).

STANFORD UNIVERSITY,
STANFORD, CALIFORNIA

ASYMPTOTIC EQUIVALENCE OF THE NAVIER-STOKES AND NONLINEAR BOLTZMANN EQUATIONS

BY

HAROLD GRAD

Abstract. Previous theory of the linear Boltzmann equation is extended to somewhat nonlinear problems. For sufficiently small initial data, solutions are shown to exist for macroscopically long times. If the mean free path is also small, the nonlinear solution is particularly well approximated by the linear solution, and it is also approximated by the macroscopic Navier-Stokes solution of an equivalent problem.[1]

Previous theory of the linear Boltzmann equation is extended to somewhat nonlinear problems. For sufficiently small initial data, solutions are shown to exist for macroscopically long times. If the mean free path is also small, the nonlinear solution is particularly well approximated by the linear solution, and it is also approximated by the macroscopic Navier-Stokes solution of an equivalent problem.

1. **Introduction.** One of the most interesting features of the use of Boltzmann's equation to describe the behavior of a gas is the possibility of a radically different macroscopic description of the gas via the Navier-Stokes or inviscid Euler equations. The fact that there is an overlapping range where both theories are believed to be valid on physical grounds suggests the strictly mathematical question of a connection between the theories of the Boltzmann and Navier-Stokes equations. The relationship is extremely singular, first because the variables used to describe the state of the gas are so dissimilar, and second because the time scales on which the gas evolves are apparently unrelated.

To exhibit this connection turns out to require much more accurate estimates of solutions than those given by any naive proofs of existence. There are strong nonlinear existence theorems in the large for the spatially homogeneous problem. There is one by Carleman [**1**] for hard spheres; one by Wild [**2**] modified by Morgenstern [**3**] for a cutoff Maxwellian potential; and there is an existence theorem by Povzner [**4**] for an artificial equation which reduces in the space-independent case to a legitimate Boltzmann equation (with a general cutoff potential). But this space-independent problem, although mathematically substantial, is physically

[1] These results were first announced at a Symposium on Partial Differential Equations at Novosibirsk, USSR, in August, 1963.

trivial; for there is no change at all in any of the macroscopic variables, and there is, of course, no fluid dynamics without spatial variation. Previous existence theorems in problems with space dependence are relatively poor.[2] Existence is shown for a time comparable to one collision time; this is quite irrelevant on any macroscopic time scale in which fluid behavior is to be observed. These limitations in the nonlinear spatially-dependent theory are not surprising when one notes that this theory should be expected to be at least as difficult as the corresponding nonlinear theory of the Navier-Stokes equations (which should arise as a special limiting case).

There are statements in the literature that one should not even expect solutions in the large for the nonlinear Boltzmann equation, and more tractable abstract replacements have therefore been suggested for the Boltzmann equation [**7**], [**4**]. Of course, there is no a priori reason to expect the existence of solutions in the large for *any* nonlinear equation. This doubt holds just as well (in the absence of any information) for the equations of fluid dynamics. But it is exactly the connection between the Boltzmann equation and fluid dynamics, especially the Navier-Stokes equations, that leads one to expect the likelihood of existence of nonlinear solutions of the Boltzmann equation in the large (at least for sufficiently small mean free path). As a matter of fact, the presence of strong results in the spatially homogeneous case where fluid dynamics is absent suggests that nonlinear estimates similar to those in fluid dynamics are exactly what is missing from the Boltzmann theory.

According to some recent usage, the term "Boltzmann equation" is taken to refer to any equation which involves a distribution function in velocity as well as physical space. We shall be more restrictive and consider the original equation of Boltzmann and Maxwell in its application to a classical gas. Even with this restriction, we deal with a general type rather than with a specific equation. A common property of all these equations is that of conservation of mass, momentum, and energy. This is violated, for example, by equations governing a neutron gas. The type of result which is usually adequate in the latter case, viz., exponential decay or exponential growth, requires relatively trivial estimates. In the linear version, the dominant feature is whether the collision operator is positive or not. For a classical gas the operator is non-negative; but the origin belongs to the spectrum as a consequence of conservation. In the spatially homogeneous case the zero eigenvalues can be discarded and we do obtain the uniform exponential decay of all solutions. In the general case we find (but this is a much more subtle result) an approximately exponential decay to a situation in which fluid behavior takes over. The state of the gas then evolves at a much slower rate and ultimately does decay to equilibrium despite the zero eigenvalues.

The variety of true Boltzmann equations is associated with the choice of intermolecular force law. There is at the present time no existence theory

[2] See [**5**, Chapter III]. The posthumous proof of Carleman [**6**, pp. 87–92] is vitally incomplete.

whatsoever for any equation with a potential that extends to infinity (infinite total cross-section). This is even true for a Maxwellian potential for which the collision operator is known to have a complete pure point spectrum with explicit polynomial eigenfunctions [**8**]. The one exception is the spatially homogeneous problem in which the solution is explicit as a sum of exponentially decaying eigenfunctions. Nothing is known about the spectrum for any other noncutoff potential, although the spectrum is known for a large class of cutoff potentials (and is, in general, not discrete) [**9**]. Even with cutoff potentials, the mathematical tractability seems to be extremely sensitive to the type of cutoff.[3] But there does exist a simple way of truncating the collision cross-section which has recently been found to be amenable to theory [**9**]. The question whether the Boltzmann equation for molecules with infinite total cross-section is mathematically sound (even in the linear case) is completely open.

Discouragement with the Boltzmann equation has led to the study of various types of modified equations. One type of modification, guided by mathematical considerations, replaces the collision operator, which is classically an operator in velocity space alone, by an operator which is nonlocal in physical space. This allows proof of nonlinear existence theorems in the large [**4**], [**7**]. But these models seem to make any property other than the bare fact of existence even more elusive than originally. For example, the identification with physical parameters is hidden; the collision operator would require re-definition near a boundary; the relation to fluid dynamics is not simple and is, in any case, not that of an ideal gas. And, of course, the basic arbitrariness in the kernel describing the space-averaging is disturbing. If the solutions could be shown to be insensitive to the precise degree of averaging in physical space, then a theory of the actual Boltzmann equation would probably ensue. This type of uniform estimate would seem to be comparable in difficulty to the uniform estimates which are required to establish the singular connection with fluid dynamics. At present there are no such uniform estimates, and the future status of these models is uncertain.

An entirely different type of modification of the Boltzmann equation, referred to as a relaxation model, is guided by physical principles and an entirely different type of mathematical expediency (e.g., see [**10**]). These equations exhibit no greater simplicity with regard to general existence theory, but they do offer practical advantages of explicit solutions in certain simple problems, [**11**, **12**] and they are more attractive for numerical work [**13**, **14**].

Existence of solutions to the linear Boltzmann equation for hard spheres was shown by Carleman [**6**, Part 2, Chapter I]. Although existence was proved in the large, the growth estimate $e^{t/\tau}$ (τ is the mean collision time) is catastrophically poor on a macroscopic time scale (typically $\tau \sim 10^{-8}$ sec.). This linear existence theory has been generalized recently to include a wide class of intermolecular potentials, and it has been improved to show boundedness for all time [**9**] and even an ultimate decay to equilibrium [**15**]. Even more important, the

[3] Personal communication from L. Finkelstein.

bounds have been shown to be independent of the mean free path (which enters as a singular parameter) and therefore carry over to the macroscopic regime. These strong estimates have been used to show the relation between Boltzmann solutions and fluid solutions, making rigorous **[16]** the Hilbert theory **[17]**; and in this paper we use the strong linear estimates to derive certain nonlinear existence results and to evaluate the legitimacy of the linear theory.

The connection between the Boltzmann equation and fluid dynamics was shown formally by Hilbert **[17]**.[4] Introducing a singular parameter ε into the Boltzmann equation (ε is the mean free path or mean collision time; cf. §2), Hilbert showed that an expansion of the solution in powers of ε has the formal property that each term in the expansion is determined by an algorithm involving the fluid state alone. A plausible argument can be given to show that Hilbert's expansion is asymptotic in ε except for a short initial layer, a narrow boundary layer, and any internal shock layers **[5**, ¶26]. The linear estimates mentioned above (uniform in ε) provide a proof that the Hilbert expansion, if suitably modified, is asymptotic to arbitrary solutions of the linear Boltzmann equation with smooth initial data **[12]**. Specifically, after an initial transient of duration $O(\varepsilon)$, the distribution function becomes approximately locally Maxwellian. The fluid state is governed by the inviscid Euler equations of fluid dynamics for a time $O(1)$ and by the Navier-Stokes equations for a time $O(1/\varepsilon)$ (the viscosity coefficient is $O(\varepsilon)$).

In this paper we use the linear estimates to prove existence of solutions to the nonlinear Boltzmann equation for a length of time which depends on the amplitude of the initial data. For sufficiently small initial amplitude, the solution exists for interesting macroscopic times, but it will be approximated by the linear equation for only a short (microscopic) part of this time. If the mean free path is small in addition, then the linear approximation is valid for much longer macroscopic times. Furthermore, both solutions are approximated by fluid dynamics (inviscid Euler or Navier-Stokes equations depending on the circumstances). The common fluid behavior for small ε is the reason for the increased range of validity of the linear approximation. The natural time of evolution of fluid properties is macroscopic and bears no relation to the mean collision time, which is the basic time scale for Boltzmann solutions.

The principal mathematical difficulty in the linear theory arises from the fact that the linear collision operator, although non-negative, is not positive definite. But it is exactly this property which provides the fluid behavior in the limit of small ε. There is a rapid approach in a time of order ε toward a state which is essentially macroscopic. This is followed by fluid behavior, largely inviscid on a finite time scale, but viscously decaying on a long time scale of order $1/\varepsilon$. Without the zero eigenvalues, all solutions would decay to zero in a time comparable to ε and both the theory and the physical behavior would be relatively trivial.

The principal difficulty in the nonlinear problem is that a priori estimates in the

[4] For a critical account of the Hilbert and Chapman-Enskog theories see **[5**, Chapter IV]; for recent developments see **[16]**.

linear problem are natural in a norm which is inappropriate for estimation of the nonlinear terms. To find estimates in compatible norms requires the use of explicit smoothing properties of a part of the linear collision operator (after removing a singular and unbounded part) and depends heavily on the assumed rectangular domain and simple boundary conditions. The rectangular domain with perfectly reflecting walls has the special property of eliminating the boundary layer which was mentioned earlier and which requires special estimates. The boundary layer is of course absent in an unbounded domain. But this case requires additional estimates of the decay at infinity in physical space; this problem is treated elsewhere [**18**].

2. **Properties of the Boltzmann equation.**[5] We consider a dimensionless distribution function $F(\boldsymbol{\xi}, \mathbf{x}, t)$ of the dimensionless arguments velocity ($\boldsymbol{\xi}$), space ($\mathbf{x}$), and time (t). The variables have been made dimensionless with respect to the parameters of a reference state which is specified by a mass density ρ_0 and mean thermal speed $C_0 = (RT_0)^{1/2}$. The distribution function has been made dimensionless by a factor ρ_0/C_0^3, the arguments $\boldsymbol{\xi}$, $\mathbf{x}$, t by respective factors C_0, a mean free path λ_0 (related to ρ_0, C_0 and molecular constants), and a mean free time λ_0/C_0. A skeleton form of the Boltzmann equation is

$$DF \equiv \frac{\partial F}{\partial t} + \xi_i \frac{\partial F}{\partial x_i} = Q(F, F). \tag{2.1}$$

The collision term Q is a quadratic operator on F as a function of $\boldsymbol{\xi}$ alone; the streaming term DF operates on F as a function of $(\mathbf{x}, t)$ alone with $\boldsymbol{\xi}$ as a parameter. Initial and boundary values can be expected to be the same as for the differential operator alone.

The dimensionless equilibrium solution (Maxwellian) which corresponds to the reference state (ρ_0, C_0) is $F = \omega(\xi)$ where

$$\omega = \frac{1}{(2\pi)^{3/2}} \exp\left(-\frac{1}{2}\xi^2\right). \tag{2.2}$$

We have

$$Q(\omega, \omega) = 0. \tag{2.3}$$

We are interested in solutions of (2.1) which are not greatly perturbed from $F = \omega$; to this end we introduce

$$F = \omega + \omega^{1/2} f \tag{2.4}$$

(the factor $\omega^{1/2}$ is convenient for normalization of f). The equation satisfied by f is

$$Df + Lf = \nu\Gamma(f, f) \tag{2.5}$$

[5] For a more detailed description and proofs of the properties quoted in this section see [**9**].

where

$$Lf = -2\omega^{-1/2}Q(\omega, \omega^{1/2}f), \tag{2.6}$$

$$\nu\Gamma(f,f) = \omega^{-1/2}Q(\omega^{1/2}f, \omega^{1/2}f) \tag{2.7}$$

and the function $\nu(\xi)$ will be defined in a moment. The linear operator L is singular and unbounded. However, for a large class of appropriately restricted intermolecular potentials, it can be shown to split into two terms,

$$Lf = \nu f - Kf. \tag{2.8}$$

The singular and unbounded part of L is given by the first term; K is a bounded (even compact) integral operator. The factor $\nu(\xi)$, the *collision frequency* of a molecule of speed ξ, is a certain unbounded positive function of ξ. The factor ν in (2.7) was removed because the remaining factor Γ will be found to be bounded in an appropriate sense.

We now quote a number of properties of the operator L which are proved elsewhere **[9]**; the required properties of Γ are derived here in the Appendix. The derivation of these properties is dependent on specific assumptions with regard to the intermolecular force law; mainly that it be repulsive, of finite total cross-section (suitably defined), and sufficiently "hard" (i.e., the force is sufficiently strong for small distances of separation). Classical hard spheres and suitably cut-off power law forces with exponent $\geqq 5$ are included.

The operators L and K are symmetric and L is non-negative; these statements are made relative to the L_2 norm in the infinite three-dimensional space $\boldsymbol{\xi}$,

$$\begin{aligned} \|f\|^2 &= \int f^2 \, d\boldsymbol{\xi}, \\ (f, g) &= \int fg \, d\boldsymbol{\xi}. \end{aligned} \tag{2.9}$$

A critical point in all the analysis is that L is not positive. The origin is a multiple eigenvalue

$$L\psi_\alpha = 0 \qquad (\alpha = 0, 1, 2, 3, 4) \tag{2.10}$$

with the explicit normalized eigenfunctions

$$\begin{aligned} \psi_0 &= \omega^{1/2}, \\ \psi_i &= \xi_i\omega^{1/2} \qquad (i = 1, 2, 3), \\ \psi_4 &= (\xi^2 - 3)(\omega/6)^{1/2}. \end{aligned} \tag{2.11}$$

The existence of these eigenfunctions is closely related to the fact that mass, momentum, and energy are conserved; and it is because L is not positive that solutions of the Boltzmann equation do not decay simply to zero but exhibit fluid-like behavior under appropriate circumstances.

The function $\nu(\xi)$ is usually monotone, it is bounded away from zero (for the class of hard potentials under consideration), and it is usually unbounded for large ξ as a power ξ^γ, $0 \leqq \gamma \leqq 1$. We shall require only the bounds

$$1 \leqq \nu(\xi) < \nu_1(1 + \xi^2)^{1/2} \tag{2.12}$$

where ν_1 is a constant. The lower bound has been taken to be 1 by a suitable choice of the normalizing dimensional mean collision time.

Since K is compact, the essential spectrum of L consists of exactly the values taken by $\nu(\xi)$. Therefore the origin is an isolated point of the spectrum, and we have

$$\begin{aligned} (f, Lf) &> \mu(f,f), \\ (f, \psi_\alpha) &= 0 \end{aligned} \tag{2.13}$$

for some positive constant μ.

We denote by κ_0 the bound of K,

$$\|Kf\| \leqq \kappa_0 \|f\|. \tag{2.14}$$

Other more refined properties of K are

$$\max |Kf| < \kappa_1 \|f\| \tag{2.15}$$

and

$$\max (1 + \xi^2)^{(r+1)/2} |Kf| < \kappa_{r+2} \max (1 + \xi^2)^{r/2} |f| \qquad (r = 0, 1, \cdots). \tag{2.16}$$

In other words, Kf is bounded if f is square integrable, and Kf decays faster than f by a factor ξ for large ξ.

There are several alternate forms of the Boltzmann equation that we shall use. If, instead of (2.4), we introduce

$$F = \omega + \varepsilon \omega^{1/2} f \tag{2.17}$$

into the Boltzmann equation (2.1), we obtain

$$Df + Lf = \varepsilon \nu \Gamma(f,f). \tag{2.18}$$

If ε is small, we are led to consider the linear equation

$$Df + Lf = 0 \tag{2.19}$$

with the expectation that solutions of this equation will approximate those of (2.18) for small ε.

A more interesting change of scale is

$$F = \omega/\varepsilon + \omega^{1/2} f \tag{2.20}$$

which leads to the equation

$$Df + \frac{1}{\varepsilon} Lf = \nu \Gamma(f,f). \tag{2.21}$$

Implicit in (2.20) is the supposition that the perturbation is not only small relative to the reference state ω/ε, but that the perturbation has a basic length scale which is long compared to the mean free path of the reference state [which is $O(\varepsilon)$ since the density is $O(1/\varepsilon)$]. It is apparent that $\varepsilon = 0$ is a singularity. Moreover, it is not immediately evident that solutions of (2.21) will be approximated by those of the associated linear equation

$$Df + \frac{1}{\varepsilon} Lf = 0. \tag{2.22}$$

Despite appearances, it will turn out that solutions of the linear equation (2.22) do approximate those of the nonlinear equation (2.21). The reason is their common fluid-like behavior in the singular neighborhood of small ε.

A final change of scale which we shall wish to consider is

$$F = \omega/\varepsilon + \varepsilon\omega^{1/2}f \tag{2.23}$$

which leads to the equation

$$Df + \frac{1}{\varepsilon} Lf = \varepsilon\nu\Gamma(f, f). \tag{2.24}$$

This equation is "linearized" to a higher order $O(\varepsilon^2)$ than the mean free path is shortened, viz. $O(\varepsilon)$. It is associated with the same linear equation as (2.21), viz. (2.22), but the relation is, in this case, more evident.

Implicit in the various scalings in ε is the assumption that the initial data are independent of ε.

3. **Boundary conditions.** We consider a rectangular domain and two types of boundary conditions, periodicity and specular reflection. The simpler case is periodicity. We take a fundamental domain with sides (a_1, a_2, a_3) and assume that the initial values are periodic in x_i with periods a_i. It is easily verified that this periodicity is retained by all functions that arise in the analysis, in particular by the solution. The periodicity property is used essentially at only one point in the analysis, to show that a boundary integral vanishes in making an a priori estimate.

The specular reflection boundary condition, also applied in a rectangular domain, states that f is an even function of the normal component of velocity at a wall

$$f(\boldsymbol{\xi}) = f(\boldsymbol{\xi} - 2\mathbf{n}(\boldsymbol{\xi}\cdot\mathbf{n})). \tag{3.1}$$

By reflection of the fundamental domain D with respect to each of three coordinate planes we obtain a domain D^* consisting of eight replicas of D. In D^* the function f satisfies a periodicity boundary condition. It is easy to verify that the symmetry of the initial function f with respect to the three planes which bisect D^* is maintained by all functions which arise in the analysis. Thus solution of the Boltzmann equation with a periodic boundary condition in D^* yields the desired solution with specular boundary condition in the subdomain D.

There are a few precautions that should be observed in passing between D and D^*. If the initial function f is required to be continuous in D^*, this implies that the boundary condition (3.1) must be satisfied by the initial function in D. A continuous initial derivative $\partial f/\partial x_1$ in D^* implies the condition

$$\frac{\partial}{\partial x_1} f(\xi_1) = -\frac{\partial}{\partial x_1} f(-\xi_1) \tag{3.2}$$

at the wall perpendicular to x_1, etc. In other words, smoothness in D involves satisfaction of certain relations beyond conventional smoothness at the boundary. These relations can be interpreted as smoothness conditions as seen by a given particle which is specularly reflected (and changes its velocity discontinuously while doing so).

The problems of initial data which do not satisfy (3.1) or (3.2), of more general discontinuous initial data, and of general nonrectangular domains are closely related but will not be considered here.

4. **Norms.** In order to properly combine estimates for the linear and nonlinear equations it is necessary to introduce an assortment of norms. We denote by N the L_2 norm in $(\boldsymbol{\xi}, \mathbf{x})$ (as distinguished from $\|\cdots\|$, previously used for the norm in $\boldsymbol{\xi}$)

$$N[f] = \left\{\int f^2 d\boldsymbol{\xi}\, d\mathbf{x}\right\}^{1/2}. \tag{4.1}$$

The simple maximum norm we denote by

$$N_0[f] = \max_{\xi,\, x} |f| \tag{4.2}$$

and more generally

$$N_r[f] = \max_{\xi,\, x} (1 + \xi^2)^{r/2} |f|. \tag{4.3}$$

We shall also use the combined norms

$$\mathsf{N}_r[f] = \max_{\xi} (1 + \xi^2)^{r/2} \left\{\int f^2\, d\mathbf{x}\right\}^{1/2} \tag{4.4}$$

and the norms of x-derivatives

$$N^s[f] = \max_{n=0}^{s} N[\nabla^n f], \tag{4.5}$$

$$N_r^s[f] = \max_{n=0}^{s} N_r[\nabla^n f], \tag{4.6}$$

$$\mathsf{N}_r^s[f] = \max_{n=0}^{s} \mathsf{N}_r[\nabla^n f], \tag{4.7}$$

where

$$|\nabla^n f|^2 = \sum_{i_1 \cdots i_n} \left| \frac{\partial^n f}{\partial x_{i_1} \cdots \partial x_{i_n}} \right|^2. \tag{4.8}$$

We shall use the symbol $\mathscr{N}$ to represent any one of the norms N, N_r^s, N_r^s. Each of the norms is evaluated at a given time, t. For the maximum with respect to t we use

$$\bar{\mathscr{N}} = \max_t \mathscr{N}(t) \tag{4.9}$$

where max is understood to be taken for $0 < t < t_0$, t_0 finite or infinite depending on the context.

Some elementary estimates are

$$N_r^s \leqq N_{r+1}^s, \qquad N_r^s \leqq N_r^{s+1}, \tag{4.10}$$

$$\mathsf{N}_r^s \leqq \mathsf{N}_{r+1}^s, \qquad \mathsf{N}_r^s \leqq \mathsf{N}_r^{s+1}, \tag{4.11}$$

$$N \leqq \pi \mathsf{N}_2, \tag{4.12}$$

the last being a consequence of the fact that $(1 + \xi^2)^{-1}$ is square integrable $[\int (1 + \xi^2)^{-2}\, d\boldsymbol{\xi} = \pi^2]$. There exists a constant s_0 depending on the domain such that (Sobolev)

$$N_r^s < s_0 \mathsf{N}_r^{s+2}. \tag{4.13}$$

From §2 we transfer the L_2 inequalities (2.13) and (2.14) unaltered to the space $(\boldsymbol{\xi}, \mathbf{x})$ and generalize (2.15) and (2.16) to read

$$\mathsf{N}_0^s[Kf] < \kappa_1 N^s[f], \tag{4.14}$$

$$\mathsf{N}_{r+1}^s[Kf] < \kappa_{r+2} \mathsf{N}_r^s[f]. \tag{4.15}$$

Similar estimates for the quadratic collision term Γ, derived in the Appendix, are

$$N_r[\Gamma(f, g)] \leqq \gamma_0 N_r[f] N_r[g], \qquad r \geqq 1. \tag{4.16}$$

and

$$\mathsf{N}_r[\Gamma(f, g)] \leqq \gamma_0 \mathsf{N}_r[f] N_r[g], \qquad r \geqq 1. \tag{4.17}$$

There is no estimate of Γ in terms of only L_2 estimates of f and g.

The above estimates of K and Γ form the basis for the entire theory. We continue with some consequences of these estimates.

From $|\boldsymbol{\xi} \cdot \nabla f| < (1 + \xi^2)^{1/2} |\nabla f|$ we obtain

$$\mathsf{N}_r^s[\boldsymbol{\xi} \cdot \nabla f] < N_{r+1}^{s+1}[f] \tag{4.18}$$

and from (2.12) we have

$$\mathsf{N}_r^s[\nu f] < \nu_1 \mathsf{N}_{r+1}^s[f] \tag{4.19}$$

from which follows

$$\mathsf{N}_r^s[Lf] < (\nu_1 + \kappa_{r+1}) \mathsf{N}_{r+1}^s[f] \tag{4.20}$$

using (2.8), (4.15), and (4.11). If f is a sufficiently regular solution of the linear Boltzmann equation (2.19), $\partial f/\partial t$ can be estimated from (4.18) and (4.20) as

$$\mathsf{N}_r^s[\partial f/\partial t] < (1 + \nu_1 + \kappa_{r+1}) \mathsf{N}_{r+1}^{s+1}[f]. \tag{4.21}$$

A vital property of all norms is

$$\mathcal{N}[\tilde{f}] \leqq \mathcal{N}[f] \tag{4.22}$$

where

$$\tilde{f}(\boldsymbol{\xi}, \mathbf{x}, t) = f(\boldsymbol{\xi}, \mathbf{x} - s\boldsymbol{\xi}, t) \tag{4.23}$$

and s is a constant (note that this would not be true if N were replaced by the stronger norm with $\max_\xi$ preceding $\int \cdots d\mathbf{x}$).

The basic formula to which all convergence estimates will be referred is the

LEMMA. *If*

$$f(\boldsymbol{\xi}, \mathbf{x}, t) = \frac{\nu}{\varepsilon} \int_0^t e^{-\nu(t-s)/\varepsilon} g(\boldsymbol{\xi}, \mathbf{x} - \boldsymbol{\xi}(t - s), s)\, ds \tag{4.24}$$

then

$$\mathsf{N}_r[f] \leqq \bar{\mathsf{N}}_r[g]. \tag{4.25}$$

If ν is a constant, this estimate for any norm is classical since f is a mean value with parameter s and total weight less than one of the functions g,

$$(\nu/\varepsilon) \int_0^t e^{-\nu(t-s)/\varepsilon} = 1 - e^{-\nu t/\varepsilon} < 1.$$

With ν a function of ξ, the estimate (4.25) is not true for the L_2 norm of N and a maximum norm with respect to ξ is needed.

For the proof, we use Schwarz's inequality to obtain

$$\int g(\boldsymbol{\xi}, \mathbf{x} - \boldsymbol{\xi}(t - s_1), s_1) g(\boldsymbol{\xi}, \mathbf{x} - \boldsymbol{\xi}(t - s_2), s_2)\, d\mathbf{x} \leqq (1 + \xi^2)^{-r} (\bar{\mathsf{N}}_r[g])^2$$

which implies

$$\int f^2\, d\mathbf{x} \leqq (1 + \xi^2)^{-r} (\bar{\mathsf{N}}_r[g])^2 (1 - e^{-\nu t/\varepsilon})^2,$$

and thus (4.25).

5. **Outline of the proof.** The linear equation (2.22) can be written

$$\frac{\partial f}{\partial t} + \boldsymbol{\xi} \cdot \nabla f + \frac{1}{\varepsilon} \nu f = \frac{1}{\varepsilon} K f \tag{5.1}$$

and transformed into the integral equation

$$\begin{aligned} f(\boldsymbol{\xi}, \mathbf{x}, t) &= f_0(\boldsymbol{\xi}, \mathbf{x} - \boldsymbol{\xi} t) \exp(-\nu t/\varepsilon) \\ &\quad + \frac{1}{\varepsilon} \int_0^t \exp[-\nu(t - s)/\varepsilon] k(\boldsymbol{\xi}, \mathbf{x} - \boldsymbol{\xi}(t - s), s)\, ds \end{aligned} \tag{5.2}$$

where

$$k = Kf, \tag{5.3}$$

and

$$f(\boldsymbol{\xi}, \mathbf{x}, 0) = f_0(\boldsymbol{\xi}, \mathbf{x}) \tag{5.4}$$

is a given initial function. We solve (5.1) by iteration on the right side, or the equivalent, iterate (5.2) and (5.3) successively. The crude estimate obtained by setting the exponentials in (5.2) equal to one yields convergent iterations with a growth $\exp(\kappa t/\varepsilon)$ in any norm $\mathcal{N}$ where κ is the bound of K in the particular norm $\mathcal{N}$. No great improvement in this growth estimate can be made by examining the iterates more carefully (unless ν is a constant; see below) because of the nontrivial nullspace of the operator L; Kf is "just as large" as νf.

But for any smooth solution f, we can obtain the a priori estimate[6]

$$N[f] \leqq N[f_0]. \tag{5.5}$$

Multiplying through the equation (5.1) by f and integrating with respect to $\mathbf{x}$ and $\boldsymbol{\xi}$, we can drop the streaming term $\nabla\cdot(\frac{1}{2}\boldsymbol{\xi}f^2)$ using periodicity in $\mathbf{x}$ and estimate the collisional term by $(f, Lf) \geqq 0$, to obtain (5.5). A simple argument shows that (5.5) obtains without unnecessary smoothness. In only the case $\nu =$ constant (cutoff Maxwellian molecules) can the uniform bound on $N[f]$ be established directly for each iteration (the L_2 norm of K is just ν). If ν is a function of ξ, we are blocked by the inapplicability of the lemma, (4.25), in an L_2 norm.

The mollifying properties of K, (2.15) and (2.16), can now be used to show boundedness of the solution as a function of ξ, and a Sobolev lemma to show boundedness as a function of x for sufficiently smooth data (all x-derivatives of f satisfy the same equation and boundary conditions and therefore the same a priori estimate). Note that all these uniform-in-time estimates are also independent of the value of ε.

Similar estimates, also independent of ε, can be found for the inhomogeneous linear equation. Using them, we iterate on the right side of the nonlinear equation (2.21). The unbounded factor ν on the right is taken care of by the strong inhomogeneous linear estimate which gives a solution decaying faster in ξ than the inhomogeneous term. A more serious problem is to obtain maximum estimates which, for the linear equation, are obtained from the a priori L_2 estimates only after losing derivatives. This is taken care of by using a norm N_r^3. Writing $f_i = \partial f/\partial x_i$, $f_{ij} = \partial^2 f/\partial x_i \partial x_j$, etc., we have

$$\begin{aligned} \frac{\partial}{\partial x_i}\,\Gamma(f,f) &= 2\Gamma(f,f_i), \\ \frac{\partial^2}{\partial x_i\,\partial x_j}\,\Gamma(f,f) &= 2\Gamma(f,f_{ij}) + 2\Gamma(f_i,f_j), \\ \frac{\partial^3}{\partial x_i\,\partial x_j\,\partial x_k}\,\Gamma(f,f) &= 2\Gamma(f,f_{ijk}) + 2\Gamma(f_i,f_{jk}) + 2\Gamma(f_j,f_{ki}) + 2\Gamma(f_k,f_{ij}). \end{aligned} \tag{5.6}$$

An estimate for $\mathsf{N}_r^3[f]$, using Sobolev, implies a maximum estimate $N_r^1[f]$. Each term on the right side in (5.6) has at least one argument of Γ which is f itself or a first derivative; i.e., at least one argument is bounded and the other one is L_2.

[6] This is essentially the linearized version of Boltzmann's H-theorem.

Thus $\mathsf{N}_r^3\Gamma[(f,f)]$ can be estimated in terms of $\mathsf{N}_r^3[f]$. In this way existence is proved for (2.18)

$$\frac{\partial t}{\partial f} + \boldsymbol{\xi}\cdot\nabla f + Lf = \varepsilon\nu\Gamma(f,f) \tag{5.7}$$

for a time of order $1/\varepsilon$ and for (2.21)

$$\frac{\partial f}{\partial t} + \boldsymbol{\xi}\cdot\nabla f + \frac{1}{\varepsilon} Lf = \nu\Gamma(f,f) \tag{5.8}$$

for a time of order 1. The two results are equivalent in that each describes existence for a long time of order $1/\varepsilon$ times the mean collision time. But the class of initial data in (5.8) is more special in that the f_0 is not only small but it is also slowly varying in space compared to the mean free path. We may obtain (5.8) directly from (5.7) by a change of scale, viz., by inserting $f(\varepsilon x)$ and changing the time scale to εt. In return for the greater specialization of initial values in (5.8), we find that the solution is more accurately linear. In (5.7) the solution is approximated by the corresponding linear solution (2.19) to within an error $O(\varepsilon)$ for a microscopic time $O(1)$; this is evident by inspection of the nonlinear equation. But a more powerful estimate of the inhomogeneous linear equation can be made in (5.8) and yields the unexpected result that the solution of (5.8) is approximated by the corresponding linear solution (2.22) for the entire (macroscopic) time of existence. The proof of this result is closely related to the proof that the solution of (5.8) is approximated by fluid dynamics. Since the parameter ε does not appear in the inviscid fluid equations, it is not surprising that a small fluid perturbation of relative size ε will remain accurately linear for the macroscopic time $O(1)$. For the "more linear" equation (2.24), existence and approximate linearity as well as fluid behavior are proved for a time $O(1/\varepsilon)$. The comparisons with fluid dynamics are contained in an earlier paper **[12]**, but we shall sketch the proofs here for completeness.

More efficient use of the same estimates that show that the solutions of (5.8) are approximately linear would give an improved existence proof for (5.8) for the longer time $O(\log 1/\varepsilon)$, but we shall not bother with this.

6. **The linear equation.**[7] Consider first the integral formulation (5.2), (5.3) with an initial function $f_0(\boldsymbol{\xi}, \mathbf{x})$ which is periodic and bounded with respect to one of the norms $\mathcal{N}$. Iterating and estimating $|f|$ by setting $\nu = 0$,

$$\begin{aligned} \mathcal{N}[f^{n+1}] &\leqq \mathcal{N}[f_0] + \frac{1}{\varepsilon}\int_0^t \mathcal{N}[k^n(s)]\,ds, \\ \mathcal{N}[k^n] &\leqq \kappa\mathcal{N}[f^n] \end{aligned} \tag{6.1}$$

we obtain a contracting sequence of iterates $\exp(-\kappa t/\varepsilon)f^n$ in the norm $\mathcal{N}$ where κ is the bound on the operator K ($\kappa = \kappa_0$ for $\mathcal{N} = N^s$, $\kappa = \kappa_{2+r}$ for $\mathcal{N} = N_r^s$ or N_r^s). We may choose to look at (5.1) with $\nu = 0$ as a dominating equation.

[7] The theory of this section is taken from **[9]**. We repeat the proofs (in a slightly different form) to make the abstract existence theory self contained (i.e., starting from stated properties of the collision operators).

The function $f(\boldsymbol{\xi}, \mathbf{x}, t)$ defined by the contracting sequence is in the space given by the completion of $\mathcal{N}$ and satisfies (5.2), (5.3). This solution is unique in the class of all functions $f(\boldsymbol{\xi}, \mathbf{x}, t)$ which have a finite norm $\mathcal{N}$ for some interval $0 \leqq t \leqq t_0$; and at any finite t, there is continuous dependence of f on f_0 in the norm $\mathcal{N}$.

The solution has the same boundedness and differentiability properties inherent in the norm $\mathcal{N}$ as the initial function. Let us first assume that $N[f_0]$ is finite. From (5.2) we deduce the existence of the directional derivative Df, and in this generalized sense f satisfies the original equation (5.1). If $\mathsf{N}_1^1[f_0]$ is finite, then $\partial f/\partial t$, $\boldsymbol{\xi}\cdot\nabla f$, and νf exist individually in (5.1) (as measurable L_2 functions). If the maximum norm $N_r^s[f_0]$ is finite and f_0 as well as the indicated derivatives are continuous, then the solution is continuous together with its derivatives by the uniform convergence in the maximum norm.

Now consider a fixed initial function f_0 with finite norm N. We can approximate f_0 by a sequence of functions $f_0^{(n)}$ with continuous first derivatives and finite (but not uniformly bounded) $N_3^1[f_0^{(n)}]$ such that $N[f_0 - f_0^{(n)}] \to 0$. By the continuous dependence on initial data $N[f^{(n)}] \to N[f]$ at any time t. But each of the smooth solutions $f^{(n)}$ satisfies the a priori estimate $N[f^{(n)}] \leqq N[f_0^{(n)}]$. This follows by multiplication through the Boltzmann equation (which is satisfied pointwise) by $f^{(n)}$, noting that $\boldsymbol{\xi}\cdot\nabla(f^{(n)})^2$ is integrable in $\boldsymbol{\xi}$ and continuous. Consequently f itself satisfies the estimate

$$N[f] \leqq N[f_0]. \tag{6.2}$$

Exactly the same argument holds for any x-derivatives of f which are square integrable,

$$N^s[f] \leqq N^s[f_0]. \tag{6.3}$$

For the linear theory alone (cf. [**9**]), it is not necessary to be so parsimonious of derivatives in deriving the a priori estimate; but it is vital for the nonlinear application.

To extend these uniform L_2 estimates to maximum estimates, we turn to the integral equation (5.2). Referring to the lemma of §4 and recalling that $\nu \geqq 1$, from (5.2) we have

$$\mathsf{N}_j^s[f] \leqq \mathsf{N}_j^s[f_0] + \bar{\mathsf{N}}_j^s[k]. \tag{6.4}$$

Using (4.14), (4.15) in (5.3), we find

$$\begin{aligned} \mathsf{N}_0^s[k] &< \kappa_1 N^s[f], \\ \mathsf{N}_j^s[k] &< \kappa_{j+1}\mathsf{N}_{j-1}^s[f], \end{aligned} \tag{6.5}$$

and inserting these in (6.4) we have

$$\begin{aligned} \mathsf{N}_0^s[f] &\leqq \mathsf{N}_0^s[f_0] + \kappa_1 \bar{N}^s[f], \\ \mathsf{N}_j^s[f] &\leqq \mathsf{N}_j^s[f_0] + \kappa_{j+1}\mathsf{N}_{j-1}^s[f]. \end{aligned} \tag{6.6}$$

Solving these recurrence inequalities for successive j and inserting the a priori estimate (6.3),

$$\begin{aligned} \mathsf{N}_0^s[f] &\leqq \mathsf{N}_0^s[f_0] + \kappa_1 N^s[f_0], \\ \mathsf{N}_1^s[f] &\leqq \mathsf{N}_1^s[f_0] + \kappa_2 \mathsf{N}_0^s[f_0] + \kappa_2\kappa_1 N^s[f_0] \\ &\leqq (1 + \kappa_2)\mathsf{N}_1^s[f_0] + \kappa_2\kappa_1 N^s[f_0], \\ \mathsf{N}_2^s[f] &\leqq (1 + \kappa_3 + \kappa_3\kappa_2)\mathsf{N}_2^s[f_0] + \kappa_3\kappa_2\kappa_1 N^s[f_0] \\ &\leqq (1 + \kappa_3 + \kappa_3\kappa_2 + \pi\kappa_3\kappa_2\kappa_1)\mathsf{N}_2^s[f_0] \end{aligned}$$

and for $r \geqq 2$

$$\mathsf{N}_r^s[f] \leqq a_r \mathsf{N}_r^s[f_0], \qquad r \geqq 2 \tag{6.7}$$

where a_r depends on $\kappa_1 \cdots \kappa_{r+1}$ only. These estimates are distinguished from the L_2 estimates (6.3) in that the constants a_r are necessarily larger than one.

For the inhomogeneous equation

$$Df + \frac{1}{\varepsilon}\nu f = \frac{1}{\varepsilon}Kf + \nu g, \qquad f_0 = 0 \tag{6.8}$$

we proceed similarly. Iterating

$$\begin{aligned} f(\boldsymbol{\xi}, \mathbf{x}, t) &= \int_0^t \exp[-\nu(t - s)/\varepsilon]\Phi(\boldsymbol{\xi}, \mathbf{x} - \boldsymbol{\xi}(t - s), s)\, ds, \\ \Phi &= \frac{1}{\varepsilon}Kf + \nu g, \end{aligned} \tag{6.9}$$

we obtain existence of f over any time interval in which the norm of νg is finite. As an a priori estimate, using the fact that L is non-negative, we have

$$N^s[f] \leqq \int_0^{t_0} N^s[\nu g]\, dt \leqq t_0 \bar{N}^s[\nu g] \leqq \pi\nu_1 t_0 \mathsf{N}_3^s[g]. \tag{6.10}$$

We obtain maximum estimates from the integral expression (6.9) by use of the lemma (4.25)

$$\begin{aligned} \mathsf{N}_0^s[f] &\leqq \kappa_1 \bar{N}^s[f] + \varepsilon \bar{\mathsf{N}}_0^s[g], \\ \mathsf{N}_j^s[f] &\leqq \kappa_{j+1} \bar{N}_{j-1}^s[f] + \varepsilon \bar{\mathsf{N}}_j^s[g]. \end{aligned} \tag{6.11}$$

Iterating these inequalities and taking $r \geqq 3$, we find

$$\mathsf{N}_r^s[f] \leqq (b_r t_0 + \varepsilon c_r)\bar{\mathsf{N}}_r^s[g], \qquad r \geqq 3. \tag{6.12}$$

Summarizing the essential results we have

THEOREM 1. *There is a unique solution to*

$$Df + \frac{1}{\varepsilon}Lf = \nu g$$

for $\mathsf{N}_r^s[f_0]$ *and* $\mathsf{N}_r^s[g]$ *finite and* $r \geqq 3$ *which satisfies*

$$\mathsf{N}_r^s[f] \leqq a_r \mathsf{N}_r^s[f_0] + (b_r t_0 + \varepsilon c_r)\bar{\mathsf{N}}_r^s[g]. \tag{6.13}$$

The constants a_r, b_r, c_r *depend only on* $\nu_1, \kappa_1 \cdots \kappa_{r+1}$, *and, in particular, are independent of* ε *and* t.

Better estimates can be made for both the homogeneous and inhomogeneous equations if f_0 is space-independent. Existence follows from the general case. We write the solution

$$\frac{\partial f}{\partial t} + \frac{1}{\varepsilon} Lf = 0 \tag{6.14}$$

as the sum of its projection into the nullspace of L and the orthogonal complement;

$$\begin{aligned} f &= \hat{f} + \tilde{f}, \\ \hat{f} &= \sum_a \rho_\alpha \psi_\alpha, \qquad \rho_\alpha = (f, \psi_\alpha), \\ (\tilde{f}, \psi_\alpha) &= 0. \end{aligned} \tag{6.15}$$

The two components satisfy

$$\begin{aligned} \frac{\partial \hat{f}}{\partial t} &= 0, \\ \frac{\partial \tilde{f}}{\partial t} + \frac{1}{\varepsilon} L\tilde{f} &= 0. \end{aligned} \tag{6.16}$$

The fluid part, $\hat{f}$, is constant in time. From (2.13), we derive

$$\|\tilde{f}\| \leqq \exp(-\mu t/\varepsilon)\|\tilde{f}_0\| \tag{6.17}$$

and conclude that $\tilde{f}$ decays exponentially to zero in a time of order ε. Exactly as before, we extend this estimate to

$$N_r^s[\tilde{f}] \leqq a_r \exp(-\mu t/\varepsilon) N_r^s[\tilde{f}_0], \qquad r \geqq 2 \tag{6.18}$$

with the same constant a_r as previously.

Next we consider an inhomogeneous term which is orthogonal to ψ_α

$$\begin{aligned} \frac{\partial f}{\partial t} + \frac{1}{\varepsilon} Lf &= \nu g, \qquad f_0 = 0, \\ (\nu g, \psi_\alpha) &= 0. \end{aligned} \tag{6.19}$$

The same decomposition (6.15) yields $\hat{f} = 0$ and the a priori estimate

$$\begin{aligned} N^s[f] &\leqq \int_0^t \exp(-\mu(t - s)/\varepsilon) N^s[\nu g(s)]\, ds \\ &< \frac{\varepsilon}{\mu} \bar{N}^s[\nu g]. \end{aligned} \tag{6.20}$$

This is improved into a maximum estimate exactly as in the space-dependent case, but we note that ε/μ takes the place of t_0 in (6.10) (the time t_0 is still implicit in $\bar{N}^s$);

$$N_r^s[f] < (b_r/\mu + c_r)\varepsilon \bar{N}_r^s[g], \qquad r \geqq 3. \tag{6.21}$$

We see that the solution is smaller than the inhomogeneous term by a factor ε in this case.

We summarize the principal results in

THEOREM 2. *The solution to the space-independent equation*

$$\frac{\partial f}{\partial t} + \frac{1}{\varepsilon} Lf = \nu g, \qquad (\nu g, \psi_\alpha) = 0, \qquad (f_0, \psi_\alpha) = 0 \tag{6.22}$$

for finite $N_r^s[g]$ *and* $N_r^s[f_0]$, $r \geqq 3$, *satisfies*

$$N_r^s[f] \leqq a_r \exp(-\mu t/\varepsilon) N_r^s[f_0] + (b_r/\mu + c_r)\varepsilon \bar{N}_r^s[g]. \tag{6.23}$$

If $\mathbf{x}$ occurs as a parameter in f_0, we merely replace N_r^s by N_r^s in this theorem.

Theorem 2 allows us to improve Theorem 1 in the space-dependent case if νg and f_0 are orthogonal to ψ_α. We write

$$f = f^1 + f^2 \tag{6.24}$$

where

$$\frac{\partial f^1}{\partial t} + \frac{1}{\varepsilon} Lf^1 = \nu g, \qquad f_0^1 = f_0, \tag{6.25}$$

$$Df^2 + \frac{1}{\varepsilon} Lf^2 = -\boldsymbol{\xi}\cdot\nabla f^1, \qquad f_0^2 = 0. \tag{6.26}$$

Applying Theorem 2 to (6.25), we have

$$\mathsf{N}_r^s[f^1] \leqq a_r \exp(-\mu t/\varepsilon)\mathsf{N}_r^s[f_0] + (b_r/\mu + c_r)\varepsilon \bar{\mathsf{N}}_r^s[g]. \tag{6.27}$$

Noting that $\mathsf{N}_{r-1}^{s-1}[\boldsymbol{\xi}\cdot\nabla f^1] \leqq \mathsf{N}_r^s[f^1]$, Theorem 1 applied to (6.26) yields

$$\mathsf{N}_{r-1}^{s-1}[f^2] \leqq (b_r t_0 + \varepsilon c_r)\bar{\mathsf{N}}_r^s[f^1]. \tag{6.28}$$

Combining these estimates, we have

THEOREM 3. *The solution to*

$$Df + \frac{1}{\varepsilon} Lf = \nu g, \qquad (\nu g, \psi_\alpha) = 0, \qquad (f_0, \psi_\alpha) = 0 \tag{6.29}$$

satisfies the estimate, for $r \geqq 3$,

$$\mathsf{N}_{r-1}^{s-1}[f] \leqq (1 + b_r t_0 + \varepsilon c_r)\{a_r \exp(-\mu t/\varepsilon)\mathsf{N}_r^s[f_0] + (b_r/\mu + c_r)\varepsilon\bar{\mathsf{N}}_r^s[g]\}. \tag{6.30}$$

If νg and f_0 are orthogonal to ψ_α, the solution rapidly decays to a magnitude of order ε; but to obtain this strong estimate, we lose a derivative of g and a factor $(1 + \xi^2)^{1/2}$.

7. The nonlinear equation. We consider the domain and boundary conditions as before and initial functions with a finite value of $\mathsf{N}_3^3[f_0]$. We look for a solution of (2.21) by iteration on the nonlinear term,

$$Df^n + \frac{1}{\varepsilon} Lf^n = \nu g^{n-1}, \tag{7.1}$$

$$g^{n-1} = \Gamma(f^{n-1}, f^{n-1}). \tag{7.2}$$

First we estimate $\mathsf{N}_3^3[\Gamma]$ from (5.6). For this purpose it is convenient to introduce the auxiliary norms

$$\begin{aligned} \tilde{N}_r[\nabla f] &= \Big\{\sum_i (N_r[f_i])^2\Big\}^{1/2}, \\ \tilde{N}_r[\nabla^2 f] &= \Big\{\sum_{ij} (N_r[f_{ij}])^2\Big\}^{1/2}, \\ \tilde{N}_r[\nabla^3 f] &= \Big\{\sum_{ijk} (N_r[f_{ijk}])^2\Big\}^{1/2} \end{aligned} \tag{7.3}$$

and similarly for $\tilde{\mathsf{N}}_r$. We note the elementary inequalities

$$\begin{aligned} N_r[\nabla^s f] &\leqq \tilde{N}_r[\nabla^s f] \leqq 3^{s/2} N_r[\nabla^s f], \\ \mathsf{N}_r[\nabla^s f] &\leqq \tilde{\mathsf{N}}_r[\nabla^s f] \leqq 3^{s/2} \mathsf{N}_r[\nabla^s f]. \end{aligned} \tag{7.4}$$

Taking norms in (5.6) and recalling (4.16) and (4.17),

$$\begin{aligned} \mathsf{N}_3[\nabla\Gamma] &\leqq \tilde{\mathsf{N}}_3[\nabla\Gamma] \leqq 2\gamma_0 N_3[f]\tilde{\mathsf{N}}_3[\nabla f] \\ &\leqq 2\sqrt{3}\gamma_0 s_0 (\mathsf{N}_3^3[f])^2, \\ \mathsf{N}_3[\nabla^2\Gamma] &\leqq 2\gamma_0\{N_3[f]\tilde{\mathsf{N}}_3[\nabla^2 f] + \tilde{N}_3[\nabla f]\tilde{\mathsf{N}}_3[\nabla f]\} \\ &\leqq 12\gamma_0 s_0 (\mathsf{N}_3^3[f])^2, \\ \mathsf{N}_3[\nabla^3\Gamma] &\leqq 2\gamma_0 N_3[f]\tilde{\mathsf{N}}_3[\nabla^3 f] + 3\tilde{N}[\nabla f]\tilde{\mathsf{N}}_3[\nabla^2 f] \\ &\leqq 24\sqrt{3}\gamma_0 s_0 (\mathsf{N}_3^3[f])^2, \end{aligned}$$

we obtain

$$\begin{aligned} \mathsf{N}_3^3[\Gamma(f,f)] &\leqq \gamma_1 (\mathsf{N}_3^3[f])^2, \\ \gamma_1 &= 24\sqrt{3}\,\gamma_0 s_0. \end{aligned} \tag{7.5}$$

Similarly, we derive

$$\mathsf{N}_3^3[\Gamma(f, g)] \leqq \gamma_1 \mathsf{N}_3^3[f]\mathsf{N}_3^3[g]. \tag{7.6}$$

From Theorem 1 applied to (7.1) we have

$$\begin{aligned} \mathsf{N}_3^3[f^n] &\leqq a_3 \mathsf{N}_3^3[f_0] + t_1 \bar{\mathsf{N}}_3^3[g^{n-1}], \\ t_1 &= b_3 t_0 + \varepsilon c_3. \end{aligned} \tag{7.7}$$

The iteration is contracting if we choose $N_3^3[f_0]$ sufficiently small. Specifically, if we take

$$4a_3\gamma_1 t_1 N_3^3[f_0] < 1, \tag{7.8}$$

then all iterates are bounded

$$N_3^3[f^n] < 2a_3 N_3^3[f_0] < 1/(2\gamma_1 t_1). \tag{7.9}$$

Taking differences in (7.1) and (7.2)

$$\begin{aligned} N_3^3[f^{n+1} - f^n] &\leqq t_1 N_3^3[g^n - g^{n-1}], \\ N_3^3[g^n - g^{n-1}] &\leqq \gamma_1 N_3^3[f^n + f^{n-1}] N_3^3[f^n - f^{n-1}] \\ &< \frac{1}{t_1} N_3^3[f^n - f^{n-1}], \end{aligned}$$

and we see that the iterations contract. From the explicit expression (7.7) for t_1, we conclude that (7.8) will be satisfied if t_0 is sufficiently small, viz.,

$$t_0 \leqq \frac{\sigma}{N_3^3[f_0]} - \varepsilon\tau \tag{7.10}$$

where $\sigma = (4a_3b_3\gamma_1)^{-1}$ and $\tau = c_3/b_3$ depend only on the collision operators L and Γ and the domain (through s_0). A bounded solution exists for $0 < t < t_0$ if t_0 and $N_3^3[f_0]$ are appropriately related as in (7.10). Uniqueness and continuous dependence on f_0 follow in the usual manner. We state

THEOREM 4. *A unique solution to the Boltzmann equation*

$$Df + \frac{1}{\varepsilon} Lf = \nu\Gamma(f, f)$$

exists for a time t_0 which is related to the initial norm $N_3^3[f_0]$ by (7.10). *The solution satisfies the bound* (7.9), $N_3^3[f] < 2a_3N_3^3[f_0]$, *over this period of time.*

Setting $\varepsilon = 1$ in this theorem yields

COROLLARY 1. *A solution to*

$$Df + Lf = \nu\Gamma(f, f)$$

satisfying the bound $N_3^3[f] < 2a_3N_3^3[f_0]$ exists for a time $t_0 \leqq \sigma/N_3^3[f_0] - \tau$.

Similarly, we obtain

COROLLARY 2. *A solution to*

$$Df + Lf = \varepsilon\nu\Gamma(f, f)$$

exists for $t < t_0/\varepsilon$ where t_0 is exactly as given in (7.10). *This result can be obtained directly from the theorem by the substitutions $\varepsilon \to 1$, $\gamma_1 \to \varepsilon\gamma_1$.*

A further corollary we distinguish as

THEOREM 5. *A unique bounded solution to*

$$Df + \frac{1}{\varepsilon} Lf = \varepsilon\nu\Gamma(f,f)$$

exists for $t < t_0 = \sigma/\varepsilon N_3^3[f_0] - \varepsilon\tau$.

This is obtained from Theorem 4 by the substitution $\gamma_1 \to \varepsilon\gamma_1$.

All four results can be summarized by the statement that a solution exists for a sufficiently small initial perturbation from equilibrium; and the length of time for which existence is proved, measured in collision times, is approximately inversely proportional to the relative size of the initial perturbation. But Theorems 4 and 5 are distinguished from the corollaries to Theorem 4 by their closer relation to the linear equation. If f^* is the solution of the linear equation

$$Df^* + \frac{1}{\varepsilon} Lf^* = 0, \qquad f_0^* = f_0, \tag{7.11}$$

the difference

$$\phi = f - f^* \tag{7.12}$$

satisfies

$$D\phi + \frac{1}{\varepsilon} L\phi = \varepsilon^i \nu\Gamma(f,f), \qquad \phi_0 = 0 \tag{7.13}$$

where $i = 0$ or 1 under the conditions of Theorems 4 and 5 respectively. From Theorem 3, recalling that $\nu\Gamma$ is orthogonal to ψ_α, we conclude that

$$N_2^2[\phi] < 4\varepsilon^{i+1}(1 + b_3 t_0 + \varepsilon c_3)(b_3/\mu + c_3)\gamma_1 a_3^2 (N_3^3[f_0])^2. \tag{7.14}$$

The right side is of order ε for the total time of existence referred to in Theorems 4 and 5. In Theorem 4, $i = 0$ and $t_0 = O(1)$, while in Theorem 5, $i = 1$ and $t_0 = O(1/\varepsilon)$. Thus f differs from f^* by an error of order ε over the entire time for which the existence of f is known. Under the conditions of Corollaries 1 and 2, the related linear solution can only be shown to approximate the nonlinear solution for a time which is short compared to the proved time of existence; [$o(1)$ in Corollary 1 and $O(1)$ in Corollary 2]. In the one case (Theorems 4 and 5) the linearization is valid for a time long compared to a mean collision time; in the other case (corollaries) only for a time comparable to a collision time.

The precise estimates of Theorem 3 could be used in the nonlinear existence proof to improve Theorems 4 and 5 (but not the corollaries). This improvement is only by a factor $\log 1/\varepsilon$; i.e., existence can be shown for $t_0 = O(\log 1/\varepsilon)$ under Theorem 4 and $(1/\varepsilon)\log 1/\varepsilon$ under Theorem 5. The improvement is so slight because the accurate estimate of Theorem 3 is obtained at a cost of reduced differentiability.

In summary we note that, although the convergence proof as given is not sufficiently delicate to distinguish those cases (Theorems 4 and 5) where the mean free path of the unperturbed equilibrium ω/ε is small compared to the length scale of variation of the perturbation f, this distinction can be made by use of Theorem 3.

We conclude this section with a brief description of the existence theorems which can be obtained by these methods for the space-independent problem (although this is not our primary purpose). First, since x does not appear, we can replace the constant γ_1 in (7.5) by γ_0. Second we may set $\varepsilon = 1$ since this only alters the time scale. We obtain a solution of

$$\frac{\partial f}{\partial t} + Lf = \nu g, \qquad g = \Gamma(f, f) \tag{7.15}$$

by iteration using (6.23)

$$N_3[f] \leqq (b_3/\mu + c_3)\bar{N}_r[g] \tag{7.16}$$

and (4.16)

$$N_3[\Gamma(f_1, f_2)] \leqq \gamma_0 N_3[f_1] N_3[f_2]. \tag{7.17}$$

We find that a solution exists for all time and satisfies the bound

$$N_3[f] \leqq 2a_3 N_3[f_0] \tag{7.18}$$

if $N_3[f_0]$ is taken sufficiently small, specifically

$$2\gamma_0(b_3/\mu + c_3)a_3 N_3[f_0] < 1. \tag{7.19}$$

By a slight modification of this analysis we can show that these solutions are not only bounded but decay exponentially to zero. First we assume in the separation $F = \omega + \omega^{1/2} f$ that ω is chosen with the parameters of the ultimate equilibrium (they are simply determined by the total mass and energy as given by f_0). Then $(f, \psi_\alpha) = 0$ and the approach to equilibrium consists in showing $f \to 0$. If we assume that $N[e^{\alpha t}\nu g]$ is bounded uniformly in t, $0 < \alpha < \mu$, then (6.20) can be improved to read (with $\varepsilon = 1$)

$$N[e^{\alpha t} f] < \frac{1}{\mu - \alpha} \bar{N}[e^{\alpha t}\nu g] \tag{7.20}$$

whence (6.23) becomes

$$N_r[e^{\alpha t} f] < a_3 \exp(-(\mu - \alpha)t) N_3[f_0] + (b_3/(\mu - \alpha) + c_3)\bar{N}_3[g]. \tag{7.21}$$

Exactly the same procedures as before yield the result that the solution to (7.15) satisfies the bound

$$N_3[f] \leqq 2a_3 N_3[f_0] \exp(-\alpha t) \tag{7.22}$$

provided that

$$2\gamma_0\left(\frac{b_3}{\mu - \alpha} + c_3\right)a_3 N_3[f_0] < 1. \tag{7.23}$$

From (7.23) we see that the decay exponent α can be taken arbitrarily close to μ if the initial value is small. This is not surprising since the equation is, in this case, approximately linear, and μ is the distance of the spectrum from the origin. For any finite initial value subject to (7.19), the ultimate decay exponent for large time is arbitrarily close to μ since $N_3[f]$ becomes small ultimately (7.22), and the theorem can then be reapplied with a new choice of α as in (7.23).

These spatially homogeneous results can be compared to others of Carleman **[1]** (also **[6**, Part 1]), Wild **[2]** and Morgenstern **[3]**, and Povzner **[4]**. Carleman's result is for hard spheres and an isotropic as well as homogeneous f; Wild and Morgenstern consider only the cutoff Maxwellian (ν = constant); Povzner's equation is comparable to ours in generality. Carleman's class of initial functions f_0 is somewhat larger; Morgenstern's and Povzner's initial functions are much more general. On the other hand, Povzner and Morgenstern prove nothing about boundedness or the approach to equilibrium, and Carleman proves a relatively weak form of the approach to equilibrium.

8. **Comparison with fluid dynamics.** That the solution of the nonlinear Boltzmann equation is approximated by a fluid flow when the mean free path is small is a consequence of known results for the linear equation **[16]** using the close correspondence between the linear and nonlinear equations that has just been shown. For completeness of this presentation we shall give a brief discussion of this theory.

Under the conditions of Theorem 4 we can show that the Boltzmann solution is approximated within $O(\varepsilon)$ by a solution of the linear inviscid Euler equations. The viscosity coefficient is of order ε; thus viscosity can be ignored to this order for a finite time. Under the conditions of Theorem 5, the Boltzmann solution is approximated within $O(\varepsilon)$ by a solution of the linear Navier-Stokes equation for the whole time for which existence is shown. Viscosity cannot be ignored for such times of order $1/\varepsilon$.

The Hilbert theory, in its linear version, expands the solution of (2.22) as a power series

$$f_H = f^0 + \varepsilon f^1 + \cdots, \tag{8.1}$$

despite the fact that $\varepsilon = 0$ is singular. The successive terms are determined by an algorithm which involves solution of an integral equation for the $\boldsymbol{\xi}$-dependence and of a linear fluid-dynamic Euler equation (for f^0) and inhomogeneous Euler equations (later terms) for the $(\mathbf{x}, t)$-dependence. The Hilbert series (8.1) is uniquely determined, term by term, by the initial fluid state (also assumed to be a formal power series). In other words, to a given fluid state the Hilbert algorithm assigns a unique distribution function f_H. The truncated series (8.1) satisfies an inhomogeneous Boltzmann equation with an inhomogeneous term that has been estimated and shown to be $O(\varepsilon^n)$ in an appropriate norm for any finite time $0 < t < t_0$. The series is therefore asymptotic to a true solution of the Boltzmann equation which has the same initial values.

The initial values that can be met by this procedure are very special. To generalize the Hilbert theory a different formal expansion

$$f_\mu(\boldsymbol{\xi}, \mathbf{x}, \varepsilon t) = f^0 + \varepsilon f^1 + \cdots \tag{8.2}$$

can be found which also satisfies the Boltzmann equation term by term. But, whereas f_H is uniquely determined by the fluid state, f_μ is uniquely determined by its orthogonal complement, and each term in the expansion of f_μ decays uniformly as $\exp(-\mu t/\varepsilon)$. Although f_H and f_μ are determined by the projections of f_0 into the nullspace of L and its complement, they are not equal to the projections, in particular, at $t = 0$. By summing, $f = f_H + f_\mu$, essentially arbitrary initial data can be matched, and we can find an appropriate f_H (satisfying a suitably modified initial fluid state) which is asymptotic, after a short transient, to general smooth solutions of the linear Boltzmann equation.

The Chapman-Enskog procedure is an alternative to Hilbert, one which uses the same terms (8.1) as functions of $\boldsymbol{\xi}$ but inserts a modified $(\mathbf{x}, t)$-dependence. Instead of Euler and inhomogeneous Euler equations, the fluid parameters in f_H are determined by Euler, Navier-Stokes, and successively higher order differential equations.

This expansion is also asymptotic to a solution of the Boltzmann equation provided that one can suitably estimate the solutions of the fluid equations. The Hilbert theory has the advantage that it can be carried to arbitrarily high order in ε by solving hyperbolic differential equations which have a known theory. For the Chapman-Enskog procedure there is no theory beyond the second step (Navier-Stokes). But the (linear) Navier-Stokes solution can be bounded uniformly for all time, whereas the equivalent Hilbert solution grows linearly with time. Thus the second Chapman-Enskog term is asymptotic uniformly in time; for our application we need its validity only for $0 < t < t_0/\varepsilon$.

We now sketch the proofs that the first order Hilbert approximation is asymptotic to the linear solution under conditions appropriate to Theorem 4, $t = O(1)$, and the second order Chapman-Enskog solution is asymptotic to the linear solution under conditions appropriate to Theorem 5, $t = O(1/\varepsilon)$; for more complete results see **[16]**.

We take an initial function f_0 of suitable regularity and construct the solution f of the linear equation

$$Df + \frac{1}{\varepsilon} Lf = 0. \tag{8.3}$$

For the first case, covered by Theorem 4, we construct a locally Maxwellian comparison function

$$f_E = \sum_\alpha \rho_\alpha(x, t)\psi_\alpha(\xi). \tag{8.4}$$

The ρ_α are related to the (linearized, dimensionless) nominal fluid state by

$$\rho_0 = \rho,$$

(8.5) $$\rho_i = u_i \qquad (i = 1, 2, 3),$$

$$\rho_4 = (3/2)^{1/2} T.$$

We specify the ρ_α in f_E as functions of $\mathbf{x}$ and t by choosing them to be solutions of the (linearized, dimensionless) Euler equations

$$\frac{\partial \rho}{\partial t} + \operatorname{div} \mathbf{u} = 0,$$

(8.6) $$\frac{\partial u_i}{\partial t} + \frac{\partial \rho}{\partial x_i} + \frac{\partial T}{\partial x_i} = 0$$

$$\frac{3}{2} \frac{\partial T}{\partial t} + \operatorname{div} \mathbf{u} = 0,$$

with initial data taken from f_0

(8.7) $$\rho_\alpha(\mathbf{x}, 0) = (\psi_\alpha, f_0).$$

The difference

(8.8) $$\phi = f - f_E$$

satisfies the equation

(8.9) $$D\phi + \frac{1}{\varepsilon} L\phi = - Df_E.$$

By the choice of initial data we have

(8.10) $$(\phi_0, \psi_\alpha) = 0$$

and, from the fact that ρ_α in f_E satisfies the Euler equations, we can easily verify that

(8.11) $$(Df_E, \psi_\alpha) = 0.$$

Inspection of Theorem 3 shows that, after a short exponential transient, ϕ becomes small of order ε. We note that it is the same estimate (Theorem 3) which shows that the linear solution approximates the Euler solution f_E and also that the nonlinear solution approximates the linear solution.

For the second case, covered by Theorem 5, we choose a slightly more complicated comparison function

(8.12) $$f_N = \hat{f}_N + \varepsilon \tilde{f}_N.$$

As before, $\hat{f}_N$ is locally Maxwellian

(8.13)
$$\hat{f}_N = \sum_\alpha \rho_\alpha \psi_\alpha,$$

but the ρ_α are now taken to satisfy the linear Navier-Stokes equations

(8.14)
$$\begin{aligned} &\frac{\partial \rho}{\partial t} + \operatorname{div} \mathbf{u} = 0, \\ &\frac{\partial u_i}{\partial t} + \frac{\partial \rho}{\partial x_i} + \frac{\partial T}{\partial x_i} = \varepsilon\eta\left[\Delta u_i + \frac{1}{3}\frac{\partial}{\partial x_i}(\operatorname{div} \mathbf{u})\right], \\ &\frac{3}{2}\frac{\partial T}{\partial t} + \operatorname{div} \mathbf{u} = \varepsilon\lambda\Delta T \end{aligned}$$

($\varepsilon\eta$ and $\varepsilon\lambda$ are the dimensionless viscosity and heat conductivity coefficients). By inspection of (8.12) one should expect f_N to approximate f to within $O(\varepsilon^2)$. This is indeed possible for a time which is $O(1)$. To accomplish this the ρ_α in f_N would have to be assigned appropriate initial values which are obtained from f_0 by a rather complex computation (see **[16]**). But, since we are interested in times of order $1/\varepsilon$, we shall only be able to show that f_N approximates f to within $O(\varepsilon)$. This, as it turns out, will permit us to use the simpler initial values (8.7). Summarizing, we specify the leading term $\hat{f}_N$ by (8.13) where the ρ_α are solutions of the Navier-Stokes equations with given initial data (8.7).

The second term in the comparison function, $f_N \bar{f}_N$, is obtained by the Chapman-Enskog algorithm. Formal substitution of

(8.15)
$$\phi = f - f_N$$

into the Boltzmann equation yields

(8.16)
$$D\phi + \frac{1}{\varepsilon}L\phi = -\,Df_N - L\bar{f}_N.$$

We would like to specify $\bar{f}_N$ to satisfy

(8.17)
$$L\bar{f}_N + D\hat{f}_N = 0$$

since this would make the inhomogeneous term in (8.16) of order ε. This is an integral equation for $\bar{f}_N$, with $D\hat{f}_N$ a known inhomogeneous term. But the non-trivial nullspace of L requires a compatibility condition on $D\hat{f}_N$ which is not satisfied. From our earlier result (8.11) we know that compatibility would be satisfied if ρ_α satisfied the Euler equations. Expanding

(8.18)
$$D\hat{f}_N = \sum_\alpha \psi_\alpha(\partial\rho_\alpha/\partial t + \boldsymbol{\xi}\cdot\nabla\rho_\alpha)$$

and replacing $\partial\rho_\alpha/\partial t$ by their Navier-Stokes equivalents from (8.14), we can set

(8.19)
$$D\hat{f}_N = \delta_0 + \varepsilon\delta_1$$

where in δ_0 we collect the Euler terms from (8.14) and in δ_1 the viscous and heat conducting terms. It is easily verified, exactly as in (8.11), that

$$(\psi_\alpha, \delta_0) = 0. \tag{8.20}$$

We therefore choose f_N not as the (nonexistent) solution of (8.17), but as the unique solution of

$$L f_N + \delta_0 = 0. \tag{8.21}$$

This leaves a formal remainder in (8.16) of order ε,

$$D\phi + \frac{1}{\varepsilon} L\phi = -\varepsilon D f_N - \varepsilon \delta_1. \tag{8.22}$$

We note that the separation (8.19) is strictly formal; the ρ_α as solutions of the Navier-Stokes equations are complicated functions of ε and, in general, are non-expandable. But the remainder in (8.22) can be estimated to be $O(\varepsilon)$, given sufficiently smooth initial data for the Navier-Stokes solution.

The solution of (8.21) for f_N is an explicit linear combination of velocity and temperature gradients with coefficients which are functions of ξ obtained by solution of the integral equation (which can be transformed into a Fredholm equation with compact kernel). It is easily verified that

$$(\psi_\alpha, D f_N) = 0. \tag{8.23}$$

This is essentially the statement that ρ_α satisfy the Navier-Stokes equations [cf. the missing orthogonality condition for (8.17), $(\psi_\alpha, D\hat{f}_N) \neq 0$]; this is, in fact, the kinetic *derivation* of the Navier-Stokes equations. We are now in a position to refer again to Theorem 3. Since the inhomogeneous term in (8.22) is of order ε (uniformly for all time by Navier-Stokes estimates) and is orthogonal to ψ_α, and since the initial value ϕ_0 is orthogonal to ψ_α, we conclude that ϕ is $O(\varepsilon)$ for $t = O(1/\varepsilon)$ [we do not obtain $O(\varepsilon^2)$ because of the factor $t_0 = O(1/\varepsilon)$ in (6.30)].[8]

The solutions of the nonlinear Boltzmann equation obtained in the previous section have been shown to approximate fluid behavior only to the extent that they are also linear. While these fluid comparisons can be improved to some extent, they cannot be greatly extended by our present methods. For example, the existence theory is basically unsuited to describe a finite strength shock wave. A shock wave of finite amplitude would have a thickness $O(\varepsilon)$ and would require handling estimates $N[\nabla f] = O(\varepsilon^{-1/2})$, $N[\nabla^2 f] = O(\varepsilon^{-3/2})$, etc. A Sobolev estimate would not be strong enough to rule out large excursions in f itself.

Under Theorem 4, a fully developed shock wave with strength of order ε would have a finite thickness, $O(1)$. Under Theorem 5, with nonlinearity of order ε^2, the fully-developed thickness would be $O(1/\varepsilon)$. Thus weak shocks, and even much

---

[8] The stronger result quoted in **[16**, p. 171**]** is in error. Although the linear Navier-Stokes solution in a bounded domain decays exponentially, the decay is slow as $\exp(-\varepsilon t)$. Terms such as $\int_0^\infty f\,dt$ will produce a factor $1/\varepsilon$ just as it arises from $t_0 \sim 1/\varepsilon$.

steeper profiles, are contained within the theory. However, the time required to observe the development of a steady limiting shock profile would be $O(1/\varepsilon)$ under Theorem 4 and $O(1/\varepsilon^2)$ under Theorem 5. We could therefore observe only the initial stages of shock formation.

One may hope that stronger nonlinear results for the Boltzmann equation will be obtained by making efficient use of nonlinear Navier-Stokes estimates.

APPENDIX. ESTIMATE OF THE QUADRATIC COLLISION INTEGRAL[9]

In a more complete notation, the term Q in (2.1) can be written

$$Q(F, F) = \int (F'F_1' - FF_1)\, d\Omega, \qquad d\Omega = B(\theta, V)\, d\theta d\varepsilon d\boldsymbol{\xi}_1. \tag{A.1}$$

Introducing f as in (2.4), we obtain the bilinear form

$$\nu\Gamma(f, g) = \int \frac{1}{2}(f'g_1' + f_1'g_1 - fg_1 - f_1g)\omega_1^{1/2}\, d\Omega \tag{A.2}$$

where

$$\nu = \int \omega_1\, d\Omega. \tag{A.3}$$

To estimate Γ we write

$$|\nu\Gamma| \leqq \nu\Gamma_1 + \nu\Gamma_2, \quad \nu\Gamma_1 = \int \frac{1}{2}|fg_1 + f_1g|\omega_1^{1/2}\, d\Omega, \quad \nu\Gamma_2 = \int \frac{1}{2}|f'g_1' + f_1'g_1|\omega_1^{1/2}\, d\Omega. \tag{A.4}$$

To estimate Γ_1 we need the bound

$$\sigma = \int \omega_1^{1/2}\, d\Omega < \alpha_0\nu \tag{A.5}$$

for some constant α_0. This is easily obtained from the explicit forms

$$\nu(\xi) = 2\pi \int B_0(|\boldsymbol{\eta} - \boldsymbol{\xi}|)\omega(\eta)\, d\boldsymbol{\eta}, \quad \sigma(\xi) = 2\pi \int B_0(|\boldsymbol{\eta} - \boldsymbol{\xi}|)\omega^{1/2}(\eta)\, d\boldsymbol{\eta}, \tag{A.6}$$

where

$$B_0(V) = \int B_0(\theta, V)\, d\theta. \tag{A.7}$$

---

[9] For the notation, transformations, and supporting estimates used in this Appendix, we refer to [9].

The bound (A.5) follows from (A.6) as an elementary exercise if, for example, $B_0(V)$ has a uniformly bounded derivative (this is true for all hard, power law potentials).

From

$$|f| < (1 + \xi^2)^{-r/2} N_r[f] < N_r[f],$$
$$|g| < (1 + \xi^2)^{-r/2} N_r[g] < N_r[g]$$

we obtain

$$\tfrac{1}{2}|fg_1 + f_1 g| < (1 + \xi^2)^{-r/2} N_r[f] N_r[g]$$

and conclude that

$$\nu\Gamma_1 < (1 + \xi^2)^{-r/2} \alpha_0 \nu N_r[f] N_r[g]$$

or

(A.8) $$N_r[\Gamma_1] < \alpha_0 N_r[f] N_r[g].$$

To estimate Γ_2, we transform the integral as in **[9]** (here we use $R(v, w)$ for the kernel $Q(v, w)$ in **[9]**)

(A.9) $$\nu\Gamma_2 = \int \frac{1}{2} |f(\boldsymbol{\xi} + \mathbf{v}) g(\boldsymbol{\xi} + \mathbf{w}) + f(\boldsymbol{\xi} + \mathbf{w}) g(\boldsymbol{\xi} + \mathbf{v})| \cdot \omega^{1/2}(\boldsymbol{\xi} + \mathbf{v} + \mathbf{w}) \frac{R(v, w)}{v^2} \, d\mathbf{v} \, d\mathbf{w}.$$

We recall that $\mathbf{w}$ is integrated over the plane perpendicular to $\mathbf{v}$, and then $\mathbf{v}$ is integrated over the full three-dimensional space. Resolving $\boldsymbol{\xi}$ into components $\boldsymbol{\xi}_1$ and $\boldsymbol{\xi}_2$ parallel and perpendicular to $\mathbf{v}$ respectively, we have

(A.10) $$\omega^{1/2}(\boldsymbol{\xi} + \mathbf{v} + \mathbf{w}) = \omega^{1/2}(\boldsymbol{\xi}_1 + \mathbf{v}) \omega^{1/2}(\boldsymbol{\xi}_2 + \mathbf{w}).$$

From equation (60) of **[9]** we have

(A.11) $$\int \omega^{1/2}(\boldsymbol{\xi}_2 + \mathbf{w}) R(v, w) \, d\mathbf{w} < Q_0 v.$$

From

$$1 + (\boldsymbol{\xi} + \mathbf{v})^2 = 1 + (\boldsymbol{\xi}_1 + \mathbf{v})^2 + \xi_2^2 > 1 + \xi_2^2,$$
$$1 + (\boldsymbol{\xi} + \mathbf{w})^2 = 1 + (\boldsymbol{\xi}_2 + \mathbf{w})^2 + \xi_1^2 > 1 + \xi_1^2$$

and

$$[1 + (\boldsymbol{\xi} + \mathbf{v})^2][1 + (\boldsymbol{\xi} + \mathbf{w})^2] > (1 + \xi_1^2)(1 + \xi_2^2) > 1 + \xi^2$$

we obtain, for $r \geqq 1$

(A.12) $$\tfrac{1}{2}|f(\boldsymbol{\xi} + \mathbf{v}) g(\boldsymbol{\xi} + \mathbf{w}) + f(\boldsymbol{\xi} + \mathbf{w}) g(\boldsymbol{\xi} + \mathbf{v})| < (1 + \xi^2)^{-(r-1)/2} (1 + \xi_1^2)^{-1/2} (1 + \xi_2^2)^{-1/2} N_r[f] N_r[g].$$

Substituting (A.11) and (A.12) into (A.9), we find

$$\nu\Gamma_2 < Q_0(1 + \xi^2)^{-r/2} N_r[f] N_r[g]\, J,$$

(A.13)

$$J = \int \frac{1}{v}(1 + \xi_1^2)^{-1/2}(1 + \xi_2^2)^{-1/2}\omega^{1/2}(\boldsymbol{\xi}_1 + \mathbf{v})\, d\mathbf{v}.$$

Introducing polar coordinates with $\boldsymbol{\xi}$ as axis in the $\mathbf{v}$-integration,

$$d\mathbf{v} = 2\pi v^2 dv d(\cos\theta),$$

then replacing the variable $\cos\theta$ by $u = \xi\cos\theta$, we have

$$J = (2\pi)^{-1/2}\xi^{-1}\int_{-\xi}^{+\xi}(1 + u^2)^{-1/2}(1 + \xi^2 - u^2)^{-1/2}\phi(u)\, du$$

where

$$\phi(u) = \int_0^\infty e^{-(u+v)^2/4} v\, dv.$$

The elementary estimate $\phi(u) \leq 2 + \psi(u)$ where

$$\psi(u) = 0, \qquad u > 0$$

$$\psi(u) = -2\pi^{1/2}u, \qquad u < 0$$

yields

$$J < \left(\frac{2}{\pi}\right)^{1/2}\frac{1}{\xi}\int_{-\xi}^{+\xi}(1 + u^2)^{-1/2}(1 + \xi^2 - u^2)^{-1/2}\, du$$

$$- \frac{2^{1/2}}{\xi}\int_{-\xi}^{0}(1 + u^2)^{-1/2}(1 + \xi^2 - u^2)^{-1/2}u\, du.$$

The second integral is explicit and the first is estimated using $(1 + u^2)(1 + \xi^2 - u^2) > 1 + \xi^2$ to obtain

$$J < 2\left(\frac{2}{\pi}\right)^{1/2}(1 + \xi^2)^{-1/2} + \frac{2^{1/2}}{\xi}\arcsin\frac{\xi^2}{2 + \xi^2} < \beta_0(1 + \xi^2)^{-1/2}$$

where β_0 can be taken as $2(2/\pi)^{1/2} + 2^{-1/2}\pi$. Thus

(A.14) $$N_r[\Gamma_2] < \beta_0\, Q_0\, N_r[f] N_r[g], \qquad r \geq 1$$

and

(A.15) $$N_r[\Gamma] < \gamma_0 N_r[f] N_r[g], \qquad r \geq 1$$

where $\gamma_0 = \alpha_0 + \beta_0 Q_0$. A trivial modification of the above arguments yields the companion estimate

(A.16) $$\mathsf{N}_r[\Gamma] < \gamma_0 N_r[f] N_r[g], \qquad r > 1.$$

Acknowledgement. The work presented here was supported by the U.S. Atomic Energy Commission under contract No. AT(30-1)1480.

References

1. T. Carleman, Acta Math. **60** (1933), 91.
2. E. Wild, Proc. Cambridge Philos. Soc. **47** (1951), 602.
3. D. Morgenstern, Proc. Nat. Acad. Sci. U.S.A. **40** (1954), 719.
4. A. Ja. Povzner, Mat. Sb. **58** (1962), 62.
5. Harold Grad, *Principles of the kinetic theory of gases*, Handbuch der Physik, S. Flugge, ed., Vol. XII, pp. 205–294, Springer, Berlin, 1958.
6. T. Carleman, *Problèmes mathématiques dans la théorie cinétique des gaz*, Almqvist and Wiksells, Uppsala, 1957.
7. D. Morgenstern, J. Rational Mech. Anal. **4** (1955), 533.
8. C. S. Wang Chang and G. E. Uhlenbeck, *On the propagation of sound in monatomic gases*, Engineering Research Inst., Univ. of Mich., Ann Arbor, Mich., 1952.
9. Harold Grad, *Asymptotic theory of the Boltzmann equation*. II, Rarefied gas dynamics, J. A. Laurmann, ed., Vol. I, pp. 26–59, Academic Press, New York, 1963.
10. E. P. Gross and E. A. Jackson, Phys. Fluids **3** (1959), 432.
11. C. Cercignani, Ann. Physics **20** (1962), 219.
12. H. Weitzner, *Steady state oscillations in a gas*, Proceedings of Fourth International Symposium on Rarefied Gas Dynamics, Toronto, July 1964 (to appear).
13. H. W. Liepmann, R. Navasimna, M. T. Chahine, Phys. Fluids **5** (1962), 1313.
14. C. K. Chu, Phys. Fluids **8** (1965), 12.
15. Harold Grad, *On Boltzmann's H-theorem*, Proceedings of SIAM von Karman Symposium, Washington, D.C., May 1964, 1965 (to appear).
16. Harold Grad, Phys. Fluids **6** (1963), 147.
17. D. Hilbert, *Grundzüge einer allgemeinen Theorie der linearen Integralgleichungen*, Chelsea, New York, 1953.
18. Harold Grad, Comm. Pure Appl. Math. **18** (1965), 345.

Courant Institute of Mathematical Sciences
New York University,
New York, New York

ON THE EXISTENCE OF SOLUTIONS OF THE STEADY-STATE NAVIER-STOKES EQUATIONS FOR A CLASS OF NONSMOOTH BOUNDARY DATA[1]

BY

J. E. EDWARDS

It is proved that, for piecewise-smooth boundary data, solutions exist to both the interior and exterior three-dimensional Navier-Stokes boundary-value problems of fluid mechanics. The results are new in that previous results concerning existence have depended strongly on boundary data regularity. The proof is completed in three steps: (1) a vector field $\mathbf{v}$ is constructed such that $\mathbf{v}$ assumes prescribed values on the boundary, $\operatorname{div} \mathbf{v} = 0$, $\mathbf{v}$ vanishes outside a neighborhood of the boundary, and $|\mathbf{v}(\mathbf{x})| \leqq \varepsilon s^{-1}$, where s is a modified distance of $\mathbf{x}$ from the boundary and $\varepsilon > 0$ is any prescribed number; (2) using this solenoidal extension field, a generalized solution of the problem is shown to exist; and (3) this generalized solution is shown to have the proper regularity in the flow region up to and including any smooth portion of the boundary. When the boundary data are smooth, the construction in step (1) reduces to that used by R. Finn (Acta Math. **105** (1961), 197–244). The functional-analytic approach used in steps (2) and (3) is based on that used by H. Fujita (J. Fac. Sci. Univ. Tokyo Sect. I **9** (1961), 59–102).
(Received February 17, 1964.)

Knolls Atomic Power Laboratory,
Schenectady, New York

[1] This research was partially financed by the Lockheed Missiles and Space Company, as part of its Independent Research Program.

TOWARD THE VALIDITY OF THE PRANDTL APPROXIMATION IN A BOUNDARY LAYER

BY

P. C. FIFE

A family w_R, p_R (R is the parameter and also the Reynolds number) of solutions of the Navier-Stokes equations $-R^{-1}\nabla^2 w + (w \cdot \nabla)w + \nabla p = 0$; $\nabla \cdot w = 0$ (2 vars.) is postulated to exist in a fixed bounded region G adjacent to a curved wall (on which $w = 0$). Let Γ be a straight line normal to the wall and bounding G, and suppose the flows all enter G through Γ. Assume (1) the term $R^{-1}\nabla^2 w_R$ is bounded in G uniformly in R as $R \to \infty$; (2) certain tangential derivatives of flow quantities are also bounded in this way; (3) the tangential component w_R^1 of w_R satisfies $w_R^1 \geqq kn$ (n is distance from the wall; k independent of R); and on Γ, the stronger condition $w_R^1 \geqq k \operatorname{Min}(R^{1/2}n, 1)$; (4) $\partial^2 w_R^1/\partial n^2$ is bounded from above by $kR^{1/2}$ (in fact, one expects it to be negative). Let $\bar{w}_R^1$ be the tangential component of a velocity field found by solving the Prandtl system. If $\bar{w}_R^1 - w_R^1 = O(R^{-1/2})$ on Γ ($R \to \infty$) and if the pressure used in the Prandtl system differs from p_R on the wall by the same order, then $\bar{w}_R^1 - w_R^1 = o(1)$ uniformly in a strip next to the wall of width $o(R^{-(1-\delta)/2})$ (rather than $O(R^{-1/2})$). Physically speaking, the above boundedness conditions exclude turbulent flows; the result is not true without some such postulates. (Received February 27, 1964.)

UNIVERSITY OF MINNESOTA,
MINNEAPOLIS, MINNESOTA

INSTABILITY AND UNIQUENESS RESULTS FOR A THIRD ORDER PDE ON A STRIP

BY

B. D. COLEMAN, R. J. DUFFIN AND V. J. MIZEL

(*) $u_t = u_{xx} - u_{xtx}$ is considered for the semi-infinite strip S: $0 \leqq x \leqq H$, $0 \leqq t < \infty$ with conditions of type (1) $u = 0$, or else of type (1) in combination with type (2) $u_x - u_{xt} = 0$, applied at the edges at $x = 0$ and at $x = H$. By a *solution* is meant a function which is C^2 on the S, and satisfies (*). With the above conditions the following results hold: (1) *For prescribed initial data* $u(x, 0) = \bar{u}(x)$ *there is at most one solution of* (*); (2) *Not all bounded initial data yield bounded solutions. In fact for arbitrary* $\bar{u}_1(x)$ *there exists for every* $\varepsilon > 0$ *functions* $\bar{u}_2(x)$ *with* $|\bar{u}_1(x) - \bar{u}_2(x)| < \varepsilon$ *such that a solution with initial value* $\bar{u}_2(x)$ *must be unbounded.* This follows from the proof of the following result; (3) *If* $H \leqq H_0$ *then the only bounded solution is* $u \equiv 0$. The value $H_0 = \pi$ is sharp for edge conditions (1). The value $H_0 = \pi/2$ is sharp for (1) in combination with (2). Equation (*) is the dimensionless form of an equation arising in the hydrodynamics of non-Newtonian fluids (see B. D. Coleman and W. Noll, Arch. Rat. Mech. Anal. **6** (1960), 355–370, equation (7.12): γ is chosen to be negative). (Received February 20, 1964.)

Note added in proof. Sharper and more embracing results on this subject are given in our paper *Instability, uniqueness, and nonexistence theorems for the equation* $u_t = u_{xx} - u_{xtx}$ *on a strip*, to appear shortly in the Archive for Rational Mechanics and Analysis.

Mellon Institute,
Pittsburgh, Pennsylvania
Carnegie Institute of Technology,
Pittsburgh, Pennsylvania

IV. GENERAL RELATIVITY, QUANTUM FIELD THEORY

EXISTENCE AND UNIQUENESS THEOREMS IN GENERAL RELATIVITY

BY

A. LICHNEROWICZ

In this lecture, my purpose is to study local existence and uniqueness theorems for the Einstein equations in different cases: the exterior case, hydrodynamic and electromagnetic cases. Some of the results are mine; mostly they are due to Y. Bruhat. Leray's theorems on hyperbolic quasilinear systems play an essential role in the theory.

I. Einstein's equations.

1. EINSTEIN'S EQUATIONS.

(a) In each relativistic theory of the gravitational field, the main element is a differentiable manifold of dimension 4: the *space-time* V_4. On V_4, we have an hyperbolic riemannian metric, with the signature $+ - - -$, which can be written in local coordinates

$$ds^2 = g_{\alpha\beta} dx^\alpha dx^\beta \qquad (\alpha, \beta, \cdots = 0, 1, 2, 3).$$

The $g_{\alpha\beta}$ are the gravitational *potentials* with respect to the coordinates. In each point $x \in V_4$ the metric defines by $ds^2 = 0$ the *elementary cone* C_x. Such a manifold admits global systems of time-like curves, but does not admit, generally, global systems of space-like hypersurfaces. Our point of view is here purely local.

(b) Let $R_{\alpha\beta}$ be the Ricci tensor of the metric and let us consider the Einstein tensor

$$S_{\alpha\beta} \equiv R_{\alpha\beta} - \tfrac{1}{2} g_{\alpha\beta} R \tag{1.1}$$

which, according to Bianchi identities, satisfies

$$\nabla_\alpha S^\alpha{}_\beta = 0 \tag{1.2}$$

where ∇ is the operator of covariant derivation.

In the general relativity, the metric satisfies Einstein equations

$$S_{\alpha\beta} = \chi T_{\alpha\beta} \qquad (\chi = \text{const}) \tag{1.3}$$

where the energy tensor $T_{\alpha\beta}$ is piecewise continuous; $T_{\alpha\beta}$ defines the sources of the field. In the domains where $T_{\alpha\beta} = 0$, we have the "exterior case."

2. Elementary analysis of the Cauchy problem. We give first an elementary analysis for the Cauchy problem of the exterior case

$$S_{\alpha\beta} = 0. \tag{2.1}$$

(a) Let Σ be a local hypersurface of V_4 which is not tangent to the elementary cones. If $x^0 = 0$ defines locally Σ, we have $g^{00} \neq 0$. Einstein's equations can be written

$$R_{ij} \equiv -\tfrac{1}{2}g^{00}\partial_{00}g_{ij} + F_{ij} = 0 \qquad (i, j = 1, 2, 3) \tag{2.2}$$

and

$$S^0_\alpha \equiv G_\alpha = 0 \tag{2.3}$$

where the F_{ij} and G_α are functions, the values of which are known on Σ, if we know the values of the potentials $g_{\alpha\beta}$ and the values of the first derivatives $\partial_0 g_{\alpha\beta}$ (Cauchy data).

The system of Einstein equations has the involution property: if a metric satisfies the equations (2.2) and, *over* Σ *only*, the equations $S^0_\alpha = 0$, it satisfies also these equations outside Σ. This is a trivial consequence of the conservation identities (1.2).

(b) Correlatively, we see that the system (2.2) gives the values on Σ of the six second derivatives $\partial_{00}g_{ij}$, which I called the *significant derivatives* for Σ. The four derivatives $\partial_{00}g_{\alpha 0}$ are absent.

We have the possibility to change local coordinates, according to

$$x^{\lambda'} = x^\lambda + \frac{(x^0)^3}{6}\{\phi^{(\lambda')}(x^i) + \varepsilon^{(\lambda)}\} \qquad (\lambda' = \lambda) \tag{2.4}$$

where $\varepsilon^{(\lambda)} \to 0$ when $x^0 \to 0$. The numerical values of the coordinates of the points of Σ and the Cauchy data are invariant. This is so also for the $\partial_{00}g_{ij}$, but the new $\partial_{00}g_{\alpha 0}$ can have arbitrary values. These four derivatives can be discontinuous through Σ. But, according to the axioms of the theory, these discontinuities have no physical meaning and vanish for convenient coordinates.

The significant derivatives can have discontinuities only if Σ is tangent to the elementary cones. The characteristics of Einstein's equations, or *gravitational waves*, are defined by the hypersurfaces $f = 0$ tangent to the elementary cones

$$\Delta_1 f \equiv g^{\alpha\beta}\,\partial_\alpha f\,\partial_\beta f = 0; \tag{2.5}$$

the *gravitational rays* are defined by the characteristics of (2.5), that is to say, by the null-geodesics of the metric.

3. Harmonic coordinates.

(a) In the following part, we use systematically harmonic coordinates: we consider an equation which admits (2.5) as characteristics

$$\Delta f \equiv \delta df = 0 \tag{3.1}$$

where d is the operator of exterior differentiation and δ the operator of exterior codifferentiation.

Harmonic coordinates are coordinates such that the

(3.2) $$F^\rho = \Delta x^\rho = g^{\alpha\beta}\Gamma^\rho_{\alpha\beta}$$

vanish. It is possible to write

(3.3) $$R_{\alpha\beta} = R^{(h)}_{\alpha\beta} + L_{\alpha\beta}$$

where

(3.4) $$R^{(h)}_{\alpha\beta} = -\tfrac{1}{2}g^{\lambda\mu}\,\partial_{\lambda\mu}g_{\alpha\beta} + f_{\alpha\beta}(g_{\lambda\mu}, \partial_\rho g_{\lambda\mu})$$

and

(3.5) $$2L_{\alpha\beta} = g_{\alpha\rho}\partial_\beta F^\rho + g_{\beta\rho}\partial_\alpha F^\rho.$$

(b) We consider the general Einstein system

(3.6) $$S_{\alpha\beta} = \chi T_{\alpha\beta} \quad \text{or} \quad R_{\alpha\beta} = \chi(T_{\alpha\beta} - \tfrac{1}{2}g_{\alpha\beta}T)$$

which implies $\nabla_\alpha T^\alpha{}_\beta = 0$. We assume that the Cauchy data for Σ ($x^0 = 0$) satisfy

(3.7) $$S^0_\alpha = \chi T^0_\alpha \quad \text{for } x^0 = 0.$$

Moreover we assume the initial harmonicity condition

(3.8) $$F^\rho = 0 \quad \text{for } x^0 = 0.$$

Let us consider now the system given by

(3.9) $$S^{(h)}_{\alpha\beta} \equiv R^{(h)}_{\alpha\beta} - \tfrac{1}{2}g_{\alpha\beta}R^{(h)} = \chi T_{\alpha\beta} \quad \text{or} \quad R^{(h)}_{\alpha\beta} = \chi(T_{\alpha\beta} - \tfrac{1}{2}g_{\alpha\beta}T)$$

and

(3.10) $$\nabla_\alpha T^\alpha{}_\beta = 0.$$

If we write a solution of (3.6) in harmonic coordinates, it is a solution of (3.9), (3.10), satisfying (3.7), (3.8) on a *space-like* Σ. Conversely such a solution of (3.9), (3.10) satisfies

$$L^0_\alpha - \tfrac{1}{2}g^0_\alpha L = S^0_\alpha - S^{(h)0}{}_\alpha = 0 \quad \text{for } x^0 = 0$$

and thus

(3.11) $$\partial_0 F^\rho = 0 \quad \text{for } x^0 = 0.$$

From the conservation identities (1.2), we obtain for this solution

$$\nabla_\alpha(L^{\alpha\beta} - \tfrac{1}{2}g^{\alpha\beta}L) = 0,$$

that is to say,

$$g^{\alpha\beta}\,\partial_{\alpha\beta}F^\rho + h^\rho = 0$$

where h^ρ is linear with respect to the $\partial_\alpha F^\lambda$. If Σ is space-like, the F^ρ satisfy an hyperbolic system which admits a uniqueness theorem: from (3.8), (3.11) follows $F^\rho = 0$ everywhere.

Thus *each solution of the system* (3.9), (3.10), *satisfying* (3.7), (3.8) *on the space-like* Σ, *is a solution of the corresponding Cauchy problem for Einstein's equations.*

II. **Leray's Theorem.**

4. Special quasilinear systems on a manifold. Let V_m be a differentiable manifold. Let us consider the differential system in

$$U(x) = (u_\sigma(x)) \qquad (\sigma = 1, \cdots, n)$$

where $x \in V_m$, defined by

$$A(x, U, \partial)U = B(x, U). \tag{4.1}$$

∂ is here the operator of ordinary derivation $\partial = (\partial_\alpha)$ $(\alpha = 1, \cdots, m)$ and A a diagonal matrix

$$A(x, U, \partial) = \begin{pmatrix} a_1(x, U, \partial) & \cdots & 0 \\ \cdot & \cdot & \\ \cdot & \cdot & \\ \cdot & \cdot & \\ 0 & & a_n(x, U\ \partial) \end{pmatrix} \tag{4.2}$$

whose element $a_\tau(x, U, \partial)$ $(\tau = 1, \cdots, n)$ is a differential operator of order $m(\tau)$.

It is convenient to associate to each u_σ an index $s(\sigma)$ and to τ an index $t(\tau)$, defined up to an additive constant, such that

$$m(\tau) = s(\tau) - t(\tau) + 1;$$

we assume that

$$B(x, U) = (b_\tau(x, U))$$

where b_τ are functions of the u_σ and of the derivatives of u_σ *of order* $\leqq s(\sigma) - t(\tau)$.

We will study the Cauchy problem for the system (4.1).

5. Leray's theorem. Let Σ be a regular hypersurface of V_m and let us introduce in the neighborhood of Σ

$$V(x) = (v_\sigma(x))$$

where v_σ has locally square integrable derivatives of order $\leqq s(\sigma) + 1$.

We assume

(1) $A(x, V, \partial)$ is *hyperbolic* in the sense of Leray-Gårding and defines two fields of half cones C_κ^+ and C_κ^- $(C_\kappa = C_\kappa^+ \cup C_\kappa^-)$ and the corresponding emissions $\mathscr{E}_\kappa^+, \mathscr{E}_\kappa^-$. The vector space tangent to Σ in x is exterior to C_κ (Σ is "space-like");

(2) $a_\tau(x, V, \partial)v_\tau - b_\tau(x, V)$ and its derivatives of order $< t(\tau)$ vanish on Σ.

A solution of the Cauchy problem for (4.1) is a solution $U = (u_\sigma)$ of (4.1) having locally square integrable derivatives of order $\leqq s(\sigma)$, such that

$$u_\sigma - v_\sigma$$

and its derivatives of order $< s(\sigma)$ vanish on Σ.

Theorem. *If $x \in \Sigma$, the Cauchy problem has, under our assumptions, at least one solution in the neighbourhood of x. If u_σ and $\bar{u}_\sigma$ are two solutions of the Cauchy problem in the neighbourhood of x and if u_σ and $\bar{u}_\sigma$ have locally square integrable derivatives of order $\leqq s(\sigma) + 1$, $U = \overline{U}$.*

III. Exterior and interior cases.

6. EXTERIOR CASE.

(a) Let us consider the Einstein system for the exterior case

(6.1) $$R_{\alpha\beta} = 0.$$

In harmonic coordinates, we have

(6.2) $$R^{(h)}_{\alpha\beta} \equiv -\tfrac{1}{2}g^{\lambda\mu}\,\partial_{\lambda\mu}g_{\alpha\beta} + f_{\alpha\beta}(g_{\lambda\mu}, \partial_\nu g_{\lambda\mu}) = 0.$$

The system of the ten equations (6.2) belongs to the type (4.1) with

$$s(g_{\alpha\beta}) = 2, \qquad t(R^{(h)}_{\alpha\beta}) = 1;$$

we consider Cauchy's data such that

(1) $g_{\alpha\beta}X^\alpha X^\beta$ is hyperbolic on the initial hypersurface Σ $(x^0 = 0)$;

(2) Σ is space-like;

(3) on Σ: $S^0_\alpha = 0$, $F^\rho = 0$.

The corresponding Cauchy problem for (6.2) admits *an unique solution* according to the theorem of Leray, if the Cauchy data are sufficiently smooth. The values of the solution at a point y corresponding to the positive side of Σ depend only on the Cauchy data in $\mathscr{E}^-(y) \cap \Sigma$, that is to say, in the past of y.

(b) According to the argument of §3, this solution is a solution of the Cauchy problem for the Einstein equations.

The uniqueness of the Cauchy problem for the Einstein system is a "*physical*" *or* "*geometrical*" *uniqueness*, that is to say the uniqueness, modulo a change of coordinates leaving invariant the numerical values of the coordinates of each point of Σ and the Cauchy data.

It is now easy to see that each solution of the Cauchy problem for $R_{\alpha\beta} = 0$ can be deduced by such a change of coordinates from the unique solution of the same problem for $R^{(h)}_{\alpha\beta} = 0$. This change of coordinates satisfies a system of the same type as (6.2) and the existence theorem for this system implies thus *the physical uniqueness theorem for the Einstein equations.*

The same argument is available for all the cases.

7. PURE MATTER CASE.

(a) If we consider only pure matter as sources, the Einstein equations can be written

(7.1) $$S_{\alpha\beta} = \chi\rho u_\alpha u_\beta$$

where ρ is the proper density and u^α the unitary 4-velocity ($g_{\alpha\beta}u^\alpha u^\beta = 1$). The conservation equations are equivalent to the system

(7.2) $$u^\alpha \nabla_\alpha u^\beta = 0$$

and

(7.3) $$\nabla_\alpha(\rho u^\alpha) = 0.$$

According to §3, we consider, in harmonic coordinates, the system defined by

(7.1′) $$R^{(h)}_{\alpha\beta} = \chi\rho(u_\alpha u_\beta - \tfrac{1}{2}g_{\alpha\beta})$$

and (7.2), (7.3). To obtain an hyperbolic system, we substitute for (7.1′), the derivative along the current lines:

(7.1″) $$u^\gamma\nabla_\gamma R^{(h)}_{\alpha\beta} = -\chi\rho\nabla_\gamma u^\gamma(u_\alpha u_\beta - \tfrac{1}{2}g_{\alpha\beta}).$$

u^α is now an arbitrary vector and the unknown functions are ten $g_{\alpha\beta}$, four u^α and ρ, that is, 15 functions; we have the system (7.1″), (7.2), (7.3) of 15 equations and this system belongs to the type (4.1) with

$$s(g_{\alpha\beta}) = 3, \qquad s(u^\alpha) = 1, \qquad s(\rho) = 1$$

and for the equations

$$t(1'') = 1, \qquad t(2) = 2, \qquad t(3) = 1.$$

The corresponding matrix A is diagonal and we have ten times the operator

$$a(1'') = u^\gamma g^{\lambda\mu}\,\partial_{\gamma\lambda\mu}$$

and five times the operator

$$a(2) = a(3) = u^\gamma\,\partial_\gamma.$$

(b) Our Cauchy data on Σ are the $g_{\alpha\beta}$ and their first derivatives and we assume that these data are such that:

(1) The relations

$$S^0_\alpha = \chi\rho u^0 u_\alpha$$

define a unitary u^α and the scalar ρ on Σ.

(2) $g_{\alpha\beta}X^\alpha X^\beta$ is hyperbolic normal; u^α being unitary, the operator A is thus hyperbolic with the main cone C_x; Σ is space-like.

(3) $F^\rho = 0$ on Σ.

From these data, we determine the second derivatives of $g_{\alpha\beta}$ by the equations

$$R^{(h)}_{\alpha\beta} = \chi\rho(u_\alpha u_\beta - \tfrac{1}{2}g_{\alpha\beta}) \quad \text{on } \Sigma;$$

we obtain thus a Cauchy problem for the system (7.1″), (7.2), (7.3) for which the Cauchy data are the $g_{\alpha\beta}$, their first and second derivatives, the u^α and ρ, and which admits an unique solution, according to the theory of Leray. This solution satisfies everywhere (7.1′) where, according to

$$u^\alpha u^\beta \nabla_\alpha u_\beta = 0,$$

u^α is unitary.

From the argument of §3, it follows that our solution is a solution of the Einstein equations (7.1). We have thus proved the existence theorem and the uniqueness theorem in this case.

IV. Hydrodynamic case.

8. Relativistic Helmholtz equations.

(a) We consider a perfect fluid with the energy tensor:

$$T_{\alpha\beta} = \rho u_\alpha u_\beta - p g_{\alpha\beta} \tag{8.1}$$

where p is the pressure, $\rho - p$ the proper density and u^α the 4-velocity. We assume that the fluid admits a state equation

$$\rho = \phi(p). \tag{8.2}$$

The conservation equations $\nabla_\alpha T^{\alpha\beta} = 0$ are equivalent to the system

$$u^\alpha \nabla_\alpha u^\beta = \frac{\partial_\alpha p}{\rho}(g^{\alpha\beta} - u^\alpha u^\beta) \tag{8.3}$$

and

$$\nabla_\alpha(\rho u^\alpha) = u^\alpha\, \partial_\alpha p. \tag{8.4}$$

I introduce the function

$$f = \exp \int_{p_0}^{p} \frac{dp}{\rho},$$

which is the *index of the fluid*, and the conformal metric

$$\overline{ds}^2 = f^2\, ds^2.$$

In the following part, we consider ρ and p as functions of f defined by means of the state equation.

(b) The *current vector* C defined by

$$C_\alpha = f u_\alpha$$

is unitary in the metric $\overline{ds}^2$ and (8.3) can be written

$$C^\alpha \overline{\nabla}_\alpha C_\beta = 0. \tag{8.5}$$

I have introduced the *vortex tensor* Ω defined by

$$\Omega = dC \tag{8.6}$$

where d is the operator of exterior differentiation; (8.5) is equivalent to

$$i(C)\Omega = 0 \tag{8.7}$$

where i is the interior product. If $\mathscr{L}(C)$ is the operator of infinitesimal transformation by C, we have

$$\mathscr{L}(C)\Omega = (di(C) + i(C)d)\Omega$$

and thus (8.7) implies

$$\mathscr{L}(C)\Omega = 0. \tag{8.8}$$

(8.8) are *relativistic Helmholtz equations.* Explicitly, we have

$$C^\rho \nabla_\rho \Omega_{\alpha\beta} + \Omega_{\rho\beta} \nabla_\alpha C^\rho + \Omega_{\alpha\rho} \nabla_\beta C^\rho = 0. \tag{8.9}$$

9. Relations between the current vector and the vortex tensor. The continuity equation (8.4) can be written

$$\delta C = i(C)\, dH(f^2) \tag{9.1}$$

where

$$H(f^2) = \log (f^{-2} p).$$

It is easy to see that

$$H'(f^2) = \frac{\phi'(p) - 2}{2f^2}. \tag{9.2}$$

From (8.6) and (9.1) we deduce

$$\Delta C \equiv (d\delta + \delta d) C = \delta \Omega + \mathscr{L}(C)\, dH(f^2).$$

But, according to (8.7),

$$\partial_\alpha H(f^2) = \partial_\alpha H(C^\beta C_\beta) = 2H'(f^2) C^\beta \nabla_\alpha C_\beta = 2H'(f^2) C^\beta \nabla_\beta C_\alpha$$

and we obtain

$$\{\mathscr{L}(C)\, dH(f^2)\}_\alpha = 2H'(f^2) C^\beta C^\gamma \nabla_\beta \nabla_\gamma C_\alpha + \psi_\alpha$$

where ψ_α depends only on C^λ, their first derivatives, $g_{\alpha\beta}$ and their first derivatives. Otherwise

$$(\Delta C)_\alpha = -g^{\beta\gamma} \nabla_\beta \nabla_\gamma C_\alpha + R_\alpha{}^\rho C_\rho.$$

We obtain thus, according to (9.2),

$$\left\{g^{\beta\gamma} + \frac{C^\beta C^\gamma}{f^2}(\phi' - 2)\right\} \nabla_\beta \nabla_\gamma C_\alpha - R_\alpha{}^\rho C_\rho - \nabla^\rho \Omega_{\rho\alpha} + \psi_\alpha = 0. \tag{9.3}$$

10. The hyperbolic system.

(a) For our fluid, we consider the following system:

$$R^{(h)}_{\alpha\beta} = \chi(T_{\alpha\beta} - \tfrac{1}{2} g_{\alpha\beta} T), \tag{10.1}$$

$$C^\rho \nabla_\rho \Omega_{\alpha\beta} + \Omega_{\rho\beta} \nabla_\alpha C^\rho + \Omega_{\alpha\rho} \nabla_\beta C^\rho = 0 \tag{10.2}$$

and the equation (10.3) obtained by the action on (9.3) of the operator $C^\lambda \nabla_\lambda$ and the elimination of $C^\lambda \nabla_\lambda \Omega_{\rho\alpha}$ by means of (10.2).

We obtain a system for the unknown functions $g_{\alpha\beta}$, $\Omega_{\alpha\beta}$, C_α. This system belongs to the type (4.1) with

$$s(g_{\alpha\beta}) = 3, \qquad s(\Omega_{\alpha\beta}) = 1, \qquad s(C_\alpha) = 2$$

and for the equations

$$t(1) = 2, \qquad t(2) = 1, \qquad t(3) = 0.$$

The corresponding matrix A is diagonal and the elements are the operators

$$-\tfrac{1}{2}g^{\beta\gamma}\,\partial_{\beta\gamma}, \qquad C^{\lambda}\,\partial_{\lambda}, \qquad C^{\lambda}h^{\beta\gamma}\,\partial_{\lambda\beta\gamma}$$

where

$$h^{\beta\gamma} = g^{\beta\gamma} + \frac{C^{\beta}C^{\gamma}}{f^2}(\phi' - 2);$$

we assume $\phi' \geqq 2$. The cone $\hat{C}_x$ defined in the dual space by

$$h^{\beta\gamma}X_{\beta}X_{\gamma} = 0$$

is exterior to the cone $g^{\beta\gamma}X_{\beta}X_{\gamma} = 0$ and does not cut the plane $C^{\lambda}X_{\lambda} = 0$. Our system is *hyperbolic*. To the field $\hat{C}$ of cones, correspond the characteristics which are the time-like *hydrodynamic waves*.

(b) We assume that our Cauchy data on Σ (the $g_{\alpha\beta}$ and their first derivatives) are such that:

(1) The relations on Σ

$$S^0_{\alpha} = \chi T^0_{\alpha}$$

define a unitary u^{α} and the scalars ρ and p on Σ;

(2) $g_{\alpha\beta}X^{\alpha}X^{\beta}$ is hyperbolic normal; Σ is space-like;

(3) $F^{\rho} = 0$ on Σ.

From these data, we deduce the values on Σ of C^{α}, their first and second derivatives and the second derivatives of $g_{\alpha\beta}$, by the means of (8.5), (10.1) and (9.3). We obtain thus a Cauchy problem for the system (10.1), (10.2), (10.3) which admits an unique solution.

It is possible to prove that this solution is a solution of the Einstein equations $S^{(h)}_{\alpha\beta} = \chi T_{\alpha\beta}$, $\nabla_{\alpha}T^{\alpha}{}_{\beta} = 0$. For analytic data, it is easy to see that the Cauchy problem for the Einstein equations admits an unique solution which coincides necessarily with the previous solution. A limit process shows then that this last solution satisfies the Einstein equations, in the case where the data are only sufficiently differentiable.

A similar process is available for the case where we have also an electromagnetic field.

The Lorentz condition for the potential vector

$$\delta\phi = 0$$

replaces the harmonicity conditions.

Bibliography

1. G. Darmois, *Les équations de la gravitation einsteinienne*, Gauthier-Villars, Paris, 1927.

2. Y. Bruhat, *Théoreme d'existence pour certains systèmes d'équations aux dérivées partielles non linéaires*, Acta Math. **88** (1952), 141–225.

3. ———, *Équations d'Helmholtz, détermination des vitesses á partir des tourbillons*, C. R. Acad. Sci. Paris **246** (1957), 3319.

4. Y. Bruhat, *Théorèmes d'existence en mécanique des fluides relativistes*, Bull. Soc. Math. France **86** (1958), 155–175.

5. ———, *The Cauchy problem*, Louis Witten, ed., *Gravitation: An introduction to current research*, Wiley, New York, 1962.

6. V. A. Fock, *The theory of space time and gravitation*, Pergamon, New York, 1959.

7. J. Hadamard, *Equations aux dérivées partielles*, Hermann, Paris, 1932.

8. J. Leray, *Hyperbolic differential equations*, Mimeographed, Institute for Advanced Study, Princeton, N.J., 1952.

9. A. Lichnerowicz, *Problémes globaux en mécanique relativiste*, Hermann, Paris, 1939; Ann. École Norm. Sup. **58** (1941), 285–304.

10. ———, *Problèmes généraux d'intégration des équations de la relativité*, Helv. Phys. Acta Suppl. **4** (1956), 176–190.

11. ———, *Théories relativistes de la gravitation*, Masson, Paris, 1956.

12. J. L. Synge, *Relativistic hydrodynamics*, Proc. London Math. Soc. **43** (1937), 376.

13. K. Stellmacher, *Zum Anfangswertproblem der gratitationsgleichungen*, Math. Ann. **115** (1937), 136.

14. A. H. Taub, *Singular hypersurfaces in general relativity*, Illinois J. Math. **1** (1957), 370.

15. J. A. Wheeler, *Fundamental topics in relativistic fluid mechanics and hydrodynamics*, Robert Wasserman and Charles P. Wells, eds., Proc. Sympos. Michigan State Univ., 1962, Academic Press, New York, 1963.

College de France,
Paris, France

SOME ALGEBRAICALLY DEGENERATE SOLUTIONS OF EINSTEIN'S GRAVITATIONAL FIELD EQUATIONS[1]

BY

R. P. KERR AND A. SCHILD

1. **Introduction. Outline of general relativity.** In Newtonian gravitational theory, the gravitational potential V satisfies the gravitational field equation

$$\Delta V = \frac{\partial^2 V}{\partial x^2} + \frac{\partial^2 V}{\partial y^2} + \frac{\partial^2 V}{\partial z^2} = 0 \tag{1.1}$$

in the absence of matter. The gravitational field of a point mass m at the origin is given by the singular spherically symmetric solution of the field equation:

$$V = -\frac{m}{r}, \tag{1.2}$$

where $r^2 = x^2 + y^2 + z^2$, and where the units have been chosen so that the gravitational constant $G = 1$. The motion of a point mass in a given external gravitational field V is

$$\frac{d^2x}{dt^2} = -\frac{\partial V}{\partial x}, \quad \frac{d^2y}{dt^2} = -\frac{\partial V}{\partial y}, \quad \frac{d^2z}{dt^2} = -\frac{\partial V}{\partial z}. \tag{1.3}$$

In the theory of special relativity, space-time is a four dimensional continuum, *Minkowski space*, with the metric

$$ds^2 = dx^2 + dy^2 + dz^2 - dt^2, \tag{1.4}$$

where units have been chosen so that the speed of light $c = 1$. The motion of a material particle is described by a curve in Minkowski space, the world line of the particle,

$$x^\mu = x^\mu(s), \tag{1.5}$$

where Greek suffixes range over 1, 2, 3, 4, and $x^\mu = (x, y, z, t)$. This curve must be time-like, i.e.,

$$ds^2 < 0, \tag{1.6}$$

[1] This research has been sponsored by the Aerospace Research Laboratory, Office of Aerospace Research, and the Office of Scientific Research (Grant 454–64), U.S. Air Force.

corresponding to the physical requirement that the speed of the particle must be less than unity, the speed of light. The arc length

$$|s| = \int_A^B |ds| = \int_A^B ds/i \tag{1.7}$$

between two points or events A and B on the world line of the particle is, physically, the time elapsed between the events A and B as measured by the particle itself, i.e., by a clock travelling with the particle. A free particle, a particle moving under no forces, has as world line a straight time-like line, a time-like geodesic which satisfies the differential equation

$$\frac{\delta}{\delta s}\frac{dx^\mu}{ds} = \frac{d^2x^\mu}{ds^2} = 0, \qquad ds^2 < 0, \tag{1.8}$$

where $\delta/\delta s$ is the absolute or covariant derivative along the curve $x^\mu(s)$.

Einstein's theory of general relativity **[1]**, **[2]** generalizes and synthesizes Newtonian gravitational theory and special relativity. Space-time is a Riemannian four space, generally curved, with metric

$$ds^2 = g_{\mu\nu}dx^\mu dx^\nu, \tag{1.9}$$

and signature $+++-$. The motion of a particle is given by a time-like world line, the arc length (1.7) being the time elapsed as measured by the particle itself. The role of the single Newtonian gravitational potential V is now taken over by the ten components $g_{\mu\nu}$ of the metric tensor, so that the gravitational field has become the geometry of space-time. A particle moving in a given gravitational field, in a given Riemannian space-time, is analogous to the free particle of special relativity. It has the straightest possible world line, a time-like geodesic:

$$\frac{\delta}{\delta s}\frac{dx^\mu}{ds} = \frac{d^2x^\mu}{ds^2} + \left\{ {\mu \atop \alpha\,\beta} \right\} \frac{dx^\alpha}{ds}\frac{dx^\beta}{ds} = 0. \tag{1.10}$$

This is the equation of motion which corresponds to the Newtonian equation (1.3). The Christoffel symbols $\{{\mu \atop \alpha\,\beta}\}$ are linear in the partial derivatives $\partial g_{\mu\nu}/\partial x^\alpha$ of the metric tensor and play the role of the gravitational potential gradient.

The curvature of a Riemannian space is characterized by the Riemann curvature tensor

$$R^\mu{}_{\nu\rho\sigma}, \tag{1.11}$$

which is a function of the metric tensor $g_{\mu\nu}$ and its first and second partial derivatives $\partial g_{\mu\nu}/\partial x^\rho$, $\partial^2 g_{\mu\nu}/\partial x^\rho \partial x^\sigma$. The vanishing of the full curvature tensor, $R^\mu{}_{\nu\rho\sigma} = 0$, is the necessary and sufficient condition for space-time to be flat, i.e., for the existence of a rectangular Cartesian coordinate system where the metric, throughout space-time, takes the form (1.4). Physically, this corresponds to the absence of an intrinsic gravitational field.

The contracted Riemann tensor is called the Ricci tensor

$$R_{\mu\nu} = R_{\nu\mu} = R^\alpha{}_{\mu\nu\alpha}. \tag{1.12}$$

The vanishing of the Ricci tensor,

$$R_{\mu\nu} = 0, \tag{1.13}$$

gives a system of ten second order nonlinear partial differential equations in the ten functions $g_{\mu\nu}$. It is a weaker condition than the vanishing of $R^{\mu}{}_{\nu\rho\sigma}$, and thus restricts the Riemannian space without requiring that it reduce to flat Minkowski space. Equations (1.13) are Einstein's gravitational field equations which in general relativity theory play the role of Laplace's equation (1.1) in Newtonian theory. The field equations (1.13) hold in the absence of matter, in vacuum, but do not require the absence of a gravitational field. The equations (1.13), like equations (1.1) in Newtonian theory, hold in regions of space-time where there is a gravitational field which is produced by matter in other regions of space-time. In those other regions, where there is matter, equations (1.13) do not hold, but must be generalized analogously to the generalization from Laplace's to Poisson's equation in Newtonian theory.

Corresponding to the static, spherically symmetric solution (1.2) of Newtonian gravitational theory, the solution of Einstein's field equations (1.13) is the famous Schwarzschild [3] metric which, in suitable coordinates r, θ, ϕ, t, is given by

$$ds^2 = \left(1 - \frac{2m}{r}\right)dr^2 + r^2(d\theta^2 + \sin^2\theta d\phi^2) - \frac{dt^2}{1 - \dfrac{2m}{r}}. \tag{1.14}$$

This very brief outline of general relativity theory is, of course, quite incomplete. It should, however, give the applied mathematician who does not know the subject at all a very rough idea of Einstein's theory of gravitation. We shall assume that the reader is familiar with the differential geometry of Riemannian spaces, with covariant differentiation, curvature tensor, etc., but we will now add some special results which are in the main specific to four dimensions or to spaces which satisfy the field equations.

A Riemannian space admits a continuous group of motions if and only if there exists a Killing vector field K_μ which satisfies Killing's equation

$$K_{(\mu;\nu)} = 0. \tag{1.15}$$

Here and throughout the semi-colon denotes covariant differentiation, round brackets enclosing suffixes denote symmetrization, e.g., $A_{(\mu\nu)} = \frac{1}{2}(A_{\mu\nu} + A_{\nu\mu})$, square brackets denote skew-symmetrization, e.g., $A_{[\mu\nu]} = \frac{1}{2}(A_{\mu\nu} - A_{\nu\mu})$. A motion or an isometric point transformation preserves, as the name implies, distances, i.e., if the neighbouring points P and Q transform into points P' and Q', then $ds(P, Q) = ds(P', Q')$. Thus the existence of a continuous group of motions or, equivalently, of a Killing vector characterizes a symmetry of the space. For example, in Minkowski space when rectangular Cartesians are used, equation (1.4), any vector with constant components is a Killing vector

$$K^\mu = \text{constant} \Rightarrow K_{(\mu;\nu)} = K_{(\mu,\nu)} = 0, \tag{1.16}$$

where the comma denotes partial differentiation, e.g., $K_{\mu,\nu} = \partial K_\mu / \partial x^\nu$. The constant Killing vector K^μ corresponds to the one parameter group of translations of Minkowski space onto itself.

Two Riemannian spaces with line elements

$$ds^2 = e^{2\sigma}\tilde{g}_{\mu\nu}dx^\mu dx^\nu \tag{1.17}$$

are said to be conformally related if, in suitable coordinates, they differ only in the conformal factor $e^{2\sigma}$ which is an arbitrary positive function of the coordinates. Weyl's conformal curvature tensor is defined by

$$C^\mu{}_{\nu\rho\sigma} = R^\mu{}_{\nu\rho\sigma} + g_{\nu[\sigma}R^\mu_{\rho]} + R_{\nu[\sigma}\delta^\mu_{\rho]} - \tfrac{1}{3}g_{\nu[\sigma}\delta^\mu_{\rho]}R, \tag{1.18}$$

where $R^\mu{}_\rho$ is the mixed Ricci tensor given by equation (1.12), and $R = R^\mu{}_\mu$ is the curvature invariant. The mixed Weyl tensor $C^\mu{}_{\nu\rho\sigma}$ remains invariant under a conformal change of the metric, i.e., under a change of the factor $e^{2\sigma}$ in the metric (1.17). In four or more dimensions, the vanishing of the Weyl tensor is the necessary and sufficient condition for the Riemannian space to be conformally flat, i.e., to be conformally related to a flat space of the same dimension and signature.

In the four dimensions of space-time, the Weyl tensor has 10 algebraically independent components, and the Ricci tensor has 10. These add up to the 20 independent components of the Riemann tensor. We shall now discuss the algebraic classification of space-times. Here it is important that we are dealing with a real four-dimensional Riemannian space of signature (3, 1). Consider the following four equations for a null direction λk^μ,

$$k_\mu k^\mu = 0, \tag{1.19}$$

which are successively stronger, in the sense that any one of the equations implies all the preceding equations:

$$k_{[\alpha}C_{\mu]\nu\rho[\sigma}k_{\beta]}k^\nu k^\rho = 0, \tag{1.20,1}$$

$$C_{\mu\nu\rho[\sigma}k_{\beta]}k^\nu k^\rho = 0, \tag{1.20,2}$$

$$C_{\mu\nu\rho[\sigma}k_{\beta]}k^\rho = 0, \tag{1.20,3}$$

$$C_{\mu\nu\rho\sigma}k^\rho = 0. \tag{1.20,4}$$

A null direction λk^μ which satisfies (1.20,1) but not (1.20,2) is called a simple Debever-Penrose direction; if it satisfies (1.20,2) but not (1.20,3) it is called double, if it satisfies (1.20,3) but not (1.20,4) it is called triple, if it satisfies (1.20,4) it is called a quadruple Debever-Penrose direction. Debever **[4]** has shown that at any point of space-time, where the Weyl tensor does not vanish, there are Debever-Penrose directions whose multiplicity adds up to exactly four.

Debever's theorem is clearest in the spinor formalism, as was first shown by Penrose **[5]**. The ten real components of the Weyl tensor are represented by the five independent complex components of the Weyl spinor

$$C_{ABCD} = C_{(ABCD)}, \tag{1.21}$$

which is completely symmetric in the four suffixes, each spinor suffix having the range 1, 2. A real null direction λk^μ has two real degrees of freedom, and is represented by the complex ratio $\zeta^1:\zeta^2$ of the two components of a spin vector ζ^A. The Debever-Penrose directions are the solutions of

$$C_{ABCD}\zeta^A\zeta^B\zeta^C\zeta^D = 0, \tag{1.22}$$

which is a fourth degree equation for the unknown ratio $\zeta^1:\zeta^2$. The multiplicity of the Debever-Penrose directions are the ordinary multiplicities of the roots of this equation. Debever's theorem now becomes obvious.

The Petrov-Pirani [**6**], [**7**], [**8**] classification of space-times can be discussed in terms of the multiplicity of the Debever-Penrose directions. If we have four simple Debever-Penrose directions, [1, 1, 1, 1], then we say that the space-time is algebraically nondegenerate or general. Otherwise we say that it is algebraically degenerate or special; this includes the five cases [2, 1, 1], [2, 2], [3, 1], [4], and finally $C^\mu{}_{\nu\rho\sigma} = 0$, the conformally flat space-times.

When Einstein's vacuum field equations are satisfied, $R_{\mu\nu} = 0$, the Weyl tensor and the Riemann tensor coincide, so that the algebraic classification of space-times can be determined by using the Riemann tensor $R_{\mu\nu\rho\sigma}$ in equations (1.20) or (1.22).

Consider a null vector field l^μ in space-time. It determines a congruence of null curves $x^\mu(u)$ in space-time, which have l^μ as tangents:

$$l^\mu = \frac{dx^\mu}{du}, \qquad l_\mu l^\mu = 0. \tag{1.23}$$

If these curves are null geodesics, then $\delta/\delta u(dx^\mu/du) = \mu dx^\mu/du$, or

$$l^\mu{}_{;\nu}l^\nu = \mu l^\mu. \tag{1.24}$$

We shall say that the null vector field l^μ is geodesic. It is then always possible to renormalize the vector field, so that

$$l^\mu = \lambda k^\mu, \qquad k_\mu k^\mu = 0, \qquad k^\mu{}_{;\nu}k^\nu = 0. \tag{1.25}$$

The normalized vector field k^μ is then the derivative $k^\mu = dx^\mu/dv$ along the null geodesics of the congruence with respect to an affine or preferred parameter v.

Sachs [**9**], [**10**] has defined the *shear* of a null geodesic congruence. We shall be concerned only with the case of zero shear, when we say that the null vector field k^μ is geodesic and shear-free. This has the following geometric meaning:

At any point P consider a 2-space S, orthogonal, but not tangent to, the null geodesic l of the congruence which passes through P (Figure 1). At any other point P' of l, consider any 2-space S', orthogonal to l, but not tangent to it. In S, draw the infinitesimal circle C with center at P. Then the null geodesics $\bar{l}$ of the congruence which pass through the points $\bar{P}$ of the circle C will meet S' in the points $\bar{P}'$ of a curve C'. The shear-free condition ensures that C' is again an infinitesimal circle with center P'.

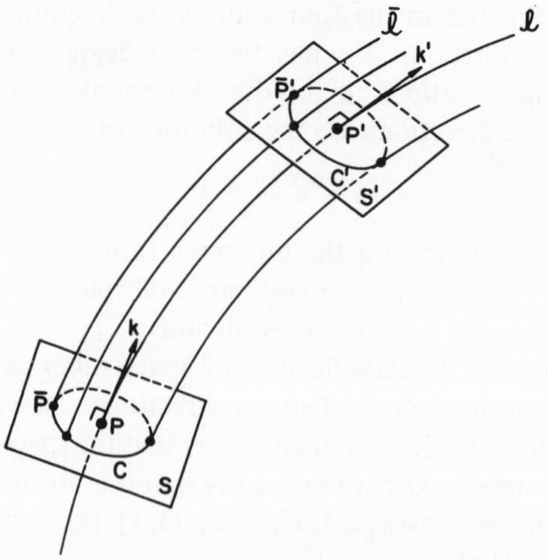

FIGURE 1

Physically, the null geodesics of the congruence represent light rays or, better, the histories of light pulses which fill space. If a small two-dimensional screen S, placed at right angles to the light rays becomes opaque for one instant of time, as determined by its own rest frame, then this will produce a shadow on another two-dimensional screen S' placed at right angles to the same light rays. The shear measures the distortion of the shape of the shadow on S' with respect to the shape of S. If there is no distortion of shape, and circles go into circles, then the light rays are shear-free.

Goldberg and Sachs have proved an important theorem **[11]**: If the vacuum field equations (1.13) are satisfied, then the space-time is algebraically degenerate if and only if it contains a shear-free null geodesic congruence; the tangent vectors k^μ to the congruence are the degenerate, i.e., multiple, Debever-Penrose vectors. Robinson and Schild **[12]** have proved the theorem under weaker conditions which are invariant under a conformal change of the metric.

It is the existence of a geodesic, shear-free field of null vectors which provides a powerful new tool for the solution of Einstein's vacuum field equations in the case of algebraically degenerate space-times.

2. **Outline of results.** In this paper the general solution of Einstein's empty space field equations (1.13) is obtained for a space-time where the metric has the form

$$g_{\mu\nu} = \eta_{\mu\nu} + l_\mu l_\nu. \tag{2.1}$$

Here $\eta_{\mu\nu}$ is the metric of Minkowski space in coordinates which are Cartesian but not necessarily rectangular, i.e., $\eta_{\mu\nu}$ are constants, with signature $+ + + -$, and l_μ is null:

$$g^{\mu\nu} l_\mu l_\nu = 0. \tag{2.2}$$

The reason for considering vacuum solutions of the form (2.1) is that the contravariant components of the metric are easily expressed in terms of the covariant components. In fact

$$g^{\mu\nu} = \eta^{\mu\nu} - l^\mu l^\nu, \tag{2.3}$$

where

$$l^\mu = g^{\mu\nu} l_\nu = \eta^{\mu\nu} l_\nu, \tag{2.4}$$

and the determinant

$$(-g) = -\det(g_{\mu\nu}) = 1. \tag{2.5}$$

It follows that if l_μ is null with respect to one of the two metrics $g_{\mu\nu}$ and $\eta_{\mu\nu}$, then it is null with respect to the other, i.e., equation (2.2) implies

$$\eta^{\mu\nu} l_\mu l_\nu = 0, \tag{2.6}$$

and vice versa.

The new vacuum solutions have the following properties:

(a) They include as special cases the Schwarzschild solution (1.14) and the exterior solution of a rotating body which was recently discovered by one of us [**13**].

(b) All vacuum solutions of the form (2.1) are algebraically degenerate, l_μ being a multiple Debever-Penrose vector and thus goedesic and shear-free.

(c) All vacuum solutions of the form (2.1) admit a one parameter group of motions. The Killing vector K^μ is at the same time a Killing vector of the flat Minkowski metric $\eta_{\mu\nu}$. In fact, with respect to $\eta_{\mu\nu}$, the motion is just a translation along a direction which may be time-like, space-like, or null in the Minkowski space. There are thus three cases:

$$\begin{aligned} \eta_{\mu\nu} K^\mu K^\nu &< 0 \qquad \text{(Case I)}, \\ &> 0 \qquad \text{(Case II)}, \\ &= 0 \qquad \text{(Case III)}. \end{aligned} \tag{2.7}$$

(d) In each of the three cases, the general solution is determined by one arbitrary analytic function of one complex variable.

(e) If $g_{\mu\nu}$ admits a Killing vector other than K^μ, it also must be a Killing vector with respect to $\eta_{\mu\nu}$.

(f) There are at most two essentially different ways of representing a vacuum metric in the form (2.1). For Case I, apart from the two special cases mentioned in (a), the representation (1.1) is, in fact, unique, so that the Riemannian space $g_{\mu\nu}$ determines uniquely the null vector field l_μ and the Minkowski space $\eta_{\mu\nu}$.

Together with their graduate student, Mr. George Debney, the authors have examined solutions of the nonvacuum Einstein-Maxwell equations where the metric has the form (2.1). Most of the results mentioned above apply to this more general case. This work is continuing.

In the following section an indication only is given of the derivation of our results. The full details of the proofs are reserved for a longer paper which is now being written.

3. **Outline of derivation. Final results.** A simple direct calculation of the Christoffel symbols $\{{}_{\mu}{}^{\rho}{}_{\nu}\}$ for the metric (2.1), (2.3), and of $\{{}_{\mu}{}^{\nu}{}_{\nu}\}$, $\{{}_{\mu}{}^{\rho}{}_{\nu}\}l^{\nu}$, $\{{}_{\mu}{}^{\rho}{}_{\nu}\}l^{\nu}l^{\mu}{}_{,\rho}$, and substitution into the vacuum field equation

$$R_{\mu\nu}l^{\mu}l^{\nu} = 0, \tag{3.1}$$

yields

$$l_{\mu,\nu}l^{\nu}l^{\mu}{}_{,\rho}l^{\rho} = 0. \tag{3.2}$$

By differentiating equation (2.6), we also have

$$l_{\mu,\nu}l^{\nu}l^{\mu} = 0. \tag{3.3}$$

Thus, in the Minkowski metric $\eta_{\mu\nu}$, the vector $l^{\mu}{}_{,\nu}l^{\nu}$ is null and orthogonal to the null vector l^{μ}. In a four-dimensional space with the signature (3,1) of space-time, a vector v^{μ} orthogonal to a null vector l^{μ} is either space-like ($\eta_{\mu\nu}v^{\mu}v^{\nu} > 0$) or else is a multiple of l^{μ}. Therefore

$$l^{\mu}{}_{,\nu}l^{\nu} = \mu l^{\mu}. \tag{3.4}$$

Also, it is easily shown that

$$l^{\mu}{}_{;\nu}l^{\nu} = l^{\mu}{}_{,\nu}l^{\nu} = \mu l^{\mu}. \tag{3.5}$$

Thus the field equation (3.1) implies that the null field l^{μ} is geodesic. We can therefore define a new null vector field $k^{\mu} = l^{\mu}/\sqrt{(2H)}$, so that

$$k_{\mu}k^{\mu} = 0, \qquad k^{\mu}{}_{;\nu}k^{\nu} = 0, \tag{3.6}$$

and

$$\begin{aligned} g_{\mu\nu} &= \eta_{\mu\nu} + 2Hk_{\mu}k_{\nu}, \\ g^{\mu\nu} &= \eta^{\mu\nu} - 2Hk^{\mu}k^{\nu}, \\ k^{\mu} &= g^{\mu\nu}k_{\nu} = \eta^{\mu\nu}k_{\nu}. \end{aligned} \tag{3.7}$$

Another simple calculation gives

$$R^{\sigma}{}_{\rho\mu\nu}k^{\rho}k^{\nu} = -\ddot{H}k^{\sigma}k_{\mu}, \tag{3.8}$$

where the dot denotes differentiation along a null geodesic $x^{\mu}(v)$ of the congruence defined by the vector field k^{μ}, with respect to an affine parameter v, i.e.,

$$\begin{aligned} k^{\mu} &= \frac{dx^{\mu}}{dv}, \\ \dot{A} &= \frac{dA}{dv} = A_{,\mu}k^{\mu}. \end{aligned} \tag{3.9}$$

Since we are considering vacuum solutions, and since in vacuum

$$R_{\mu\nu} = 0, \qquad C^{\sigma}{}_{\rho\mu\nu} = R^{\sigma}{}_{\rho\mu\nu}, \tag{3.10}$$

equation (3.8) shows that the Debever equation (1.20,2) is satisfied by k^μ. Thus k^μ is at least a double Debever-Penrose vector, space-time is algebraically degenerate, and k^μ is geodesic and shear-free.

Using the shear-free character of k^μ and the remaining field equations, a long and intricate calculation gives all the vacuum solutions of type (2.1). This derivation will be omitted here, and only the final results will now be given.

We introduce complex conjugate coordinates $\bar{\zeta}$, ζ and real coordinates v, u in Minkowski space which are related to x, y, z, t of equation (1.4) by

$$\begin{aligned} \zeta &= \frac{1}{\sqrt{2}}(x + iy), & \bar{\zeta} &= \frac{1}{\sqrt{2}}(x - iy), \\ v &= \frac{1}{\sqrt{2}}(z - t), & u &= \frac{1}{\sqrt{2}}(z + t), \end{aligned} \tag{3.11}$$

so that

$$ds_0{}^2 = \eta_{\mu\nu} dx^\mu dx^\nu = 2d\zeta d\bar{\zeta} + 2du dv. \tag{3.12}$$

They are called null coordinates.

The field equations provide us with a Killing vector field K^μ whose contravariant components are constants, thus showing that K^μ is a translational Killing vector of the Minkowski space $\eta_{\mu\nu}$.

In Case I, when K^μ is time-like, we perform a Lorentz transformation so that K^μ points along the t-axis or, by equation (3.11), the $(u - v)$-direction. The metric $g_{\mu\nu}$ is then a function of $\bar{\zeta}$, ζ and $u + v$ alone.

Similarly, in Case II, we let K^μ point along the z-axis, so that $g_{\mu\nu}$ is a function of $\bar{\zeta}$, ζ and $u - v$ alone. In Case III, we let K^μ point along the u-axis, so that $g_{\mu\nu}$ is a function of $\bar{\zeta}$, ζ and v.

The general solutions are as follows:

Case I.

$$\begin{aligned} ds^2 &= 2d\zeta d\bar{\zeta} + 2du dv \\ &\quad - 4\sqrt{2}\, m \operatorname{Re}\left(\frac{1}{F_Y}\right)\left[\frac{du + Y d\bar{\zeta} + \bar{Y} d\zeta - Y\bar{Y} dv}{1 + Y\bar{Y}}\right]^2, \end{aligned} \tag{3.13}$$

where m is a real constant, Y is a complex variable, F_Y is the partial derivative with respect to Y of the function

$$F(Y, \bar{\zeta}, \zeta, u + v) = \phi(Y) + [Y^2\bar{\zeta} - \zeta + (u + v)Y], \tag{3.14}$$

where ϕ is an arbitrary analytic function of the complex variable Y, and where, finally, Y is determined as a function of the coordinates by the equation

$$F = 0, \qquad \phi(Y) = -Y^2\bar{\zeta} + \zeta - (u + v)Y. \tag{3.15}$$

In the following two cases the notation and explanation is the same.

Case II.

$$(3.16)\qquad ds^2 = 2d\zeta d\bar{\zeta} + 2dudv + 4\sqrt{2}\, m \,\mathrm{Re}\left(\frac{1}{F_Y}\right)\left[\frac{du + Yd\bar{\zeta} + \bar{Y}d\zeta - Y\bar{Y}dv}{1 - Y\bar{Y}}\right]^2,$$

$$(3.17)\qquad F(Y, \bar{\zeta}, \zeta, u - v) = \phi(Y) - [Y^2\bar{\zeta} + \zeta + (u - v)Y],$$

$$(3.18)\qquad F = 0, \qquad \phi(Y) = Y^2\bar{\zeta} + \zeta + (u - v)Y.$$

Case III.

$$(3.19)\qquad ds^2 = 2d\zeta d\bar{\zeta} + 2dudv - 4\sqrt{2}\, m \,\mathrm{Re}\left(\frac{1}{F_Y}\right)(du + Yd\bar{\zeta} + \bar{Y}d\zeta - Y\bar{Y}dv)^2,$$

$$(3.20)\qquad F(Y, \bar{\zeta}, \zeta, v) = \phi(Y) + \zeta - vY,$$

$$(3.21)\qquad F = 0, \qquad \phi(Y) = vY - \zeta.$$

The points where $F_Y = 0$ are true singularities of the Riemannian space. Also, in general, Y is a multivalued function with these singularities as branch points.

We shall now consider the special solution in Case I, where

$$(3.22)\qquad \phi = -\sqrt{2}\, iaY, \qquad a \geqq 0.$$

The line-element (3.13) becomes

$$(3.23)\qquad ds^2 = dx^2 + dy^2 + dz^2 - dt^2 + \frac{2m\rho^3}{\rho^4 + a^2z^2}\left[dt + \frac{z}{\rho}dz + \frac{\rho}{\rho^2 + a^2}(xdx + ydy) + \frac{a}{\rho^2 + a^2}(xdy - ydx)\right]^2,$$

where we have reverted to the rectangular Cartesian coordinates in Minkowski space given by equation (3.11), and where ρ is given by

$$(3.24)\qquad \frac{x^2 + y^2}{\rho^2 + a^2} + \frac{z^2}{\rho^2} = 1.$$

This is the exterior gravitational field of a rotating body [**13**]. When we put $a = 0$, so that $\rho = r = (x^2 + y^2 + z^2)^{1/2}$, this reduces to the Schwarzschild metric in a form first given by Eddington [**14**].

References

1. a. A. Einstein, *Zur allgemeinen Relativitätstheorie,* S.-B. Preuss. Akad. Wiss. (1915), 778–786.

b. ———, *Zur allgemeinen Relativitätstheorie* (*Nachtrag*), S.-B. Preuss. Akad. Wiss. (1915), 799–801.

c. ———, *Die Feldgleichungen der Gravitation*, S.-B. Preuss. Akad. Wiss. (1915), 844–847.

2. A. Einstein, *Die Grundlage der Allgemeinen Relativitätstheorie*, Ann. Physik **49** (1916), 769–822.

3. K. Schwarzschild, *Über das Gravitationsfeld eines Massenpunktes nach der Einsteinschen Theorie*, S.-B. Preuss. Akad. Wiss. (1916), 189–196.

4. R. Debever, *La supr-énergie en relativité générale*, Bull. Soc. Math. Belg. **10** (1958), 112–147.

5. R. Penrose, *A spinor approach to general relativity*, Ann. Physics **10** (1960), 171–201.

6. A. Z. Petrov, *Classification of spaces defining gravitational fields*, Kazan. Gos. Univ. Uč. Zap. **114** (1954), 55–69. (Russian)

7. ———, *On spaces of maximal mobility which define a gravitational field*, Dokl. Akad. Nauk SSSR (N.S.) **105** (1955), 905–908. (Russian)

8. F. A. E. Pirani, *Invariant formulation of gravitational radiation theory*, Phys. Rev. **105** (1957), 1089–1099.

9. R. K. Sachs, *Gravitational waves in general relativity*. VI. *The outgoing radiation condition*, Proc. Roy. Soc. London Ser. A **264** (1961), 309–338.

10. F. A. E. Pirani and A. Schild, *Geometrical and physical interpretation of the Weyl conformal curvature tensor*, Bull. Acad. Polon. Sci. Sér. Sci. Math. Astronom. Phys. **9** (1961), 543–547.

11. J. N. Goldberg and R. K. Sachs, *A theorem on Petrov types*, Acta Phys. Polon. **22** (1962), suppl., 13.

12. I. Robinson and A. Schild, *Generalization of a theorem by Goldberg and Sachs*, J. Mathematical Phys. **4** (1963), 484–489.

13. R. P. Kerr, *Gravitational field of a spinning mass as an example of algebraically special metrics*, Phys. Rev. Lett. **11** (1963), 237–238.

14. A. S. Eddington, *A comparison of Whitehead's and Einstein's formulae*, Nature **113** (1924), 192.

THE UNIVERSITY OF TEXAS,
AUSTIN, TEXAS

NONLINEAR PARTIAL DIFFERENTIAL EQUATIONS IN QUANTUM FIELD THEORY

BY

I. E. SEGAL

1. **Introduction.** These are all quasi-linear equations of evolution, in their fundamental forms. From a classical local viewpoint they appear quite well behaved, as nonlinear partial differential equations go. This is however somewhat deceptive, for the relevant problems are rather different in character from those of, say, classical fluid mechanics, being more reminiscent of those of the theory of turbulence. There are the following gross differences in the nature of the relevant problems:

(i) Only global solutions, throughout space and time, are surely significant; in fact only those global solutions which are small near infinity in space. A purely local solution need have no physical significance, while a global solution which is only bounded near infinity in space has an ambiguous interpretation.

(ii) In elementary particle theory, which is the main *raison d'être* of these equations, the unknown function is "quantized," i.e., is supposed to have values which are linear operators, which need not commute at different points of spacetime.

(iii) The connection between the theory and the empirical situation can be made to depend virtually entirely on the asymptotic character of the solutions, for very early and very late times. The solutions for finite times have no established connection with experiment.

The central difficulty has been the second, primarily because it is not, like the others, a purely mathematical one, but is equally a matter of formulation and interpretation. The quantized theory is, as Dirac has emphasized, one of great architectural mathematical beauty; in fact, he indicates this as the primary motivation for its study, rather than any numerical empirical implications, which were nonexistent at the time he wrote this, some twenty years after the founding of the theory. It is, however, not a theory at all in the contemporary mathematical sense, but a consensus of scientific feelings and putative approximations whose expression is mathematical in appearance. In the past fifteen years, a number of independent investigations of possible formulations of nonlinear quantum field theory in harmony with reasonable standards of clarity and mathematical precision have been made, but most of these have eliminated the connection with nonlinear partial differential equations, and concrete models of quantum fields exhibiting some of the features which have been under abstract investigation are only beginning to emerge.

This is not to paint a dark picture of the situation, and indeed the developments of the past decade have been quite encouraging, but only to indicate some of the background within which the role of nonlinear partial differential equations in elementary particle theory must be evaluated. The relation between the classical (i.e., unquantized, or numerical-valued) solutions of the nonlinear equations of the theory and the quantum solutions—assuming such exist—has not been at all clear cut, nor can it be in the nature of things, as long as the quantized theory is itself ambiguous.

This ambiguity stems from the circumstance that the quantized theory deals not with strict operator-valued functions, but only weak such functions; in other terms, only the suitably smoothed-out space-time averages of the unknown function has meaning. Nevertheless, the equations are, and this is in fact a crucial part of their rationale, *local*, i.e., expressed in terms of the values of the function at a point. The nonlinear parts of the "equation" then give rise to expressions of which powers of the Dirac delta function are a highly simplified prototype. The celebrated divergences of quantum field theory do not appear only when computations are attempted but are intrinsic in the statement of the axioms of the theory, being visible in the lack of definite mathematical meaning for the partial differential equations which define the "theory."

It may be interesting and helpful to contrast the situation with that in the theory of turbulent flow. This theory involves the difficulties (i) and (iii) in lesser degree, but not (ii); however, the unknown function, while not an operator, is in many theories not really numerical-valued, but rather has values which are random variables. Such are virtually the same as a commuting set of hermitian operators in a Hilbert space, apart from their expectation values, which have their parallel in quantum theory in the expectation values in the so-called "vacuum" state. In both theories the connection with quantitative empirical results is made through the corresponding low-order moments, the so-called correlation functions in the case of turbulent flow, and the vacuum expectation values of products of the field in quantum theory. This is just as in applied probability classically, but just as in the mathematical theory of probability, the moments are an inconvenient and bulky tool for theoretical and especially for general investigation. It is natural to turn to the characteristic function instead, as Hopf did for the theory of turbulence and Schwinger for quantum field theory. Unlike the moments, this satisfies a simple differential equation for its temporal propagation, but it has proved difficult to make effective use of this equation.

Although the partial differential equations for these two theories are of different types, hyperbolic in the case of quantum theory, parabolic in that of the theory of turbulent flow, the theory of the classical solutions of these equations shows certain similarities. In both theories, global existence has been shown in a number of important cases, but the uniqueness of the solution to the Cauchy problem remains open in some of the most interesting of these cases, and appears to require quite new methods for resolution. However, global uniqueness of weak solutions remains in doubt in both theories for a number of significant cases.

There is also an historical similarity, in that both theories have only recently emerged from periods of relative quiescence, following fundamental work about thirty years ago. They are important not only in themselves and as sources of new pure mathematical developments but as prototypes of complex systems whose temporal development is governed by nonlinear but local partial differential equations, in which stochastic features ultimately play an essential role in making the connection with the material world. Before there is a sound basis for hopeful anticipation of a similarly succinct and far-reaching mathematical model for a biological system, such as the brain, these two relatively simple systems should achieve a much more solid level of theoretical understanding than has yet been reached. The present report will be confined essentially to the equations of quantum theory.

The present state of the theory of the classical solutions of these equations will be indicated, with emphasis on those questions relevant to quantum theory. It will then be indicated how quantum field operators may be represented by differential operators in the solution manifold of the classical equation. The problem of giving an appropriate interpretation to these operators as operators in a Hilbert space leads to the theory of nonlinear stochastic partial differential equations. This theory and some of the specific equations considered have a relatively broad relevance in applied mathematics, but these aspects cannot be covered in our report.

2. **The differential equations.** The physically best established nonlinear partial differential equations of relativistic quantum theory are those of quantum electrodynamics. In their usual form, the equations have two unknown functions on space-time, A and ψ, the so-called photon and electron-positron fields, each of which has values in a four-dimensional representation space of the Lorentz group, the so-called vector and spinor representations, and with the use of certain operators γ_j on the spinor space, whose defining characteristic is that they provide an irreducible representation for the Clifford algebra determined by the fundamental indefinite form of special relativity, may be expressed as

$$\Box A_j = -e\psi^*\gamma_j\psi,$$
$$(1)\qquad \left(i\sum_j \gamma_j\partial_j + m\right)\psi = -e\sum_j \gamma_j A_j\psi,$$

where e and m are physical constants and ψ^* denotes the natural "adjoint" spinor to ψ. It may be noted that the left-hand sides indicate the action of hyperbolic linear, and in fact relativistically-invariant, differential operators, while the right-hand sides have components which are homogeneous polynomials of second degree in the components of A and ψ. Essentially because the direct product of the spin representation with its conjugate contains the vector representation of the Lorentz group exactly once, these are the unique relativistically-invariant equations of this type having the given left-hand sides.

These form a beautiful set of equations, of remarkable mathematical symmetry, embodying essentially both the Maxwell and Dirac equations, which are two of the most fruitful in mathematical physics, and which are coupled thereby in a uniquely simple way. However, in addition to constituting a system rather than a single equation, they involve several complications not present in the case of a number of equations of an equally relativistic and local character, of a probably more phenomenological character. The concept of locality turns out to be rather complex in quantum theory, and the locality of the equations (1) is somewhat specious to begin with. This is because the potentials A which intervene in (1) are not conceptually observable or even fully unique, but only the electromagnetic field strengths, definable as the coefficients of the derivative of the first-order differential form in space-time defined by the A_j; on the other hand it is only when the potentials are used that the coupling between the Maxwell and Dirac equations which defined quantum electrodynamics is described by local partial differential equations. This ambiguity in the potentials could be removed by replacing the Maxwell equations by those for a similar field whose particles however had a nonzero mass, but the equations would continue to have the property that their classical energy functional was indefinite, making it impossible to apply one of the most effective classical techniques. Recently L. Gross has obtained very precise results on the global solution of equation (1) throughout space, permitting the propagation through limited time intervals of quite general Cauchy data. This improves the possibilities for obtaining global weak solutions, but even if a smooth manifold of such could be shown to exist, there would remain the complication that two different species of quantum statistics are involved in the quantum treatment of the equation.

Lacking in these complications, but equally lacking in understanding from a fundamental quantum-field standpoint, has been the popular equation

$$\Box\phi = m^2\phi + g^2\phi^3, \tag{2}$$

where m and g are constants. It has been generally believed that a solid understanding of the system defined by equation (2) would lead to one for systems such as that defined by equation (1). In any event, equation (2) is a quite plausible semi-phenomenological one for mesons. The interaction term ϕ^3 is somewhat better-behaved from the relevant analytical point of view than those of other equations such as (1), whose analytical character is better represented by higher powers of the field as the interaction term, and there is no empirically compelling reason why the interaction term must be represented by a polynomial, so that the more general equation

$$\Box\phi = m^2\phi + F(\phi), \tag{3}$$

where F is a given function of a real variable, is appropriately studied. The same equation is of interest also in classical applied mathematics. It is reasonable to assume that F is a smooth function, say infinitely differentiable, and it is no essential loss of generality to assume it vanishes to higher order near 0. It can be regarded as describing the "self-interaction" of a scalar field with self-interaction given by the function F of the field.

The notion of a self-interacting field may appear less intuitive than that of the interaction of two or more distinct fields. There is however no difficulty in formulating analogues to these equations involving the coupling of distinct fields, for example in place of (2) the following equations could be considered:

$$\Box\phi = m^2\phi + g^2\psi^2\phi, \qquad \Box\psi = n^2\psi + h^2\phi^2\psi, \tag{4}$$

describing the interaction of scalar fields ϕ and ψ of masses m and n respectively, with interaction constants g and h. Most of the developments applicable to equation (2) will carry over with obvious changes to equations such as (4), and similarly for (3) in relation to equations involving separate fields. With algebraic modifications for present purposes irrelevant, (4) defines the motion of charged mesons in an electromagnetic field, which could be treated similarly. On the other hand, the essential elements in these equations are quite parallel to the corresponding ones for equation (3), and the abstract theory used in the treatment of equation (3) is directly applicable to them. For succinctness and clarity of exposition equation (3) will be used in our report as a prototype for all such equations.

The Yukawa equation for the interaction between nucleons and mesons is from a partial-differential-equations viewpoint similar to, although somewhat simpler than, equation (1). The so-called four-fermion and six-fermion interactions are in some ways algebraically simpler than equation (1) and involve only one species of quantum statistics, but as classical equations they lack positive-definite energy functionals, and the nonlinear (interaction) terms are more highly singular in the relevant analytical sense.

The most general nonlinear partial differential equation usually envisaged in relativistic field theory is for an unknown function ϕ having values in a finite-dimensional representation space V of the Lorentz group, and has the form

$$L\phi = p(\phi), \tag{5}$$

where L is a linear differential operator with constant coefficients which commutes with the action of the representation, and p is a function on V to V each component of which is a polynomial in the components of the unknown function $\phi(x)$, at the point x at which L is formed, of a fixed degree $d > 1$, which is likewise invariant under the action of the representation. L is necessarily hyperbolic, by virtue of its relativistic invariance, while the invariant polynomials are determined by the theory of invariants of the orthogonal group, which provides an explicit basis by virtue of the pseudo-orthogonal character of the Lorentz group. Not all such equations are admissible from a quantum-field-theoretic viewpoint. Conventionally, it has usually been required that in some sense, the "associated quantum field," which as already noted has been a highly intuitive conception, should admit a "vacuum," i.e., an invariant state relative to which the energy spectrum of the field is non-negative. Even if this requirement were not ambiguous, it would be a highly implicit restriction on the quantum field. A related requirement, and one which is much easier to deal with, is that the classical energy functional be positive definite, in the event that only fields of integral spin are involved. Neither of these restrictions will be relevant in the present exposition until later.

It is difficult to treat the global theory of the solutions of equation (5) in the relativistic form in which it is given. Much as a manifestly relativistic approach to this theory might be wished for, it is much simpler to treat the existence, uniqueness, and asymptotic properties of solutions to the Cauchy problem in a particular Lorentz frame, as well as perhaps more fundamentally physical. The equation may then be put in the form of an ordinary differential equation for a Banach-space-valued function, of the type

$$u' = Au + K(u), \tag{6}$$

where the hyperbolicity of L means that the unbounded A which intervenes generates a full one-parameter group of bounded linear operators, and K is a nonlinear operator on the given Banach space $\mathscr{B}$. While there is some degree of arbitrariness in the choice of $\mathscr{B}$, there is a natural family of Hilbert spaces to employ in this connection, for which this one-parameter group consists of unitary operators. There are two distinguished spaces in this family: that in which the energy norm is used, and that in which the relativistic norm is used. In the linear case in which K is absent, the theory is essentially the same for all of these spaces, although for only one is it relativistic; however, in the case of the nonlinear theory, the energy norm is materially easier to work with than the relativistic one, as regards the classical solution theory of the partial differential equation.

To illustrate this reduction to equation (6), let $u(t)$ for any time t denote the pair $(\Phi(t), \Phi'(t))$, where $\Phi(t)$ is a function of the space variables $\mathbf{x}$, of the form

$$\Phi(t)(\mathbf{x}) = \phi(\mathbf{x}, t),$$

ϕ being the function under consideration in equation (3). This equation then takes the form $\Phi''(t) + B^2\Phi(t) = J(\Phi(t))$, where B is the positive self-adjoint square root of the self-adjoint operator $m^2I - \Delta$, and J is the nonlinear operation carrying ϕ into $-F(\phi)$. In terms of $u(t)$ this gives equation (6) with A given by the matrix

$$\begin{pmatrix} 0 & I \\ -B^2 & 0 \end{pmatrix}$$

and K the operation sending (ϕ, ψ) into $(0, -J(\phi))$. A is readily given a precise interpretation as a self-adjoint operator in the Hilbert space $\mathscr{K}_a = [\mathscr{D}_a] + [\mathscr{D}_{a-1}]$, where $\mathscr{D}_a$ denotes the domain in the Hilbert space $\mathscr{H}$ of all square-integrable functions of the space-variables of B^a, a being real, while the notation $[\mathscr{D}_a]$ is to indicate that the norm employed is not that in $\mathscr{H}$, but rather the norm in $\mathscr{H}$ after the action of B^a, and that the space is completed in this norm (this completion is needed if $m = 0$ or $a < 0$). On the other hand, the nonlinear operation K will be well defined only if a is sufficiently large, in relation to the number of space dimensions, its required magnitude being given directly by the Soboleff inequalities;

for smaller values of a, K will be an unbounded nonlinear operator in general taking a function in $\mathcal{D}_a$ into one which is not in $\mathcal{D}_{a-1}$. In the cases when K is an operation from $\mathcal{D}_a$ into $\mathcal{D}_{a-1}$, it is additionally continuous, and in fact (when F is infinitely differentiable) infinitely differentiable in the sense of the differential calculus on Banach spaces.

There is of course a certain disparity between the strict solutions of equation (5), which are ordinary smooth functions on space-time, and the abstract solutions of equation (6). The additional structure inherent in the classical strict solution does not seem to be of any significance for the applications being considered here, and in any case is readily recovered from supplementary consideration of the abstract solution. It is appropriate therefore to turn attention now to the general theory of equations such as (6).

3. **Abstract quasi-linear equations of evolution.** The general such equation

$$u' = A(t)u + K_t(u) \tag{7}$$

with time-dependent linear and nonlinear operators $A(t)$ and K_t is indirectly relevant, since it includes the case of the first-order variations to such equations as (6), and a variety of quasi-relativistic equations, such as those involving given external potentials. In certain respects it is as easy to treat as equation (6); this more general treatment clarifies the method; at the same time the theory is rendered applicable to all types of equations (including elliptic ones).

An elementary but fundamental point is that it is mathematically effective as well as physically more natural to treat the integrated form of the equation. By a *temporal propagator* on the time interval T, on the Banach space $\mathcal{B}$, will be meant a map $W(s, t)$ on $\mathcal{B}$ to $\mathcal{B}$ defined for s and t in T and $s \geqq t$, with the properties: $W(r, s)W(s, t) = W(r, t)$; $W(t, t) = I$; $W(s, t)$ is a continuous function of s and t jointly in the strong operator topology. If the maps are linear, the propagator is called linear. Such a linear propagator is an integrated form for the differential equation $u' = A(t)u$, i.e., a generalized elementary solution for a generalized equation of this type. In these terms equation (7) has as its integrated form

$$u(t) = W(t, t_0)u_0 + \int_{t_0}^{t} W(t, s)K_s(u(s))\, ds, \tag{8}$$

employing a Banach-space-valued integral. The method of successive approximations shows that if W is a given continuous linear propagator, say on the interval $[a, b)$, and if K_t is a locally Lipschitzian function uniformly on every finite t-interval, then equation (8) has a solution in some interval $[a, c]$ with $c > a$. It will be unique in the maximal interval of its existence, concerning the length of which various information follows. For example, if the $W(s, t)$ are uniformly bounded in norm, and if K_t is uniformly Lipschitzian (as a function of u) on every finite t-interval and every bounded set in $\mathcal{B}$, then either the solution exists on all of T, or else $\|u(t)\|$ becomes unbounded. It is possible to prove existence under somewhat less restrictive conditions on $K_t(u)$, but the indicated condition cannot be greatly improved if a general theory is desired which will be useful for physical purposes, since uniqueness and smoothness features which are relevant may then be impaired. Under the cited conditions, a nonlinear continuous propagator is defined by the "differential equation" (8).

It follows in particular that in the case of equation (6), if A is the generator of a one-parameter semi-group $W(t)$ on the interval $T = [0, \infty)$, and if K is Lipschitzian on every bounded set, then for any given vector u_0 in $\mathscr{B}$, the integrated form of (6) with initial datum u_0 at time t_0 either exists globally on T, or $\|u(t)\|$ is unbounded on the interval of existence. If additionally $\mathscr{B}$ is a Hilbert space and if A is a normal operator such that $A + A^*$ is bounded from above, it follows that either the solution exists throughout T, or else $\operatorname{Re} \int_{t_0}^{t} (K_s(u(s)), u(s))\, ds$ becomes unbounded. The latter eventuality can in a significant number of cases be excluded through the use of conservation or boundedness of the energy. In particular, in the case of the equation

$$\Phi''(t) + B^2\Phi = J(\Phi) \tag{9}$$

cited earlier, there is global existence provided there exists a nonpositive continuously differentiable functional $E(\Phi)$ on D_a whose Frechet differential is the given function $J(\Phi)$. To indicate what this means in a special case, this in turn leads directly to the conclusion that the solution of equation (3) which exists locally if F grows sufficiently slowly at infinity also exists globally if F is the derivative of a non-negative function. This hypothesis is satisfied, of course, if F is Lipschitzian, but it is also satisfied in such non-Lipschitzian cases as that of equation (2), and the abstract content of the results first obtained by Jörgens **[2]** on these equations of classic interest is obtained.

Specifically, the equation

$$\Box\phi = m^2\phi + g\phi^p \qquad (p \text{ odd}, g \geqq 0) \tag{10}$$

has global solutions for the Cauchy problem in the indicated abstract sense without further restriction in the case of one or two space dimensions, and for $p = 3$ in the case of three space dimensions. For negative values of g, the solution definitely does not exist globally; the energy functional is indefinite, and by classical methods Keller has given explicit upper bounds for the integral of existence in a number of such cases; the situation is similar for even values of p. The case of a larger value of p in three or more space dimensions is puzzling, and indicative of the difficulties which may arise in the case of more complex equations, such as those of quantum electrodynamics. It is not a serious restriction to assume the initial data are infinitely differentiable and have compact support, and it is then possible to solve in a well-controlled way the Cauchy problem locally in time, throughout space, inasmuch as the map $\phi \to \phi^p$ takes $\mathscr{D}_a$ into $\mathscr{D}_{a-1}$ if a is sufficiently large (exceeding a value depending on the space dimension), and is indeed infinitely differentiable from the one space to the other. It seems however to be extremely difficult to obtain any a priori bounds on the solution except in the case $a = 1$ corresponding to the energy integral, which is too low a value of a for any cases except those cited. The energy bounds can be used to obtain weak solutions for any number of space dimensions, and any odd p; such weak solutions would be virtually as useful as strong ones for quantum-theoretic purposes if they were under effective analytic control, but even the uniqueness of the solution to the Cauchy problem is not known in these cases, and seems to be quite difficult to settle. It seems very possible that weak solutions of (10) which are initially infinitely differentiable and of compact support may lose all but the one derivative assured by the energy bound in the course of propagation.

Scattering theory concerns the asymptotic character of the solutions of such an equation as (7) in relation to those of another such equation; the scattering operator gives the overall *relative* field motion determined by the equation. There are thus two equations involved, one the "physical" (or "perturbed," or "interacting") equation for the actual motion of the system, and the other the "reference" (or "unperturbed," or "free") hypothetical motion of the system in the absence of interaction. In practice, the reference equation is usually a linear one of the form

$$u' = A(t)u, \tag{11}$$

and in fact almost always $A(t) = A$ is time-independent, but this is not too important for the general theory. It does however facilitate the exposition to describe the theory for the case in which $A(t) = A$ and in which the physical equation has the form (7) while the reference equation is of the form $u' = Au$. The most common procedure is to transform to the "interaction representation," i.e., to replace the unknown function $u(t)$ in equation (7) by the function $v(t) = e^{-At}u(t)$ which satisfies the equation $v' = L_t(v)$, where $L_t(v) = e^{-At}K(e^{At}v)$. The "wave" operator W in this representation is that taking a given datum v_0 at time $-\infty$ into the solution of the Cauchy problem

$$v(t) = v_0 + \int_{-\infty}^{t} L_s(v(s))\, ds. \tag{12}$$

The method of successive approximations gives a simple criterion for the existence of a unique solution to this equation, as well as for the forward wave operator propagating from time t to time $+\infty$, and thereby (if the domains and ranges of these operators match suitably, as can be a nontrivial consideration) the complete scattering operator S propagating the datum v_0 from time $-\infty$ to time $+\infty$.

4. **Scalar relativistic equations.** The general scalar relativistic equation (3)

$$\Box\phi = m^2\phi + F(\phi),$$

where F is a smooth function vanishing to higher order near 0, is as already indicated, an appropriate point of departure for the construction of quantum fields. If the vacuum is to be set up as the transform under the wave operator of the free vacuum, it is necessary first to deal with the existence of a suitably smooth classical wave operator. This question leads very quickly to the question of the rate of decay of solutions of the linear tangential equation at $\phi = 0$, i.e., the so-called Klein-Gordon or scalar meson equation

$$\square\phi = m^2\phi. \tag{13}$$

It is easily seen that the L_2-norms of the solution ϕ and its spatial derivatives do not decay in time, due to the conservation of energy, so that the estimates for the decay of $\sup_{\mathbf{x}}|\phi(\mathbf{x}, t)|$ as $|t| \to \infty$ which are needed in the consideration of the wave operator can not be obtained from such L_2-estimates.

In joint work with A. R. Brodsky, it has been shown that the decay is $O(|t|^{-1})$ in three space dimensions, if at any time ϕ is twice differentiable in L_2. If F is any smooth function with bounded derivative which vanishes near 0, it can be deduced that the equation (3) has a unique global solution for the Cauchy problem with data of finite energy, and that if the data have compact support, the solution is asymptotic for early or for late times to a solution of equation (13). The operation S taking the asymptotic solution at time $-\infty$ into that at time $+\infty$, i.e., the scattering operator, then exists and is relativistically invariant. This provides the only nontrivial class of examples of relativistic S-operators which are presently established.

In the case of the equation (2) with $m = 0$, Strauss **[6]** has obtained very interesting estimates establishing the existence of wave operators for slightly modified equations, among other results. However, for application to quantum fields, quite precise information is required about the scattering and wave operators. In order to define transformations of quantum states, and not merely classical ones, it is necessary that they define "measurable" transformations in function space, in the sense of the theory of integration in such spaces. Unlike the situation in the theory of integration in finite-dimensional spaces, a continuous or even infinitely differentiable transformation on Hilbert space need not be at all measurable. In order to deal with this question, the Frechet differential of the scattering and wave operators must be investigated, with a view to determining, for example, the Hilbert-Schmidt norm of the deviation of the differential of the scattering operator from the identity, in the appropriate Hilbert spaces (which belong to the families indicated earlier). This Frechet differential is in fact the scattering operator for the corresponding first-order variational equation. In other terms, to deal with the quantum field associated with equation (3), it is necessary to have quite precise information of the type indicated on the scattering and wave operators for all the equations

$$\square\psi = m^2\psi + V(\mathbf{x}, t)\psi, \tag{14}$$

where V is of the form $F'(\phi)$.

Present indications are that the necessary measurability can be established for the propagation of states of the quantum field represented by normal distributions in function space of covariance matrix $|A|^a$ for sufficiently high a, where A is the skew-adjoint operator in the free classical field space indicated earlier: The free vacuum corresponds however to the case $a = 0$, so it is uncertain whether it can rigorously be propagated. There is no physically compelling reason why it must be. It appears possible to approximate arbitrarily closely in the empirically relevant sense the conventional free particle states of interest, of which the vacuum is the simplest case (that of no particles) by states which can be represented in terms of normal distributions which can indeed be propagated.

At this point it is clear that a number of interesting and difficult classical problems concerning equation (3) are involved in its quantization, but it remains to indicate how these problems originate.

5. **The concept of "quantum field."** Canonical commutation relations involving infinitely many variables were introduced by Dirac as an entirely formally motivated analogy with their successful introduction by Heisenberg for finite systems. There is a large substantial difference between the two sets of commutation relations, in that the Heisenberg relations for finite systems essentially are a way of describing physical space as euclidean (and would be altered if space were of a different character), and involve Planck's constant h, while the field commutation relations are entirely independent of the nature of physical space (in fact would remain equally applicable in theories in which no such concept appears), and do not involve h. Nevertheless Dirac achieved definite success, and the extension to relativistic fields by Heisenberg and Pauli has been a dominant influence in fundamental mathematical physical thought for many years.

Again the essential ideas are well represented by consideration of the case of equation (3). The "quantized field" $\phi(x)$ associated with this equation was assumed to have values which were linear operators and to satisfy the following general formal conditions:

i. Canonical commutation relations: writing $x = (\mathbf{x}, t)$, then for $t = t'$,

$$\begin{aligned} &[\phi(\mathbf{x}, t), \phi(\mathbf{x}', t)] = [\dot\phi(\mathbf{x}, t), \dot\phi(\mathbf{x}, t)] = 0, \\ &[\phi(\mathbf{x}, t), \dot\phi(\mathbf{x}', t)] = iG\delta(\mathbf{x} - \mathbf{x}') \qquad (G = \text{"scale of field"}); \end{aligned} \tag{15}$$

ii. Satisfaction of the differential equation:

$$\Box\phi = m^2\phi + F(\phi);$$

iii. Relativistic invariance: for any Lorentz transformation L, there should be an operator $U(L)$ such that

$$U(L)\phi(x)U(L)^{-1} = \phi(Lx) \quad \text{for all } x.$$

This was the formal basis; the precise nature of the "operators" $\phi(x)$, or even the space they operated on, was left quite ambiguous. However, it was understood that when necessary, it should be possible to form positive definite expectation values relative to given states, represented by vectors in the space on which the field variables $\phi(x)$ operated, whatever that might be. To a mathematician, and even to some physicists, the extreme ambiguity of the formalism is apt to seem peculiar, but looking backwards from this time, it is clear that it was not at all a matter of negligence but represented a certain type of scientific insight, to recognize that a real theory had been discovered, but one of such novelty that even the terms for discussing in a clear-cut way had not and could not be invented until the theory had received substantial intuitive development.

On the other hand, this development was slow and confusing, and the equation ii appeared to be coming no closer to a plausible and meaningful mathematical interpretation. This has led partly to a loss of interest in fundamental quantum field theory and partly to the development of schools of the subject in which any specific dynamical equation such as ii is eliminated (in fact, even the commutation relation in i with nonvanishing right-hand side has been eliminated in many axiomatic treatments). Although the early ideas of Lehmann, Symanzik, and Zimmermann on the subject seemed quite promising, the momentum of this development was not sustained. The related axiomatic approach emphasized by Haag and Wightman, and developed from a more concrete viewpoint by Källén, has received considerable continuing attention, but despite the weakening of the axioms involved in giving up the cited equations, no nontrivial example, i.e., one involving real creation or annihilation of particles, of the type of field being considered by them has yet been shown to exist.

It is however possible to give a meaningful reformulation for the equations ii, as well as explicit solutions which satisfy the additional desiderata i and iii, by the use of function theory in the manifold of all classical solutions of the partial differential equation. Consider the case of equation (2); the corresponding quantized equation is meaningless as it stands because $\phi(x)^3$ is purely symbolic. Consider however the commutators $[\ddot{\phi}(x), \phi(x')]$ and $[\ddot{\phi}(x), \dot{\phi}(x')]$ at equal times; since the $\phi(x')$ and $\dot{\phi}(x')$ are presumed to form an irreducible set of operators as $\mathbf{x}'$ varies, t' being held fixed, these commutators suffice to determine $\ddot{\phi}(x)$ at the same time, within a relatively insignificant additive constant. Thus it is just about as good to have equations for these two commutators in terms of ϕ and $\dot{\phi}$ at time $t = t'$, and a simple computation shows that formally these are given by the equations

$$(16)\qquad \begin{aligned} [\ddot{\phi}(x), \phi(x')] &= 0, \\ [\ddot{\phi}(x), \dot{\phi}(x')] &= i\Delta_x \delta(\mathbf{x} - \mathbf{x}') - 3i\phi(x)^2 \delta(\mathbf{x} - \mathbf{x}'). \end{aligned}$$

These equations are still lacking in mathematical meaning, due to the $\phi(x)^2$ term on the right-hand side. However, consider the commutators of each of the two commutators given by equation (16) with $\phi(x'')$ and $\dot{\phi}(x'')$ at a second point with $t'' = t' = t$; the knowledge of these commutators would determine them within additive constants, and hence determine $\ddot{\phi}(x)$ itself within a linear inhomogeneous expression in the field ϕ and its "conjugate field" $\dot{\phi}$. A computation similar to the foregoing one shows that formally these four commutators are given by the equations

$$(17)\qquad \begin{aligned} [[\ddot{\phi}(x), \dot{\phi}(x')], \dot{\phi}(x'')] &= 6G\delta(\mathbf{x} - \mathbf{x}')\delta(\mathbf{x} - \mathbf{x}'')\phi(x), \\ [[\ddot{\phi}(x), \dot{\phi}(x')], \phi(x'')] &= [[\ddot{\phi}(x), \phi(x')], \dot{\phi}(x'')] \\ &= [[\ddot{\phi}(x), \dot{\phi}(x')], \phi(x'')] = 0. \end{aligned}$$

This is a perfectly regular equation, in as much as distinct points x, x', and x'' are involved. The mass m has disappeared from the equation, which at first glance might seem unfortunate, but which is actually advantageous, since the so-called "bare" mass m of this equation is frequently considered to be an infinite or at best fictitious quantity which must be eliminated through "mass renormalization." The true, physical mass m' can be regarded as arising as a type of constant of integration in the solution of the equations just derived in accordance with relativistic invariance. The equation (17) thus implicitly consolidates in a simple and natural mathematical way the ad hoc rules and "physical" arguments ordinarily used in connection with mass renormalization.

As operator equations for $\ddot{\phi}(x)$, after regularization by multiplication by smooth functions of the variables involved followed by integration, (17) is quite approachable but not at all trivial. The solution depends on the "representation" of the canonical commutation relations involved in the field at time t. In the standard free field representation, the so-called Wick product $:\phi(x)^3:$ would be a solution, as would also be the case if the exponent 3 were replaced by n, for the corresponding nth order equation. In the "interaction representation" treatment of quantum field theory, or more or less equivalently that in terms of Feynman graphs, the analytical treatment is expressible entirely in terms of free fields, which explains why the corresponding perturbation theory is largely expressible in terms of Wick products. The interaction representation was used as the basis of an approach to the foundations of the subject along related lines to these in **[11]**, but it has not yet proved possible to determine whether equations such as those considered here induce a one-parameter group of automorphisms of a representation-independent algebra such as that considered there. That is to say, it is quite an open question whether the interaction representation form of equations (17) admit solutions. The present form, in the so-called Heisenberg representation, is presumably more fundamental, since it involves no hypothesis as to the asymptotic structure of the field, but the representation in which equation (17) must be solved is a "floating" one which can only be implicitly specified by the integrability of the Lie conditions (17) together with the solubility in the large of the abstract ordinary differential equation which then results. This is considerably more formidable than the usual floating boundary value problem, and it is reassuring that there is a simple explicit solution for the equations i, ii, iii, with ii replaced by equation (17).

6. **Quantized fields as differential operators in the classical solution manifold.** The set of all solutions of a nonlinear equation such as (3) forms an infinite-dimensional manifold. The solution manifolds of equations of evolution seem most naturally and generally treated through the use of the strong operator topology rather than the uniform one employed in the most familiar abstract treatments. While this means that the familiar finite-dimensional theory cannot be carried over directly, it makes for no essential difficulty. On the other hand, it is also necessary to consider vector fields of a generalized sort, which does make for

essential difficulties, in fact precisely those of the theory of unbounded operators. This is visible in its simplest form through the consideration of a continuous one-parameter unitary group in a Hilbert space, e.g., that induced by translations in L_2 on the line; by concrete analytical standards, this is an extremely smooth group of homeomorphisms, yet it does not correspond to any vector field, but rather to one which assigns at each point of the Hilbert space a generalized vector not strictly within the space.

The general theory provides a sound framework for the treatment of the solution manifold to such a concrete equation as (3). The tangent vectors to the solution manifold M in the differential geometric sense may be identified with "tangent functions," i.e., solutions of the first-order variational equation in the vicinity of the point of M (or solution of M) in question. Second-order hyperbolic equations are distinctive from this standpoint in providing a natural symplectic structure for the solution manifold, which may be described as follows. Suppose λ and λ' are two solutions of the first-order variational equation

$$\Box\lambda = m^2\lambda + F'(\phi)\lambda. \tag{18}$$

The fundamental second-order differential form Ω is then defined by the equation

$$\Omega_\phi(\lambda, \lambda') = \int [\lambda(\mathbf{x}, t)\dot{\lambda}'(\mathbf{x}, t) - \lambda'(\mathbf{x}, t)\dot{\lambda}(\mathbf{x}, t)]\, d\mathbf{x}; \tag{19}$$

this formulation gives Ω the appearance of being dependent on t and on the Lorentz frame, but it may be shown that this is not the case. Ω is a Lorentz-invariant closed nondegenerate form on M which plays a role quite analogous to that of the fundamental form in the phase space of a holonomic dynamical system. In particular, any smooth function on the manifold gives rise to a "symplectic" vector field, i.e., one whose infinitesimal displacements preserve Ω, by forming its differential followed by converting this to a vector field via the duality provided by Ω. For example, the classical energy functional for (3), i.e., the functional

$$((m^2 - \Delta)\phi, \phi) + (\dot{\phi}, \dot{\phi}) + \int G(\phi)$$

where $G' = F$ and these are inner products and integrals over space for a fixed time, is precisely that giving rise to the vector field generating the one-parameter group on M consisting of temporal displacement, $\phi(\mathbf{x}, t) \rightarrow \phi(\mathbf{x}, t + t')$.

The form Ω contains in concentrated form much information concerning the elementary solutions of all the first-order variational equations to equation (3), and is closely related to the quantum-field-theoretic commutator function. More specifically, let $D_\phi(x, x')$ denote the solution of (18), as a function of x, which vanishes for $t = t'$, and has its first derivative with respect to t equal to $\delta(\mathbf{x} - \mathbf{x})$; as is well known, the Cauchy problem for equation (18) is soluble directly in terms of D_ϕ. Although the definition is not at all symmetrical between x and x', it may be shown that $D_\phi(x, x')$ is in fact skew-symmetric in x and x'. It may also be shown that Ω and $D_\phi(x, x')$ essentially determine each other, e.g., in the relation

$$\Omega_\phi(X_f, X_g) = \int\int D_\phi(x, x')f(x)g(x')\, d_4x\, d_4x',$$

where f and g are smooth functions of compact support on space-time, and X_f is the vector field on M which may be characterized as depending linearly and smoothly on f, and which is the integral over t of the vector field which at any time t displaces the Cauchy data for ϕ by $f(\cdot, t)$. It may be shown that for a linear equation with variable (space and time dependent) coefficients, such as equation (14), in which case $D_\phi(x, x')$ is independent of ϕ, it is precisely the quantum field commutator, in the conventional sense, apart from constant factors. It has in fact been intensively investigated in this connection for free equations on curved space-time manifolds from a local point of view by Lichnerowicz [**9**], who has also treated similarly the first-order variational equations of the general theory of relativity and the anti-commutator functions relevant to the quantization of fields of half-integral spin [**10**]. His quite explicit results for these linear cases are more in the direction of elucidating the connection between quantization and the curvature of space-time, than the global analytical character of quantization, and are based on Leray's general theory of hyperbolic equations rather than the use of abstract equations of evolution.

The explicit solutions of the nonlinear quantized field equations indicated earlier may be described most succinctly in unregularized form: if M is the solution manifold of equation (2), then the quantized field is given by the equation

$$\varphi(x) = -i\frac{\partial}{\partial\phi(x)} + \frac{1}{2}\phi(x),$$

as a linear operator on the space of smooth functionals over M. More precisely, the regularized field $\int \phi(\mathbf{x}, t)f(\mathbf{x})\, d\mathbf{x}$ is the operator

$$\Phi(f, t) = -iX_{f,t} + \frac{1}{2} M_{\int f\phi}, \tag{20}$$

where $X_{f,t}$ is the vector field on M which generates the displacement of the Cauchy data for ϕ by a vector proportional to f, while $M_{\int f\phi}$ denotes the operation of multiplication by $\int f(\mathbf{x})\phi(\mathbf{x}, t)\, d\mathbf{x}$, acting on functions of the general element ϕ of M. These operators satisfy the relations indicated earlier which are characteristic for the quantized field associated with equation (2). Although not defined in a manifestly relativistic way, they do indeed transform appropriately under the action of the Lorentz group, as well as satisfy the basic partial differential equation and the canonical commutation relations. Some further properties are given in [**15**], where in particular expressions are given from which the quantized field commutators at unequal times may be derived, modulo the solution of the corresponding classical equation. Similar definitions are applicable to considerably more general equations, including those having space or time dependent coefficients.

7. **Conclusion and discussion.** It remains to interpret the operators described in the preceding section in Hilbert space, or more significantly from a physical viewpoint, to show how they relate to the propagation of states of the quantum field from a very early to a very late time. In this brief account we can only refer to the closely connected §4 for necessarily quite condensed indications on this matter; see also [**14**] and [**15**].

Qualitatively, the representation theory here indicated is reminiscent of general relativity, with curved space-time replaced by a curved manifold in function space. There is the difference that the present manifold is symplectic, while that of general relativity is Riemannian. There are however indications that the present solution manifolds have a natural Kähler structure containing the indicated symplectic one. Moreover, quantization appears to depend only on the solution manifold as a structured differentiable manifold with a given (Lorentz) group of automorphisms, the differential equation serving basically as a means of setting up the manifold, rather as a set of polynomials determine an algebraic variety.

It would be natural to explore the possible applicability of quantum-field-theoretic ideas in the theory of turbulence. An attempt at a precise formulation of the steady-state turbulence sought in [**6**] might be made via scattering theory for the Navier-Stokes equations in relation to its linear part (or a suitable linearized version) in the role of the free-field equation. The Banach limit as $t \to \infty$ of the characteristic functional corresponding to a given initial probability distribution in function space should then be nontrivial, corresponding to the nondissipative character of the relative flow, and could lead thereby to a reasonable equilibrium distribution describing pure turbulence (cf. [**15**] on the quantum field counterpart to this).

8. **Acknowledgement.** The new material presented in this report is based in part on fairly current, and in some cases continuing, work of several younger mathematicians, whose relevant research has been carried out partly under our general supervision. In addition to A. R. Brodsky and Walter Strauss, this group includes John Chadam, Jan Chaiken, and Roe Goodman.

Bibliography

A. Classical relativistic equations.

1. P. Dionne, *Problème de Cauchy pour les équations hyperboliques*, J. Analyse Math. (1962).

2. Konrad Jörgens, *Das Anfangswertproblem im Grossen für eine Klasse nichtlinearer Wellengleichungen*, Math. Z. **77** (1961), 295–307.

3. J. L. Lions, $\Box u + u^p = f$, Séminaire Leray sur les equations aux derivées partielles, 1963.

4. Irving Segal, *Non-linear semi-groups*, Ann. of Math. (2) **78** (1963), 339–364.

5. ———, *The global Cauchy problem for a relativistic scalar field with power interaction*, Bull. Soc. Math. France **91** (1963), 129–135.

6. Walter Strauss, *Les operateurs d'onde pour des equations d'onde non lineaires independentes du temps*, C. R. Acad. Sci. Paris **256** (1963), 5045–5046.

B. Quantized or stochastic fields.

7. G. K. Batchelor, *The theory of homogeneous turbulence*, Cambridge Univ. Press, Cambridge, 1959, 197 pp.

8. E. Hopf, *Statistical mechanics and functional calculus*, J. Rational Mech. Anal. **1** (1952), 87.

9. A. Lichnerowicz, *Propagateurs et commutateurs en relativité genérale*, Inst. Hautes Études Sci. Publ. Math. No. 10 (1961), 1–56.

10. ———, *Champs spinoriels et propagateurs en relativite genérale*, Bull. Soc. Math. France (1964).

11. Irving Segal, *Foundations of the theory of dynamical systems of infinitely many degrees of freedom*. I, Mat.-Fys. Medd. K. Danske Vid. Selsk. **31** (1959), no. 12, 1–39.

12. ———, *Quantization of nonlinear systems*, J. Mathematical Phys. **1** (1960), 468–488.

13. ———, *Mathematical characterization of the physical vacuum for linear Bose-Einstein fields*, Illinois J. Math. **6** (1962), 500–523.

14. ———, *Explicit formal construction of non-linear quantum fields*, J. Mathematical Phys. **5** (1964), 269–282.

15. ———, *Quantum fields and analysis in the solution manifolds of differential equations*, Proc. Conf. Anal. in Function Space, 1964, pp. 129–153, Cambridge Univ. Press, Cambridge, 1965.

16. ———, *Differential operators in the manifold of solutions of a non-linear differential equation*, J. Math. Pures Appl. (to appear).

Massachusetts Institute of Technology,
Cambridge, Massachusetts

AUTHOR INDEX

Boldface numbers refer to the first page of articles by authors in this volume.
Italic numbers indicate pages where a complete reference to a work by the author is given.
Roman numbers refer to pages where an author's name is mentioned.
Some roman page numbers have one or more superscript numbers. These superscripts are bibliographical reference numbers used on the page in place of an author's name.

SUBJECT INDEX